# APPLES

## *to*

# OYSTERS

*A Food Lover's Tour of Canadian Farms*

**MARGARET WEBB**

**VIKING
CANADA**

VIKING CANADA

Published by the Penguin Group

Penguin Group (Canada), 90 Eglinton Avenue East, Suite 700, Toronto, Ontario,
Canada M4P 2Y3 (a division of Pearson Canada Inc.)

Penguin Group (USA) Inc., 375 Hudson Street, New York, New York 10014, U.S.A.
Penguin Books Ltd, 80 Strand, London WC2R 0RL, England
Penguin Ireland, 25 St Stephen's Green, Dublin 2, Ireland (a division of Penguin Books Ltd)
Penguin Group (Australia), 250 Camberwell Road, Camberwell, Victoria 3124, Australia
(a division of Pearson Australia Group Pty Ltd)
Penguin Books India Pvt Ltd, 11 Community Centre, Panchsheel Park,
New Delhi – 110 017, India
Penguin Group (NZ), 67 Apollo Drive, Rosedale, North Shore 0745,
Auckland, New Zealand (a division of Pearson New Zealand Ltd)
Penguin Books (South Africa) (Pty) Ltd, 24 Sturdee Avenue, Rosebank,
Johannesburg 2196, South Africa

Penguin Books Ltd, Registered Offices: 80 Strand, London WC2R 0RL, England

First published 2008

1 2 3 4 5 6 7 8 9 10 (RRD)

Copyright © Margaret Webb, 2008

The author gratefully recognizes assistance from the Canada Council for the Arts,
the Ontario Arts Council, and The Banff Centre.

Manufactured in the U.S.A.

ISBN-13: 978-0-670-06624-7
ISBN-10: 0-670-06624-9

Library and Archives Canada Cataloguing in Publication data available upon request.

Visit the Penguin Group (Canada) website at **www.penguin.ca**

Special and corporate bulk purchase rates available; please see
**www.penguin.ca/corporatesales** or call 1-800-810-3104, ext. 477 or 474

*For my family, my farmers and Nancy*

# Contents

# Recipes

# Introduction

# THE ELECTRIC CARROT

David Greenberg became a farmer because of a carrot.

Many years back, David, a schoolteacher then, plucked the pedestrian vegetable from the soil of Prince Edward Island, with the warmth of the sun—and that gorgeous red dirt—still on it. He bit in and fell instantly in love with the "electric orange taste." It was like no other carrot he had ever eaten, and his mind leapt immediately to the possibilities of growing food that could taste "that amazing."

A few years later, my partner and I caught up with David at the Tempest restaurant in Wolfville, Nova Scotia. We were swooning over his tender Greenberg Greens, in a salad that exploded with a deep nutty, tart sweetness. The intense complexity of flavours surprised us, since the greens were dressed with but the slightest misting of oil and herbs. Although I was writing an article for *The Globe and Mail* about the best places to enjoy East Coast seafood at its freshest, chef Michael Howell desperately wanted me to meet David, one of the local farmers he relied on for fresh veggies, fruits and meats. Howell knows that a great dish starts with great ingredients, so he buys from suppliers who raise food the way he cooks—with love, on an intimate scale, and with passion.

So on that beautiful summer day, under a canopy of grapevines on Tempest's patio, as we sipped L'Acadie Blanc Reserve from the nearby Domaine de Grand Pré winery, Howell, resplendent in his chef's whites, introduced us to David, whose hands were stained a bronzy hue from his life's work in the soil. "What we really need," Howell said, "are more farmers like David."

But, as I would quickly discover, farmers like David are actually obsessive nuts—chefs of the soil, tractor-seat philosophers, self-trained geologists and biologists, thingamajig implement inventors and food educators all hard-wired into an ever-ready labourer who often works from sun-up until sundown.

David invited us to visit the farm he then owned, a tiny ten-acre patch with a mere three acres under cultivation. It was nestled in the Annapolis Valley, which is enjoying something of an agricultural renaissance with wineries, thriving farmers' markets, artisan cheese-makers and organic vegetable farmers. "The soil has fantastic mineral content," David told us, his voice pitching up with excitement.

The man was even more enthusiastic about manure. From his rows of carrots, David scooped up a handful of compost and pressed his nose deep into what originated not so long ago from a cow's behind. Or more precisely, he told me, it was one-part cow manure on straw to one-part horse manure on peat moss, a soup David simmered and aged under a blanket of black plastic before applying it to his soil. He insisted that I have a good smell. I admit, the stock was actually rather pleasant, like the deep woods fragrance of a forest after a rain. David, however, pronounced the dark earthy matter as "pure ecstasy."

Then his hands began conducting a wild symphony of thoughts as he explained that great compost is as critical to farming as quality ingredients are to cooking. As you might expect, he lambasted large-scale, industrial farming, which emphasizes low prices and quantity over taste and quality. Rather than relying on good soil and enhancing it, industrial farming looks to chemicals and genetic modifications to increase yield; to fight insects, weeds and disease; and also to extend "freshness" for weeks, from harvest and shipping to sitting on supermarket shelves. This farming protocol may maintain a broccoli's texture and colour, but the taste and nutrition of broccoli is but a flickering memory.

Yet, surprisingly, David was no fan of many modern organic practices either, calling it "reductive organics" to simply replace chemicals with other approved processes such as fertilizing with blood meal and fish by-products. To him, soil is a living thing to be tended and nurtured lovingly. Yes, even in the plant world, we are what we eat.

David's prize compost was food, which kept his soil alive, which nourished his exquisite Greenberg Greens. Certainly, you can feed chemical fertilizers to soil. Even in ground depleted of minerals, plants will readily absorb such fertilizers and respond with vigour. But the veggies will also taste of ammonium nitrate, rather than the soil. Or *terroir*, as the French so poetically describe it. Or "Annapolis Valley dirt," as David fondly called it.

artists of the soil and sea. If we care about our food, we should support and celebrate what our farmers do well—and push many to do better.

Yes, modern farming is complicated. Organic, natural, fair trade, sustainable—there are so many labels we barely understand. But I have a simple mantra: What we do not grow in this country, we cannot really know.

I GREW UP on a farm in Simcoe County, some ninety kilometres north of Toronto, just beyond the Holland Marsh, better known as Ontario's vegetable patch. When I look back, I realize that we really had two farms, radically different.

There was the commercial side of our operation that fed people in the city and generated income to support our family. For this, we ran a beef feedlot—a fat farm for cows, if you will—and grew corn and hay for cattle feed. On corn, six-to-eight-month-old cows fatten fast for market—usually in four to five months—but not without stress. We nursed them through winter colds and pneumonia with antibiotics. Thankfully, we raised cattle before the advent of growth hormones and feed supplements made from animal parts, the culprit in mad cow disease, for I'm quite sure my father would have embraced these methods. He thought of himself as modern and progressive.

But my father fell ill in his prime, for reasons we still do not fully understand, and my oldest brother, Graham, took over the reins of the family farm. He quickly expanded it to eleven hundred acres at its peak, a small farm now by today's standards. From the very start, he faced enormous economic pressures. The price of corn is lower now than when he started farming thirty-four years ago. My brother, an astute businessman, reasoned that the only way to keep up with the rising costs of machinery, fuel and seed was to increase his efficiency—to go big—and to produce more. When he started farming, he was able to harvest about 80 bushels of corn per acre; he can now harvest more than 140. But pumping up yields to this degree requires significant doses of agriculture's version of steroids—chemical fertilizers, pesticides and herbicides. Most of the stuff that he puts in his planter and goes on the food we eat comes with hazard signs and handling instructions to wear a face mask and gloves.

Today, agricultural lingo refers to this method of farming as "conventional," a perversion of a definition that makes us think of something tried and true and old-fashioned, though it is anything but. When a great chasm opened between consumer and farmer, giant agribusinesses—chemical and seed companies—stepped in to steer the course of modern agriculture into a style better described as "industrial" or "chemical." In this new scenario, food has become an abstract business term, a commodity.

The giant meat packers and food processors who buy commodities from industrial farms operate according to that most essential law of economics: supply and demand. Both buyers and sellers are chiefly motivated by two things: quantity and price. If supply is huge—as is often the case in Canada with wheat, corn and soybeans—prices are low. Seed and chemical companies, of course, encourage farmers to embrace industrial-style farming on an even larger scale, to play the supply side of the game so they use more chemical inputs. But in the quest to become large and efficient, to grow more for less, many of these farmers have lost touch with what they actually do produce; they've forgotten that the commodity they harvest with tractors and haul by trucks to market is actually *food*. I am continually shocked by how little most industrial farmers think about the taste or nutrition of their crops and livestock, how little they know or care about what might seem a fundamental aspect of their work. Clearly, they have become as divorced from their groceries as consumers.

The other farm of my childhood brought in no income, yet it nourished and delighted us. I remember walking through the feedlot with my father, learning to pick out the best and healthiest heifer to be butchered for our own freezer. He stocked the pond on our farm with speckled trout. We picked apples and pears from our own orchard and travelled to nearby Collingwood and Niagara for cherries and peaches. My mother kept a massive garden, and the only fertilizer that ever went on it was the fresh stuff from the cows, which replenished the soil year after year. We weeded by hoe, harvested by hand. The garden grew enough to feed us through the summer and also the winter, as mom bagged corn, peas and beans for the freezer and stored potatoes, onions, carrots, squash and turnips in our root cellar.

My mother was far from being a fancy cook. She made simple suppers from what we grew, or picked from other orchards and farms. She used virtually no spices or sauces other than a sprinkling of salt and pepper, a few dollops of butter. Unwittingly, for she would call herself a meat-and-potatoes cook, her minimalist style served her fresh ingredients well. For what do new baby potatoes want but a sprinkle of salt? Or crunchy yellow beans and sweet young peas but a drizzle of butter and dash of pepper?

When I look back, I think my mother was more farmer than cook, for she was obsessed with harvesting vegetables fresh—the same day we were to eat them. A tomato could not just be ripe, it had to be perfectly ripe. Indeed, she would send me to the garden a half hour before supper to cut the new asparagus that had shot up in that day's sunshine. She would not let us husk corn until she had filled the pot with water and put it on the stove to boil. My brothers, sister and I learned to pick sweet corn her way—by sneaking down a strip of the husk to determine that it was not underripe (and therefore, white and tasteless) nor overripe (and therefore, yellow and starchy), but exactly ripe, at its magic-hour best, a pale yellow, juicy, sweet perfection.

Our regular family suppers were made special by the appearance of a new vegetable coming into season. The first rhubarb! The first strawberries! The first beans! These were occasions to compose whole meals around that singular ingredient. My father delighted in packing the first Spanish onion between two slices of Mom's homemade bread. I snacked on big beefsteak tomatoes as if they were apples. My mother would make her entire lunch of new yellow beans. When my brother, Joe, was sent to pick strawberries, he ate so many off the vine that Mom threatened to weigh him before and after—and charge him for the meal.

I remember meals tasting like the season. Spring is green, tender and tart. Summer is red, seductive and juicy. Fall is golden, sweet and thick. Winter is a hearty stew made from frozen vegetables—a rainbow of colours, spicy, smouldering.

One summer dinner stands out, a delicious surprise. There is supper and then a late-night supper. Neil Armstrong is going to walk on the moon. I barely remember that "one giant leap for mankind," yet I vividly recall the walk my father and I took after dinner, to the maple bush at the back of our farm, me running to keep up to his long purposeful strides. We shuffled through ankle-deep leaves, searching for the season's crop of morels, a curious-looking sponge-like mushroom that grows in the wild. Dad knew exactly where to find the patch. After we picked a bag, we returned to the pond. There, in the dusk of that soft evening, he and my brothers quietly cast lines in the water to fish for speckled trout.

Later, we all gathered around the TV—uncles, aunts, grandparents. While Neil Armstrong bounced on the moon in his big moon boots, we ate earthy, meaty morels and fresh speckled trout, both fried up in butter, along with thick slices of Mom's homemade bread. The adults washed their meals down with icy bottles of Red Cap beer, while I, just seven years old, drank a glass of cold water from our well.

WHEN I LEFT the farm for university in Toronto, I felt constantly hungry. Certainly, homesickness played a part in my craving—nearly every Saturday morning I visited Kensington Market just to stare at the carcasses of beef hanging in butchers' windows, to ogle the mounds of fresh vegetables and fruit. Looking back, I know I was craving taste. University cafeterias and city restaurants tried to supply it with spices, sugar and sauces. Supermarkets more often carried California strawberries, Mexican corn, New Zealand apples than fresh local produce. Later, I sought out intensely spiced foods— Mexican, Thai, Indian. But the experiments left me wanting—chocolate, sugar, butter, salt, fat, *taste.*

Then, a few years ago, my partner and I moved into a downtown Toronto neighbourhood that has the good fortune of hosting a weekly farmers' market. We started buying directly from small organic farmers and, very quickly, our meals transformed almost completely. I went back to eating much like I had as a child.

Most nights, we have a small piece of naturally raised chicken or organic beef alongside an exquisitely fresh vegetable and salad. The minimalist meal is more than enough. It is perfect. Give me a tangy tart local apple or fresh strawberries, and I will pass on the pie. Hold the sour cream and salsas and give me a free-range chicken breast—tender, juicy, plump. While eating better, we eat less. With quality, we no longer crave quantity. Finally, I had discovered what I had been craving—intense, authentic local flavour, the taste of fresh, the nutrition of quality food.

Such foods are more expensive, but many artisans make their produce affordable by selling directly to consumers, cutting out the intermediary sales agents, processors and supermarkets that take the lion's share of food profits. Community-supported agriculture farms enable you to buy a share of the seasonal harvest in advance for as little as $30 a week. Some will let you participate in the harvest, and save more, by visiting the farm to pick produce or select animals to be butchered for your freezer.

But many small family farms are struggling and going out of business. This is a terrible time for agriculture in Canada. Yet it is also a hopeful time. There are many more farmers like David Greenberg, as I delightfully discovered on the enormous journey of researching this book, a series of cross-Canada trips that took me two years to complete. Of course, there were too many to write about, so I chose as my subject a signature food of each province and the North—what the region is chiefly known for—then I searched for a farmer who produces that food with passion, in an environmentally sustainable way, and, hopefully, with innovative ideas to meet the huge economic challenges of modern farming. This wasn't easy. In some cases, chefs suggested favourite farmers; I discovered others through agricultural organizations; or I simply stumbled upon them in my own eating adventures. I tried to visit each farm at a key moment, generally harvest. This also wasn't easy, with eleven farms to explore during Canada's short growing season. Perhaps this best explains the organization of the book: Rather than a coast-to-coast sprint that might have placed me in the Prairies in February, I hopscotched about regions and presented my discoveries in a way that hopefully makes more delicious sense, a three-course smorgasbord of Canadian foods and farmers.

Along the way, these generous farmers endured my fumbling attempts to work alongside them, opened their hearts to me during long truck rides in the country and invited me into their homes to share meals and recipes and to meet their families. I am grateful for what they taught me about farming and food and for reconnecting me with a life I had missed so terribly. I am hopeful that these innovative producers will restore what industrial farming nearly severed: Our connection to the foods that come from our incredible food regions and to the people who nourish us. This, of course, also depends on us, to consider that critical ingredient too often missing from our discussions of food, our farmers.

# Appetizers

# Prince Edward Island

# JOHNNY FLYNN'S OYSTERS

*The oyster's a confusing suitor;*
*It's masculine, and feminine,*
*and even neuter.*
—Ogden Nash

I first tasted Johnny Flynn's cultivated oysters at the funky Oyster Boy restaurant in Toronto. His were my first experience of eating one raw. My partner, Nancy, who grew up in Nova Scotia, had been urging me to try one for years, seducing me with all manner of cooked oysters, but I resisted this adult rite of passage to a spinsterly age for two reasons. First, it takes but a second to swallow an oyster, but five years to grow one to market size in Canada's chill East Coast waters. Perhaps more alarming, raw means—at least in the case of oysters—that the creature is very much *alive*. Yes, the plump rise of flesh, which so resembles *that* part of the female anatomy, meets its death in your mouth. Or stomach if you do not chew. But you must chew, Oyster Boy owner Adam Colquhoun had told me, not only to release the heady flavours but to ensure the creature is still alive and fresh, and therefore not dead and skanky.

Contemplating the half decade of life that would be sacrificed for my one second of pleasure, my mind swirling with images of sex and death, I placed my finger on the sensuous swell of meat. Springy! I raised the shell to my nose and sniffed the ocean liquor. Fresh! Tipped the tender morsel into my mouth and chewed. And, oh perverse, addictive pleasure.

My partner and I began haunting the top oyster bars in Toronto—Starfish, Oyster Boy, Rodney's. We sampled our way through platters of the luscious libertines—fished from the wild, cultivated on a farm, flown in from the east coast, west coast, United States, Europe. To our palates, no other oyster could rival Colville Bay's classic sharp hit of salt, followed by a tingling sweetness and steely clean finish.

We were not alone in our lust for these gems. Adam Colquhoun told us that he is so keen to bring in the first shipment of spring oysters after ice breakup that he has flown down to Prince Edward Island, stayed with the Flynns, donned hip waders and rubber gloves, and helped with the harvest himself.

While passing a lazy afternoon at Starfish slurping up a few of the sweet sensations, I watched a chef and his wife visiting from Chicago polish off a massive platter filled with a sampling of every oyster the bar stocked. After, they each flipped over a shell, declared it their favourite, then ordered a half dozen more of, yes, Colville Bays.

Patrick McMurray is the proprietor of Starfish. He holds a Guinness Book world record for shucking (thirty-three Cape Breton Aspy Bays in one minute) and is uncommonly obsessed with the bivalve. If he were an oyster, he told me, he would want to be a Colville Bay. To the couple from Chicago—growing smugger by the minute for their discerning taste—he waxed on about its beautiful teardrop shape, deep cup, the gorgeous green of the shell, the crisp texture and bright flavour of the meat, even the tiny tuft of seaweed Johnny leaves on the shell, which makes for an eye-popping presentation of half shells on a plate of ice. "It's a perfect little oyster," Patrick pronounced. "You can't get a prettier oyster than a Colville Bay."

Across town, there are none on the menu at Rodney's Oyster House, though Rodney Clark, the man who started the oyster bar craze in Toronto in the 1990s, would dearly love to have them. As Johnny Flynn's American distributor told me, he could sell twenty-five times more Colville Bays than he does—if only Johnny would raise more. But, apparently, Johnny likes to play hard to get.

The more I learned about the Colville Bays, the more intrigued I became. With his cultivated version, Johnny Flynn had managed to improve upon what many consider the world's finest oyster—the PEI Malpeque. But how, I wondered. Was it the water, the breeding, the technique of a slow rubber-gloved hand? When my curiosity reached a fever pitch, I decided to make a date with Johnny, to find out the secrets of his craft.

THE SHOULDER SEASONS—spring and fall—are splendid times to visit Prince Edward Island. The crowds of tourists drawn to this gleaming pearl of summer heaven are at their thinnest, while the oysters are at their fattest. Arriving the last week of June, Nancy and I are pushing the season, but I have no worries. I did my research. Summer oysters are perfectly safe to eat, though after spawning, which occurs here in late summer, they can be thin and copper-tasting. As a conservation measure, Prince Edward Island closes its wild fishery from July 15 to September 15, which may explain why that old English parson's warning against eating oysters in months without an *r* in the name still holds sway, even here. But oysters fished in hot weather need only be refrigerated once out of the water—something the Romans surely knew, packing them back from Brittany on ice.

Yet, when I called Johnny to make arrangements for our visit, he said something about it not being an ideal time, as it would be lobster season, and he still fishes lobster. That information hit my East Coast partner particularly hard, for she thinks the only thing sexier than eating oysters is eating oysters and lobster. We booked a cottage with a full-size kitchen.

Our two-hour drive from Prince Edward Island's Confederation Bridge to Johnny's hometown of Souris, on the southeastern tip of the island, takes us through a sumptuous summer day. Scenery unfolds as if from an *Anne of Green Gables* novel: rolling farmland, shimmering copper beaches, glistening blue ocean. While I drive, Nancy reads aloud recipes from the oyster bibles we have brought along—M.F.K. Fisher's *Consider the Oyster* and Karen Warner's and Lonnie Williams' *Oysters: A Connoisseur's Guide and Cookbook*.

Her sensuous reading of recipes I had earmarked suddenly makes me wonder about our relationship. Being two women has nothing to do with my anxiety. We have been growing ever happier during our decade together and have developed a strong partnership, albeit one with rather more defined domestic roles than I had ever expected. While I throw myself into exotic food adventures and lustily seek out new recipes, she is usually content to remain at home, by hearth and wine fridge, perfecting my first flawed dishes. Ah, but the oyster has changed all that, drawing us inexorably into this adventure together.

And that thought turns my mind to wondering if the little devils (literally called that by the Mi'kmaq Natives of Malpeque Bay) really are an aphrodisiac. Certainly, they have a storied reputation—as a staple at any half-respectable Roman orgy or at the breakfast table of a cavorting Casanova who stoked his libido by sucking back a dozen a day. One PEI bumper sticker we see hails them as "Nature's Viagra."

From my research, I gleaned that oysters are very good for you, but not that there's a direct spark from a wee oyster to, well, let's just say they're packed with zinc, which helps metabolize testosterone, which makes the prostate gland healthy and happy indeed. Their few modest calories are also chock full of protein and a medicine shelf of vitamins, plus iron, copper, magnesium, calcium and phosphorous. To get your recommended daily allowance of all this good stuff, you need only eat four or five medium-sized oysters a day. My theory is that a famished Roman soldier or starving American colonialist would feel pretty good after eating five, sated with a dozen and raring to reproduce after a few bushels.

And Johnny? According to one long yarn circulating through a Toronto oyster bar, he saves the shell of every oyster he ever eats—and there's a massive pile of them behind his house in Prince Edward Island. Which makes me wonder, should we be expecting a Don Juan in hip waders?

THE COLVILLE BAY OYSTER COMPANY crouches on a poetic, windswept stretch of red sand shoreline across the water from Souris. The company sign hangs discreetly on the side of a cedar-shake garage, not on the front where you might actually see it from the road. Inside is a tiny twenty-six-by-thirty-two-foot government-inspected processing plant where Johnny and his family grade and pack the catch for shipping two times a week. A few steps down the beach is the Flynns' old family homestead, a small white bungalow where Johnny's eighty-two-year-old mother still lives. And there, standing in a small boat in the turbulent ocean inlet of Colville Bay, is Johnny Flynn himself.

He looks every inch the typical fisherman, wearing a sou'wester, red-plaid wool jacket and rubber boots. And although he could use any modern mechanism to gather oysters on his private beds, he is fishing, as islanders have done for more than a century, with tongs that resemble giant salad forks, scooping the molluscs off the ocean floor. As he rows into shore, I take in his trim black beard salted with grey, his massive suntanned forearms and a handsome cherub face that manages to look happy and sad all at once. And then those Irish blue eyes, the very colour of the sun-splashed sea.

He's shaking my hand before he's out of the boat, inviting us into the house to meet his mom, who's suffering badly with arthritis. Soon the whole Souris clan is dropping by—Johnny's wife, Mary Jane, a smart and attractive redhead; his younger brother, Leo, who lives across the street; an assortment of Johnny's three children and Leo's two; neighbours and cousins from town. The gathering seems like a family reunion, but this is just watching six o'clock news with mom.

Oyster farming, Johnny tells me, has enabled him to bring his family even closer together. Back in 1998, when the business began showing "a glimmer of hope," Johnny, then forty-one, persuaded Leo, then thirty-eight, to leave his home renovation business and join Johnny fishing lobster and raising oysters. Last year, Mary Jane left her job as a nursing manager to keep the books and fill orders. A major goal, Mary Jane tells me, is to build a company that will enable their children to stay home and make a living. As Johnny says, "I get Darwin, but I'm also spiritual. I guess I believe that community-minded sorts are the fittest to survive."

Well, this is something I wasn't expecting—an oysterman with profound ideas. I feel a weird twinge. But maybe it's just Johnny's gentle ways—he kisses his mom goodbye before he leaves. Or maybe it's the soft salt air. Or maybe it's the oysters, for Johnny, bless the man, sends us to our rental cottage with three dozen.

OUR HOME for the next week could not be more perfect for our mission to learn about Johnny's oyster operation. Situated on a high shore cliff, it has a wraparound deck with a hot tub and panoramic views of Colville Bay. At the southeast end, the bay opens onto the Northumberland Strait and dramatic sunrises. At the northwest end, it channels into the mouth of the Souris River—site of Johnny's farm and heart-swelling sunsets. Incoming and outgoing tides create a natural flush that funnels plankton-rich tidal waters right over Johnny's oyster beds. Not that we can see them, as it's high tide and whatever magical contraption he employs is under water. Still, I sense what's lurking there will help the PEI oyster industry find its way back from nearly a century of hard times.

· A bit of history is required at this point. Although Prince Edward Island is the oyster's most northerly home, the bivalves were once so plentiful in Malpeque Bay, which gives its name to the island variety, that early settlers—the Acadians—fished them out of the bay and spread them over the land as fertilizer. The completion of the Intercontinental Railway in 1876 connected Canada's eastern provinces to markets in Montreal and Toronto and beyond, and Prince Edward Island quickly became famous for its Malpeques—prized not only for their exquisite taste but also for their hardiness.

The island's harsh winters have much to do with both. The oyster feeds hard through the spring, summer and fall, packing on so-very-sweet-and-good-for-you glycogen-rich protein. Then, when the water plunges below freezing, the oyster seals its shell and hibernates until spring. While a limpid Florida cousin might last a week out of the water, Malpeques, with proper refrigeration, can survive up to four months (easily a month in your refrigerator—though so will the smell), making them easier to ship to distant markets. When the PEI oysters arrived at a 1900 Paris exhibition, judges declared them the best in the world. During that heady time, some five hundred boats hauled four million pounds a year out of Malpeque Bay alone.

Alas, the fishers virtually cleaned out the bay. Oystermen brought in stock from New England to replenish it—likely the source of a mysterious and contagious disease that, by 1915, nearly wiped out the fishery. Though it had no effect on humans, Malpeque disease killed 90 percent of the oysters in the bay.

To restore its wild fishery, Prince Edward Island looked to cultivation techniques developed in France in 1857 under Napoleon III. Surviving PEI stock had developed a resistance to the disease, so experts here set out collectors (anything from egg crates to drainage tile covered in a fresh thin-set coat of cement) to capture young oysters, called seed or spat. They redistributed the spat to shallow bays and estuaries, in the hopes of establishing new oyster beds. Easier said than done. As late as the 1980s, the entire island produced just two million pounds, half the haul of Malpeque Bay in its glory years.

In the early 1990s, a few large PEI mussel producers travelled to France to study oyster cultivation first-hand. Mussels—dubbed the poor man's oyster—grow in the same waters but are much easier to cultivate, and the producers had scored big, building a $24-million-a-year industry that produces thirty-seven million pounds of the famous Island Blue. They intended to do the same with oysters. The mussel men and a number of commercial fishers, using a government aquaculture program that offered interest-free loans for five years, invested millions of dollars attempting to adapt the French technology to mass-producing the finicky oyster. They lost millions.

Johnny is telling me this story in the middle of the night. Why has he woken me up to tell me this? Oh, right. It's pitch-black and spitting rain, and Johnny, Leo and I are on our way to fish lobster. My wake-up call came at 3:15 A.M. Leo still seems half asleep, but, this time of the morning, Johnny's a regular chatterbox. He tells me that in 1993 he bought eight boxes of mature oysters and tossed them in a saltwater inlet up the coast, to see if they would survive the winter. Back then, he was fishing cod along with lobster, but, stung by the 1992 moratorium on cod, he was casting about for ways to make money and "keep busy" the ten months of the year he wasn't fishing lobster. He had tried other careers as a young man—worked on northern survey crews and western oil rigs, considered teaching history and spent a year studying at the University of Prince Edward Island, did a stint in the Coast Guard—but he was always drawn back to Souris. He grew up here on the mixed farm his father worked on as a labourer—lean support for Johnny and his three brothers. But the idea of combining his father's passion for farming with his own for fishing appealed to him. After ice breakup in spring, when Johnny discovered his experimental oysters had lived, he invested $3000 in oyster seed and equipment and jumped into his new venture with both rubber boots.

The most critical choice an oyster farmer can make, he says, is selecting the water. Turns out, the best piece of ocean for raising oysters Johnny's way was right out front of the old Flynn homestead, on Colville Bay. As Johnny says, "The opportunity was looking me right in the eye."

As we motor out of East Point harbour in Johnny's boat, I ask him why we're heading out in the middle of the night to fish lobster. "After all, they're in the traps," I say. "No fear of them going anywhere." I might ask why he's fishing lobster at all, with his oyster farm thriving.

"Well, there's tradition," Johnny hollers over the motor, "and the sea's usually calmer. And I guess if there's a breakdown, there's time to fix the boat and get back out there."

Well, that's the rational explanation. Then Johnny admits that he loves the ocean. He loves her fierce, calm, warm, cold. He loves her changeable ways. "Nothing wrong with a snowstorm in winter," he says. "Gives you a chance to stay in and read a book." But I suspect he loves the ocean most in the still quiet dark, just before sunrise.

The sea wears a black silk dress. The air is a soft kiss, the moon a steady pull.

"Big spring tide at a full moon," Johnny says. "Old-timers called them bull tides."

"Really," I say. "That's kind of suggestive."

"Hmm," he says.

Although he was raised Catholic and takes his children to church—"more for the community" than anything—Johnny seems to worship a more elemental spirit. He's always saying things like, "Mother Nature will look after you." Or, "You have to work with Mother Nature." Or, "no matter what, she'll always give you a good kick or two in the arse."

Johnny and I have only a few minutes to chat before he locates the first set of traps with his Global Positioning System. His brother, Leo, slipping a hook into the water, catches the yellow buoy marker. Johnny winches up the first trap, hefts the hundred-pound wooden cage the last couple of feet over the side of the boat by hand. He pushes it along the side to Leo, who shakes out the lobsters, baits the trap with herring and pushes it to the back of the boat in time to catch the next one Johnny winches up. They work, steadily, without talking, until they've fished the six traps. Johnny wheels the boat in a circle while Leo pushes them back in the water, then Johnny speeds onto the next set—fifty in all; we will fish some three hundred traps over the next seven hours.

Leo gives me the easiest job, using a bander to slip elastic bands on the snapping claws of market-size lobsters. I work hard. I want to impress Johnny. I'm not sure why. Maybe it's the oysters we ate last night.

The sea drips with sex. Leo flips over every lobster to check for females—males have larger and harder forelegs. Ovulating females have great grape clusters of black eggs bulging from the outside of their tails. Leo throws these back in the water along with large females between about two and four and a half pounds (good breeders). As well as all the little ones, those under half a pound.

Leo uses a gauge to measure. Sometimes he'll size a lobster two or three times—not for the measure to go his way but the lobster's. With a four-and-a-half-pound female, it's like tossing twenty bucks back into the sea. Leo will say, "That'll make Johnny cry." And Johnny will holler, "Nope, I don't care."

It's not as though any authority on shore is going to measure as thoroughly. But the two brothers have made their pact with the ocean. They look after her, she'll look after them.

This spring, they're getting $4 to $6 a pound for lobster, some $100,000 for two months' work; their expenses take about half that. In the off-season, many lobster fishers go on unemployment—virtually an East Coast ritual that irks the brothers.

"This is easy compared with oyster farming," says Leo.

"This is a two-month paid holiday!" shouts Johnny.

Finally, the sun pushes light into the sky, and the sea changes into a smoky grey outfit, then a shimmering blue silk as the sun pops over the horizon. With that blast of orange comes warmth. And Rankin Family tunes from the stereo in Johnny's wheelhouse.

We were alone in the dark, now the water is dancing with lobster boats, springing between traps and flinging about buoys to the tune of fiddles and flutes. At 8:30 A.M., when my hand is cramped from banding, we stop for sandwiches. At 10:30, when I'm about to flop face first into my bin of lobsters, we're finished and cracking open cold beers, soaking up the sun.

"I think I could enjoy this," I say, "on a day like this."

"First nice day we've had since the start of the season," says Johnny. "But one nice day makes you forget all the rest."

On the way into harbour, Johnny tells me that he named his boat after an Irish king. "Well, after buying it, I guess I'm Owen Mor, too."

Then he sends me home with a dozen lobster.

I RETURN to the cottage exhausted, famished and somewhat perturbed, for when Johnny drops me off, he tells me that on top of oyster farming, on top of lobster fishing, he has been doing research on his family tree. He located his long-lost American cousins and invited them to Prince Edward Island and, lo and behold, they accepted *immediately*. He expects them to arrive any minute. His voice quivers with excitement. Mine does not. For they, rather than I, will get to hang with Johnny for the next two days.

Nancy and I turn our attention to eating. She has been up just long enough to fetch a pot of fresh sea water, to boil up the lobster I have brought home. We lunch on the front deck, with Johnny's oyster beds in constant view. The tender claws are full and bursting with sweet ocean flavour. We make a dessert of raw oysters, tarted up with a drop of fresh lemon juice or twist of pepper or a dollop of Tabasco and two of vodka.

There is just enough time for an afternoon nap and then, deliciously, it is supper. We shuck and slurp raw oysters while cooking up a pasta sauce of lobster and oysters in cream and tarragon. And then, after a hot tub, it is time for a bedtime snack—oysters sautéed in a dash of butter, garlic and wine and slathered on toast.

The next morning, we breakfast on oyster and lobster Benedict, then hurry our morning hot tub to make an oyster chowder for lunch, which goes very nicely with a lobster roll. But as we eat, dreamily looking over Johnny's oyster beds, we start to wonder about that other old saying—that you are what you eat. This is disconcerting, for oysters are shamelessly lascivious creatures. Juveniles born into the sea settle down quickly enough, secreting a gluey substance that cements them in one place for life, usually an old shell in an oyster bed. They then pass the rest of their days gorging on seafood and enjoying staggering amounts of group sex.

Not surprisingly, the lusty little molluscs have only a few lonely cells dangling in place of a brain. Yet, they possess prodigious sex glands that swell during spawning to obliterate all other organs. And what adaptable and potent gonads they are. Maybe male one season, perhaps female another— all the easier to seduce whoever lives next door—the transsexual trollop spews millions of eggs or billions of sperm into the water each season. A group of presumably excited mathematicians once calculated that if a single oyster's ova were fertilized through five generations, she could produce a brood of full-grown offspring equal to 250 times the volume of the earth. Such is the fecundity of a species that has staked its four-hundred-million-year existence almost entirely on passion. If Darwin had confined his studies to the oyster, he may well have coined a different theory: survival of the sexiest. Yet, an oyster has only a one in a million chance of surviving to adulthood, which is where the finicky work of the oyster farmer comes in.

After an afternoon snack of grilled oysters à la M.F.K. Fisher—pop open a shell, add a little butter, "some pepper, some breadcrumbs," close and set on the barbeque for a minute or two—we decide that we simply cannot stand it anymore.

"I can't wait until Tuesday to see Johnny Flynn," I confess.

"Neither can I," Nancy also admits.

This is odd. Worse, it's only Sunday.

We stroll to the end of Souris Beach for a closer look at Johnny Flynn's oyster beds. We flop cross-legged on the sand not far from an endangered piping plover nesting area. We crack open beers and contemplate our predicament: We are two gay women falling increasingly fond of a PEI oyster farmer.

"It's the oysters," I say.

I'm not sure if Nancy believes me. Her right eyebrow shoots up. "Would you turn straight to be with Johnny Flynn?" she asks.

"No," I say, "Absolutely not."

"But what if Johnny turned into a woman?"

"He'd have to shave his beard…."

But we are not oysters. Unlike them, we cannot change our sex willy-nilly. Nor do we want to.

"It's nothing," I say. "We're running out of oysters, that's all."

"Maybe," says Nancy. "When do you think we can get some more?"

After much debate, we decide finally, and to our great relief, that we have come to care for Johnny like a brother. Which makes us think instantly of a scheme to lure him to us—a family reunion, hosted by us. So what if we are not family? We will invite Johnny, Leo, their wives, their children and all their American cousins—the whole damn clan of Flynns back in Ireland if they show up—for oysters at our cottage at happy hour.

I call Johnny, and he's thrilled with the invitation—and I know why. He's haunted, even inspired, by his father's struggle to forge a living on this tiny, remote end of Prince Edward Island, rather than leave as so many others have, as his cousins' mother did. Johnny's bursting with pride for this place, and he wants to show his American cousins the island's huge potential and even bigger heart.

But the man's not one for boasting, at least not about himself. The locals we rent the cottage from are stunned to find out his oysters sell in Toronto—let alone that we're here to write about Johnny. When we ask for Colville Bay oysters at a pub in Souris that overlooks the bay, the waitress says she'd never heard of such a thing. Johnny himself jokes about an elderly woman in town who always asks how his mussels are growing. He always says, "Great, they're doing just great."

So I will play the Food Writer from Toronto, and we will spread the glory of Johnny. The thought makes us giddy.

We drive an hour and a half to the island's lone winery at Little Sands, returning with a Rossignol Chardonnay, and also a fruit cranberry wine, which goes surprisingly well with oysters. We set up a shucking bar in the kitchen. Nancy whips up her irresistible version of Oysters Rockefeller, which has very little to do with the classic recipe other than the oysters.

At six o'clock, Johnny, Mary Jane and Leo arrive with their American Cousins. They are three middle-aged sisters from Pennsylvania who have never shucked an oyster, reel at the thought of eating one raw and know nothing of Johnny's fame. They are putty in our hands.

As Johnny sits at our makeshift oyster bar, arms crossed, beaming, we teach the sisters to shuck. We tease and cajole them into trying raw oysters, to much shrieking and delight. Finally, we move the party to the deck for the pièce de résistance, a view of Johnny's oyster beds at sunset, served up with Nancy's Fellers—an oyster on the half shell, doused in garlic butter, topped with grated Gruyère cheese, then broiled for two minutes.

Mary Jane, who doesn't like raw oysters, loves Nancy's Fellers. Leo, who has never eaten a cooked oyster, laps them up. Johnny eats three in rapid succession, cheese dripping into his beard.

And the American Cousins?

They pounce on them and they do not stop eating, until there is only one. The oldest sister points out the conundrum. The middle sister suggests sharing it. The youngest sister says, "I will stab you with my fork if you so dare as touch it." And then, before the older sisters can take the dare, the youngest plunges her fork into the heart of the Feller and eats it.

Nancy and I bask in our happy success, for the Cousins have fallen as hard for Johnny and his oysters as we have. Alas, Johnny departs, though not before leaving us with another bag of oysters.

WE FILL THE NEXT DAY by visiting other farms. There are some 750 private oyster leases in Prince Edward Island. The Department of Fisheries and Oceans charges only $10 an acre for oyster and mussel leases, but it isn't issuing many more, as new housing developments are getting dibs on the island's increasingly precious shoreline. Consequently, farmers can turn around and "sell" established, successful leases for anywhere from $5000 to $15,000 an acre.

But visiting other oyster farms makes us homesick for Johnny's. At one, run by a large mussel producer, employees do the actual fishing while the owner works a calculator back in the processing plant. At another, ten employees alight on the beds one day a week to harvest, grade and ship. This operation seems more like banking than farming. Rather than raising oysters from seed, they purchase two- and three-year-old oysters, deposit them on the ocean bottom, then withdraw them two or three years later when the oysters have reached the minimum market size of three inches. Two partners show off the farm by driving us around in a state-of-the-art, $50,000 harvester boat that blows water onto the ocean bottom and stirs the oysters up a conveyor belt. The thing sounds like an industrial vacuum cleaner and would surely scare the life out of Johnny's endangered piping plover, not to mention any birds nesting along these shores.

Between visits to farms, we manage to sample the island's bounty of cooked-oyster dishes. Tyne Valley, near Malpeque Bay, is home to the Canadian Oyster Festival and The Landing Restaurant, where the specialty is an old family recipe—oysters coated in a light batter and deep-fried for one minute. The delectably tender morsel is perfect for an oyster virgin's first taste—the deep-frying mutes the commanding notes of sea and mineral.

At Carr's Oyster Bar at Stanley Bridge, we spend a sunny afternoon on the deck overlooking the harbour, sampling oysters steamed in a wine and garlic broth, an easy and delicious dish to whip up at home.

When it is time for dinner, we visit the gorgeous Dalvay by the Sea, a stand-in for the White Sands Inn in the movie *Road to Avonlea*. Here, we sample chef Andrew Morrison's latest specialty: six oysters seared with lemon, cilantro and black truffle oil. The taste is otherworldly.

But the highlight of our tour is a sampling of PEI varieties with champion shucker John Bil.

But first, a few tasting notes. Like wines, oysters can be distinguished by their species (think Chardonnay), their region (say, Napa Valley) and the waters (like vineyards' soils) they grow in. Starting with species, three are widely available commercially.

The *Crassostrea gigas*, or Japanese oyster—such as the Kumamoto—is now cultivated in the Pacific coastal waters of the western United States and Canada. We suspect it migrated to Toronto oyster bars only because East Coast varieties are iced under in winter. Connoisseurs with their sophisticated palates will wax on about the gigas possessing hints of melon, cucumber, grass and metal. Which means they taste like seaweed and copper.

The *Ostrea edulis*, or European oyster, is the variety the French predominately cultivate and consume—some 143,000 tons a year. Call me a home girl, but I nearly gagged after tasting their notes of rusting metal.

Our clear favourite is our own *Crassostrea virginica*, which grows along the east coast of North America from the Gulf of Mexico to their northernmost range in Prince Edward Island. The Florida Gulf, Maine Glidden Point, Cape Cod Cotuit, New Brunswick Caraquet and PEI Malpeque are all from the same family, yet there's a reason why folks in New Orleans douse their regional oysters in Tabasco and hot salsas while islanders here chase theirs down with nothing more than a cold beer.

As M.F.K. Fisher suggests, a southern oyster is like a Southern belle— "listless and bland." But our PEI oyster—courted by four seasons, from sultry summer to frigid winter—is a tangy tart, bursting with flavour.

And yet, as John Bil so aptly shows us, all island oysters are not the same. Malpeques can grow in waters just ten minutes apart and taste different, which is one of the reasons farmers like Johnny Flynn name their brands, usually after the water they harvest in. Water temperature, salinity, bottom soil, vegetation and even current conspire to make each unique. Tasting PEI brands side by side is rather like tasting Chardonnays from different vineyards in a region or even different slopes in the same vineyard.

So we sample, slurp and chew. Trying each is still like the first raw one I ever had—there is that ritual, a hot and bothered buildup to that tiny explosion of salt tang on the tongue.

We find that the oysters from the south shore, which opens to Northumberland Strait—from Hillsborough River, Clyde River and Bedeque Bay—have decidedly less salt. They're both milder and creamier, with a soft vegetable aftertaste. Oysters from the north shore and eastern tip, which opens to the Gulf of St. Lawrence and the vast Atlantic—Cascumpec Bay, Conway Narrows, Raspberry Point, Stanley River, South Lake and Colville Bay—have that classic Malpeque flavour. They're saltier, with a sweet hit on the chew, and a clean-steel finish. We prefer the north shores, and still love Colville Bays the best.

Our loyalty may well explain why a pek (a box of 100 to 120 small-size choice oysters) wholesales for 10 percent more than most Malpeques. As John Bil explains, oysters are still an esoteric product that requires a huge amount of trust. "A brand shows that the producer is taking care. And every time you open a box of Colville Bays, it's a great box of oysters."

But today we have none.

WE AWAKE, stirring to fantasies of gravel flying from the wheels of the American Cousins as they leave Prince Edward Island. *Ciao bellas!* Finally, we will have Johnny to ourselves. And today we are to see his oyster beds.

But at noon, Johnny calls. Big tears in his voice. He spent the morning saying goodbye. It clearly got to him. It's his daughter's last day of school and, to cut his long story short, he's throwing over the Food Writer from Toronto for his kid's school-end concert.

"At least the guy's got his heart in the right place," Nancy says when I hang up the phone.

I hiss until I have released a good bit of steam. Then grin. For I have worked Johnny's guilt to secure two dates for the next day—one to see his oyster beds right after lobster fishing, the other for dinner with Johnny and Mary Jane at our cottage.

But the next day, he doesn't call at noon as we had agreed. Or at one o'clock, or two. At three, I call him on his home phone. I call him on his cell phone. Ring, ring, ring. Outside, big storm clouds gather over Colville Bay. As lightning cracks and thunder rumbles, the Food Writer from Toronto marches out to the shore cliff, stamps her foot and screams with the fury of Lear: "What the hell do we have to do to get into Johnny Flynn's oyster bed?"

Five o'clock arrives, but Johnny does not. At six, just as we're about to throw in the towel on our dinner date, Johnny and Mary Jane appear, right on island time, apparently. Johnny offers me ten lobsters, a bag of oysters, a loaf of his mom's homemade bread and an apology. Johnny refuses to hand over the bread until I forgive him. The loaf lingers between us.

Family is only half his excuse this time. One of the giant mussel producers on the island who also cultivates oysters dropped by for a visit. Johnny says the two spent the afternoon as farmers do when it rains, "standing in the workshop talking about how to grow a better oyster and solve the world's problems."

I would have loved to hear that conversation. In clandestine cell phone calls Johnny made to me during the Cousins' visit (he has an endearing habit of thinking deeply about my questions, then calling me later with his answers), he talked on and on about limiting production, keeping prices high so farmers can take the time and care to produce a quality product and still make a fair buck. He credits the big producers for helping rebuild the PEI oyster fishery into a $7.5-million concern, but also criticizes them for being secretive. "They don't share research that could help others get a start and be successful," Johnny told me. "I'd hate to see two or three monopolize the industry. I'd rather have competition from a hundred small producers like me." Indeed, he served as president of the island aquaculture association for six years, playing, as he says, "cheerleader" to other producers. He claims his door is open for anyone to come and see his operation. "I've got nothing to hide," he says now. "Anyone can come and see my oyster beds."

"Except the Food Writer from Toronto," I say.

Johnny whips back the loaf of bread and comes out with the other half of his excuse. After the oyster producer left, he says it started to storm. And his eighty-two-year-old mom gets nervous in a thunderstorm, so Johnny sat through it with her.

*Damn it,* I think. *Family, again.* Still, I remind him that I'm here to write about him, that we've flown sixteen hundred kilometres to see his oyster beds and that tomorrow is our last day and we really have to see them.

He promises, right after lobster fishing. Crosses his heart even.

I take the loaf of bread.

THE NEXT MORNING, I refuse to let Johnny out of my sight, which means I am back on the boat fishing lobster at 4 A.M. Today, the ocean swells with eight-foot rollers, and I nearly lose my week's oyster gorge. After emptying the traps, we must haul in all three hundred of them for the winter, which takes a few trips back and forth. Our day drags on, to three o'clock in the afternoon.

Then, finally, we are pushing off shore into Colville Bay—to see the Promised Land at last. We motor the few feet out to the rearing grounds on an aluminum barge, a platform Johnny and Leo use to work on the water. Sarah, Johnny's youngest, comes along with us. She's a bright sprite of a ten year old, but was just a glint in Johnny's eye when he started in the oyster business over a decade ago, so we call her Oyster Girl.

She has carrot-orange hair and her father's determined blue eyes, and she makes one thing clear to us: We are taking her dad away from his real responsibility on end-of-fishing day, which is helping her build a bonfire on their beach, where the Flynns will all gather the next night to watch Canada Day fireworks soar over Colville Bay.

Compared with the other farms we visited—some as large as two hundred acres—Johnny's operation is tiny, comprised of Johnny's fifteen acres and Leo's ten. Rather than specializing in one aspect of oyster cultivation, they do everything—raising the seed from spat to finish, a seed-to-harvest cycle that takes a minimum of four to five years. "It's the farmer in us, I guess," says Johnny. "It takes patience and sometimes being stubborn, but we get real satisfaction from seeing an oyster grow up."

Johnny kills the engine and Oyster Girl hands him an oar—clunking me on the back of the head as she does. In a quiet hush, he poles us over three acres of oyster-rearing grounds. Here, Johnny's secret is finally revealed, though, as Johnny kept telling me all week, it's not much of a secret. While the big mussel producers tried to adapt the French Table method to grow oysters cheaper and faster, Johnny read up on the traditional approach and stayed true to it.

In August, about three weeks after the oysters spawn, Johnny and Leo put out some four hundred collectors at the mouths of two rivers at opposite ends of the island. In days, millions of wild spat—each the size of a grain of pepper—will cement themselves to the collectors. After the brothers retrieve the collectors, they knock off the minute flecks—a laborious process they perform by gloved hand. They then take the minuscule oysters out to the French Tables, which are foot-wide, wire-grate platforms that sit in long rows about a foot above the ocean floor. Attached to these by bungee cords are hundreds of Vexar bags made of a heavy plastic mesh. Johnny pulls a bag on board—it's slightly larger than a ten-pound potato sack. Inside are thousands of seeds the size of Oyster Girl's baby fingernail. They're exposed at low tide, covered at high. The "baring off," Johnny believes, makes the oysters "feed harder" when they are submerged. This is organic farming at its best—the oysters feed naturally on phytoplankton in the water while also filtering hundreds of gallons of water a day, which actually cleans the water.

If all goes well, the spat will grow to the size of a dime before winter, add an inch over the next summer, reach two inches by their third summer, at which time they're ready to spread on the bottom of Colville Bay, to reach their full size over the next summer.

But as the oysters grow, Johnny and Leo have to thin each bag several times during the year—if overcrowded, an oyster won't feed well and can even suffocate. They bring the bags to shore and empty the oysters onto a grader—three wire grates with holes of varying sizes. When they shake them through, the grater knocks off irregular shell formations and sorts the oysters into like-sized piles. Over the years, Johnny has discovered that oysters grow better if returned to a bag with similar-sized mates. It's one of the tricks, as Mary Jane teased at dinner the night before, that Johnny has picked up from walking around his farm at low tide "thinking like an oyster."

Johnny's meticulous approach requires a huge amount of work. Each thinning takes up to three weeks. During their busiest season, fall leading up to Christmas, they can spend twelve hours a day tonging, grading and packing oysters into plastic-coated cardboard boxes for shipping in refrigerated containers, by truck or plane. And each winter, to prevent freezing in the shallow waters, they must sink the bags in about twelve to fourteen feet of water. From seed through packing, Johnny estimates they will handle each oyster at least a dozen times—that's a lot of contact when you consider Colville Bay ships about a half million a year.

"Most people find the French Table method too labour-intensive," Johnny says, "but it works for us." So he holds true to it, using only the help of two university students during the summer. His philosophy is to be both his own boss and his own employee, responsible for getting things done and close to the action to know exactly what needs to be done. "You have to get your rubber boots and rubber gloves on and go out and work it yourself."

Johnny drops the bag back into the water. As he poles on, Oyster Girl scoops a starfish from the deck and places the creature in the palm of my hand.

"They eat baby oysters," she says.

"Hmm," agrees Johnny. "Suction cups on the legs pry open the shells just a crack, then it slides its stomach inside the shell and eats the oyster right there."

But the Vexar bag protects the oyster from the nasty starfish and other predators. The tables also keep the wee guys from sinking into the silt bottom of the ocean and suffocating.

We glide over to the maturing beds, covered at high tide by about six and half feet of water. The bottom is studded with thousands of oysters that glow an eerie grey under the surface. "They just sit there," says Johnny, "but we can't ever forget they're living creatures. We try not to step on them. We try to treat them with dignity."

Before Johnny can ask for them, Oyster Girl races for the set of tongs lying on the front of the deck. Nancy and I duck this time as she swings the ten-foot-long sticks over our heads and hands them to her father. Johnny scolds her to be careful. She sulks but not for long, for, with one scoop, Johnny tongs up about fifty market-size oysters, and Oyster Girl is at his side, begging him to shuck one for her. She's the only one of Johnny's children who likes raw oysters. As we contemplate the freshest ones we'll ever eat—right out of the water—she whips the half shell to her lips and her face breaks into a wide smile as she swallows the mouthful of summer ocean. For me, it is more like a mouth-puckering hit of warm salt that leaves me gasping for a cold beer.

As Johnny shucks us another round, I ask him about future plans. Will he get bigger? Expand into South Lake, where he also has a lease?

He looks over his oyster beds and shakes his head. "Really," he says, "we're right where we want to be." There's always risk in working with Nature—say a poor spat season, another Malpeque disease, a red-tide algae bloom that can close shellfish waters for a season, even years. But things are going his way now. After losing half his oysters through the first two winters, he has reduced mortality to about 10 percent a year. About 80 percent of the oysters he raises are choice, which commands top price. He's also starting to sell directly to restaurants, including Catch in Calgary, and he'd like to do more of that. "The trick now," he says, "is to just keep doing what we've been doing, keep consistent, keep in the rhythm of it all." And then, he says, he will consider expanding.

And if someone were to come along, I ask, and offer him a million bucks for it all? I regret the question as soon as I ask, for Johnny's sea-blue eyes water up.

"No," he says. "No, I couldn't ever. This is home."

He hands the tongs back to Oyster Girl, who dances them to the front of the barge. Johnny starts up the motor and steers us back to shore. As Nancy and I step onto the beach, Johnny nods to the pile of freshly fished oysters and asks if we want to take some back to Toronto.

Truthfully, we want to take everything home—Johnny Flynn, his family, his oyster farm, his sunrises and his sunsets. But we will settle for his oysters, if we must.

# Prince Edward Island

## Nancy's Fellers

This is a seductively easy appetizer to make, and your guests will fall in love with them, if not you for serving it. Even friends who don't like raw oysters lap these up. Count on 3 to 4 shucked oysters per person, so buy 12 to 16 for four people.

You can cheat the shucking by placing the oysters on a baking sheet in an oven preheated to 350°F (180°C) for 5 minutes. The shells will open slightly. Discard any that don't open, as they could be funky. With a knife, pry off the top shells and discard. Reserve the bottom shell with the oyster meat. Run a shucking knife or sharp knife under the oyster to cut the adductor muscle from the shell, but return the oyster to the shell.

For the cheese, Gruyère or Monterey Jack work nicely.

| 3 | cloves garlic, minced | 3 |
|---|---|---|
| 1/2 cup | butter | 125 mL |
| 12–16 | shucked oysters on the half shell | 12–16 |
| 1/2 lb | grated sharp cheese | 250 g |

Sauté the garlic in the butter in a sauté pan over low heat.

Turn the broiler on to high. Place the oysters in the half shell on a baking sheet. Spoon the garlic butter over each oyster; top with the grated cheese. Broil the oysters until the cheese browns, about 1 to 2 minutes.

Serve the oysters still in the half shell, but beware: The shells will be hot to the touch. Accompany with thick slices of baguette.

*Makes 4 servings.*

Credit: Nancy Lyons, Toronto, Ontario.

## Oyster Boy Oyster Stew

Adam Colquhoun, owner of Oyster Boy on Queen Street West in Toronto, runs a "Shuck U" class one Saturday a month. While teaching a small group of students how to shuck, he dispenses eclectic knowledge of the mollusc and spouts Zen-like aphorisms such as, "Oysters give their life to you."

This recipe comes with a caveat: Boil the stew gently and do not overcook the oysters—unless you like them rubbery. The ingredients in this recipe are too delicate to reheat, which means you'll have to eat this delicious stew all in one sitting, but that won't be too difficult.

Oyster liquor is the juice inside the shell; when shucking, catch and reserve any of this juice running off to use in the recipe.

| | | |
|---|---|---|
| 2 tbsp | unsalted butter | 25 mL |
| 2 tbsp | minced shallots | 25 mL |
| 2 tbsp | minced leek (white part only) | 25 mL |
| 1 cup | cubed cooked PEI potatoes | 250 mL |
| 1 tsp | finely chopped fresh thyme | 5 mL |
| 1/2 cup | dry white wine | 125 mL |
| 2 tsp | Worcestershire sauce | 10 mL |
| 2 cups | 35% cream | 500 mL |
| 1/4 cup | oyster liquor | 50 mL |
| 4 drops | hot sauce (such as Tabasco) | 4 drops |
| 12 | raw, shucked oysters | 12 |
| | salt | |
| | freshly grated nutmeg for garnish | |
| | chopped parsley for garnish | |

Melt the butter in a saucepan over medium-low heat. Sauté the shallots and leeks in the butter until soft. Add the potatoes, thyme, wine and Worcestershire sauce; cook for 3 to 4 minutes. Stir in the cream, oyster liquor and hot sauce. Bring to a gentle boil. Add the oysters; heat through, about 30 seconds. Season with salt. Top with freshly grated nutmeg and chopped parsley.

*Makes 2 servings.*

Credit: Adam Colquhoun, Oyster Boy, Toronto, Ontario.

# New Brunswick

# THE SALAD FROM THE SEA

*I once heard a story about a certain village somewhere in
Canada's Bay of Fundy area where everyone ate dulse.
After a hundred years or so they had to shoot
an old fellow just to start a graveyard.*
—Roland Flagg, founder, Roland's Sea Vegetables

If Grand Manan Island and its dulse industry were to promote themselves, their advertisements might go something like this:

*Grand Manan Island—undiscovered temperate maritime paradise in the mouth of the Bay of Fundy, Canada's other Vancouver Island. Home to whales, traditional fishing communities, naturalists, kayakers and artists. Stunning beauty may overwhelm you.*

*Dark Harbour Dulse—an edible seaweed that you eat like a potato chip but works like a multivitamin. May ward off cancer and obesity. Considered the best in the world though largely unknown outside Atlantic provinces.*

The ads would be classifieds, set in very small type, and likely placed in the community newspaper. In other words, the island and its dulse industry are about as discovered as they want to be.

Grand Manan is the largest island in an archipelago of tiny islands scant kilometres from the U.S. border and a ninety-minute ferry ride from Blacks Harbour, New Brunswick. On some crossings, lucky passengers have spotted the endangered North Atlantic right whale—the mouth of the Bay of Fundy is the whale's summer feeding grounds.

It is mid-August when Nancy and I land here, the morning of the fifteenth to be exact. Sandy Flagg, who runs Roland's Sea Vegetables, started by his father, Roland, known as the King of Dulse, suggested the timing of our visit to coincide with the dulsing tides, which occur on the full and new moons, every other week. Then, the massive Fundy tides recede by as much as twenty-two feet—exposing the red seaweed that grows luxuriously at the low-water mark and giving pickers about a two-hour window to harvest the island's most famous crop.

Yet, when we arrive, the tides are off. Dulsers, as pickers call themselves, break the news to us at the drying grounds surrounding Sandy's house and a tiny store marked with a hand-painted sign: Roland's Sea Vegetables. Sandy's miscommunication—accidental? intended?—strikes me as odd, but, then, so did the full answering machine I encountered whenever I tried to leave a message during the two weeks leading up to our arrival.

"Are you sure?" I ask.

"Tide book's our bible," says Dale Parker, forty-five, a tall, handsome man with a teenager's grin. He's been married to Sandy's youngest sister, Cindy, forty-two, for twenty-five years. Winters he works as a deckhand on a lobster boat. Summers he's Cindy's right-hand man picking dulse. "Dulsing's her thing," he says. "She knows more about the dulse business than I ever will."

The drying grounds, located on high ground in the middle of the island, are five acres of tightly packed beach rocks the size of softballs. A group of five dulsers, who look like they've been friends since high school, stand on the edge, waiting for the morning dew to burn off so that they can spread the last of the previous week's harvest on the rocks to dry.

In a few minutes, Cindy returns with takeout coffees for the group. She's a small woman but a force of energy, with a deep tan, dark flashing eyes and impressive legs—dulser's legs, chiselled from hours of picking a trail through slippery beach rock. She greets us with a friendly smile and firm handshake. No, Sandy has not told her we're coming, so, no, she has no idea who we are, but, yes, we're welcome to drop by their cabin in Dark Harbour to talk about dulsing and, yes, the jammed answering machine certainly sounds like Sandy.

Then she looks at Dale, who looks at her, and they seem to have decided, in this wordless exchange, that the rocks are dry, for suddenly they are rolling a net over the rocks, then spreading the dulse on the net. The others follow their lead. Dale explains that, in a few hours, they'll roll up the net, flip it, and unroll it, to let the dulse dry on the other side.

Then, as soon as Dale and Cindy finish, they hop in their truck and head off, only god knows where on this small island, but in an awful hurry.

ONE LOCAL GUIDEBOOK claims that Grand Mananers have been harvesting dulse commercially since 1876. Before United Empire Loyalists settled on the island in 1784, Passamaquoddy-Penobscot Natives canoed from the mainland to fish, hunt seals and gather dulse from the northwest, or back side, of the island, accessible by the natural sea cove of Dark Harbour. Even without a lab to provide analysis, local tribes knew that this "salad of the sea" was chock full of good stuff—vitamin C (percentage-wise, almost as much as an orange, though drying reduces it), protein (14 percent, compared with 30 percent for lean beef), soluble and insoluble fibre (so much that it may cause flatulence in some), as well as vitamin A, calcium, thiamine (keeps nerves and muscle tissue healthy), riboflavin (helps the body absorb iron) and more. Clearly, we can learn a thing or two about their version of the 100-mile diet. In the early 1600s, Samuel de Champlain's French colony of Port Royal in Nova Scotia suffered horribly from scurvy until First Nations folks introduced the men to soups made from birch bark and dulse.

This particular species, *Palmaria palmata*, grows widely along the Pacific Northwest and North Atlantic coasts, along both North America and Europe, but geographic conditions on the Dark Harbour shoreline conspire to produce what many consider to be the finest in the world. The towering cliffs on the backside of the island shade the dulse at low tide, protecting it from burning sunlight. At high water, the massive Fundy tides—the highest in the world—pump nutrients to the plant while waves bounce back from the cliffs to create a sloshing action that prevents mud, mussels and other sea creatures from collecting on the dulse.

Dulsers here say they can easily spot the difference between superior Dark Harbour and what grows elsewhere, including Passage dulse they collect off shallow pebble beaches on the front side of the island just kilometres away. Companies on the island sell Dark Harbour dulse whole only, whereas Passage dulse is ground into seasoning flakes—possibly along with the mud and tiny sea creatures that cling to it.

The island's claims about the superiority of Dark Harbour dulse is not just local boasting. "The area is unique," says James Craigie, a specialist in marine plants with the National Research Council in Halifax. "The conditions give you an extremely good-quality dulse. It affects the taste, texture, colour, mouth feel—everything."

Yvonne Yuan, a professor at the School of Nutrition at Toronto's Ryerson University, started researching Dark Harbour dulse after several high-profile studies cited the health benefits of seaweeds such as kelp and nori. In the past, herbalists used seaweed to cure ulcers and cuts (it is high in zinc, which promotes healing) and treat obesity (it is packed with iodine, which helps thyroid function, regulating metabolism). Now researchers believe that antioxidant-rich seaweed has cancer-suppressing qualities and may emerge as a leading player in the fight against that disease. But Yuan realized that international researchers were overlooking North American seaweed. "Dulse here differs from a nutritional and chemical perspective," she says. "Plus Dark Harbour dulse is harvested in the spring, summer and fall, and that's good for its antioxidant qualities. It is also shaded from the sun and therefore needs greater pigment for photosynthesis, which is responsible for its rich, dark purple colouration." Yet, Yuan proves as coy as Grand Mananer dulsers when I ask about her research. "The unique compounds I'm interested in are natural sunscreens produced by the plant…. There's speculation that these may have some pharmaceutical applications, but that's all I want to say."

WHEN WE CALL on Sandy Flagg, he looks like he would rather jump in a dory and sail up the coast than face the swelling tsunami of interest in dulse. He sits in his home office—the kitchen table—as we talk, hands clasped tightly, face pinched. He's forty-six. He's been having stomach troubles. Nerves. The phone rings several times. He ignores it. Health food stores and now doctors and raw-food restaurants have been calling from California.

Sandy says he's still trying to catch up from weeks of dismal weather in the spring and can't fill orders for his regular customers. The dulsers who supply him stopped picking because the fog was so thick, they couldn't dry their harvest. "It's like haying," he says. "You need the sunshine."

The season runs roughly from mid-May to mid-October—not that dulsers can't pick through the winter, but they need the strong, steady summer sun to dry it, a good six hours, and that's on a sunny, breezy day. Fresh water—rain or even mist—will leach out sea salt, altering the taste and pocking the dried-black fronds with white marks. More than a sprinkle of rain and the dulse becomes compost.

Sandy was a picker before taking over his father's business and says he misses the life—seasonal work outdoors on a gorgeous beach and with no boss to answer to except the pull of the moon. When he was a boy, about ten families camped out in shacks on the natural seawall at Dark Harbour and spent summers gathering dulse. "Even as kids, we had to fill and spread a bag before we went to play," says Sandy. "It only took us an hour or so, and then we could spend the rest of the day swimming and rowing in the punt. It was my parents' way of teaching us how to work, I guess."

Roland built his business by doing what few islanders like to do—leaving the island. Although they can find every nook and cranny on the twenty-eight-kilometre back side of the island, even in a thick fog, most dulsers admit that they get lost as soon as they hit a mainland highway. But Roland, a lifetime lobster fisherman, figured if another local could sell dulse off the island, then so could he. He secured his first customer in Saint John and was soon buying dulse from others and selling to stores across the Atlantic, then to supermarkets, and, increasingly, health food stores across North America and by mail order as far away as Australia. When Roland and his wife, Flora, retired, they gave this bungalow and business to their only son, Sandy. Then they bought a lot down the road and built an identical house. Now, Sandy might buy $100,000 worth of dulse a season, paying pickers $4.75 a pound for first-quality dried dulse and $2.75 for second-quality (still Dark Harbour but perhaps salt pocked or silted), which he grinds into flakes. His only processing is packing the dulse in bags—"crispy dulse" is packed right off the rocks, whereas "soft dulse" sits in his shed for the night to collect moisture. (I recommend the crispy—you can soften it yourself by leaving some out on the countertop in a bowl. Plus paying by dry weight makes for a better deal, with a one-and-a-half-ounce bag selling retail in the $3 range.)

Sandy's company and two others ship about seventy-five thousand pounds each year, but that is a paltry drop in the bucket in the $5.5 billion seaweed business worldwide, much of that crop cultivated at sea by Japan,

China and the Philippines. But what happens on Grand Manan is natural aquaculture—the sea does the farming, so to speak. Here, nature provides a crop that requires no seeding, tending or input of chemicals or fertilizers. Nature even regulates the harvest—dulse regenerates itself from a root-hold on rocks every two weeks, which coincides with the biweekly dulsing tides, making it impossible to overpick. The only processing involved is drying the dulse outdoors, then packing it into plastic bags and closing them with a twist tie. Sealed from oxygen and stored in the freezer, dulse will last indefinitely.

Although Sandy has a premium natural product that is clearly in short supply, he has no interest in taking advantage of that demand. Indeed, he's more concerned with hanging on to the business he has—a small, traditional cottage industry. And so, it seems, are the other two dulse-buying companies here—one run by Sandy's cousin, Gerry Flagg. They agree on the price they'll pay dulsers each year. The hundred or so dulsers, in turn, remain loyal, picking for one company rather than trying to sell off-island. And the companies remain loyal to their long-term customers, filling their orders rather than taking on newer and potentially higher-paying ones. "I'm not in this to be a billionaire," says Sandy. "I'm not out to beat anyone. I'm interested in making a living is all."

As SANDY STILL INSISTS that dulsers are picking this week, Nancy and I hurry over to Dark Harbour after our chat. The winding road slows us down, luckily, as six deer explode from the dense bush and spring across the highway in front of our Jeep, then disappear into the bush on the other side. Finally, the trees give way to the towering cliffs of Dark Harbour and the road ekes through a crevice to plunge sharply to sea level.

The harbour is not nearly as bleak as the name suggests, at least not by late morning, when sunlight has finally seeped over the cliffs to flood the blue waters below. The cliffs are tagged with bright graffiti—high school graduates proudly paint their names high atop the rocks, alongside their graduation years. The few shacks that remain on the natural breakwater are abandoned. Now, many dulsers stay in a string of tidy cabins set back in the trees, while their colourful dories line the pebble beach in front.

But today the beach is empty, save for one dulser. He picks his way toward us through soccer-ball size rocks, a large plastic bag bulging with dulse slung over each shoulder. Elton, as he introduces himself, actually looks like a forty-something pop star—thin, with wire-framed glasses and sandy shoulder-length hair. He says there wasn't much to pick today in this neap, or dead, tide, but he wasn't doing anything, so he figured he would try to collect a bag or two. "It's a walk on the beach as much as anything," he says.

When I explain why we're here, he sets down his bag and leads us to the water's edge. Between the incoming tide and dry beach is a swath of wet, mossy rocks. Elton makes his way through the slippery boulders like a nimble deer, while we hurry after him, slipping, stumbling, cursing. I couldn't imagine calling two hours of this, lugging a bag or two of dulse, a walk on the beach.

Finally, Elton stops at a rock covered in drooping translucent purple fronds—dulse. Farther out, he says, at low tide in a good picking area, every rock is covered like this.

He shows me how to pull off a handful—it snaps easily and is cool and soft to the touch, like tender camera film and not at all slimy. "That's the way I eat it," he says, tucking a piece into his mouth and chewing it like gum. I try a mouthful and pass some to Nancy. It's odd what people find icky. While I must still go through a hot and bothered buildup before eating a raw oyster, Nancy can slurp back a half dozen in a wink. And although she grew up eating dried dulse, loves maki sushi and the nori it's wrapped in, she balks at trying this—a bit of fresh wet seaweed. To me, it smells like the ocean—briny and lusty—and simply tastes saltier, albeit with a slightly fishy aftertaste—or is that grassy? She mutters something about dead fish.

"Some don't like it," Elton shrugs.

He peels off another leaf to chew, and so do I.

A FEW DAYS LATER, we hear through the dulsing grapevine that Dale and Cindy are heading out winkling: picking periwinkles, the small snails that burrow in sand on the beach and which Sandy also sells off-island. We drop by their Dark Harbour cabin in the hopes that they might take me out in their dory for a look at dulsing grounds along the coastline—and maybe give me a short lesson in picking.

Cindy greets us at the door as if we were old friends, then disappears to run errands, leaving Dale to regale us with stories of their dulsing adventures.

Their cabin has no electricity, but it's a beautiful place, built with island woods that Dale cut with a handsaw. A massive picture window overlooks a front deck and the harbour. They spend most of their summers here. Winters, they live in a house on the corner of Dark Harbour Road. During the fall hunting season, they head to yet another cabin, in the woods—both Cindy and Dale are avid deer hunters.

"We like doing all the same things," says Dale. "We do pretty good together."

With three houses within a twenty-minute drive of each other, they clearly enjoy the island lifestyle. Still, they've endured their share of tragedy: Five years ago, their eldest son died in a car accident at age eighteen. Their youngest son is now twenty-one. He works at odd jobs around the island after the fish processing plant he worked at closed.

With the demise of various fisheries on the East Coast, Dale says more islanders are turning to dulsing. About a hundred pick the back side of the island—the companies control the numbers by buying only from their list of pickers. Dale says there is occasional talk of licensing dulsers or leasing dulsing grounds so that everyone has a patch to work. For the purposes of calculating winter unemployment payments, the federal government classifies dulsers as fishers, but Dale claims no one wants dulsing to be constrained by that industry's regulations. They prefer the thrill of open rivalry.

"Fishermen are fishermen," Dale says. "We're competitive. Everyone wants to catch the most and get the most. [With dulsing] we're competing for space on the beach. We're all neighbours and we know each other, so there are no fist fights or anything, but you might tell someone to back off if they're picking too close. Someone might see our haul and say, 'Wow, you did good,' and ask, 'Where's that?' And I'll say, 'Too bad, it's all gone.' That's about all the information we'll share."

When the dulsing tide's on—when the tide reaches its highest and lowest levels, pulled by a full or new moon—Cindy and Dale might pick twice a day for a solid week—at the night low tide and again twelve hours later at the afternoon low tide. Often, it will take them an hour or more to motor their dory to a desired spot. As Dale says, "You try to figure when everyone else is going to be there, and then you go a half hour earlier." They pick at night with miner's hats and headlamps, in fog with the help of a compass and in rain, sinking their harvest in bags in Dark Harbour until it's sunny enough to dry. Only rough weather—when it's too stormy to land their dories on the beach rock—stops them.

During the first few days of a dulsing tide, they might pick as much as 480 pounds a day, which dries to about sixty pounds—an 8 to 1 ratio of wet to dry. As the tide wears on, the hunt for dulsing grounds that haven't been picked over becomes more intense and harvests fall off to thirty dried pounds or even nothing.

"It's back-breaking work," says Dale. "You spend the whole time bent over picking. You're carrying heavy bags over slippery rocks. There's lots of twisted and stuck ankles. You're pulling dulse off the rocks with your bare hands, so you lose all your fingernails. Then, if you get that harvest back to the drying grounds and it rains, you've done all that work for nothing."

Well, not exactly nothing.

Suddenly, Cindy reappears and announces that it's time to go winkling. She and Dale don't expect to pick many but hope to make enough money to pay for the gas for their dory. Although this is their week off from dulsing, they still want to spend time on the beach. As Cindy says, "I see this view and I never take it for granted. Some people do, but I never do."

As for me enjoying that view with them, well, that's another issue. "I like being by myself," Cindy says before I can even ask to go along. "I love my boy, but I don't even like him coming with us."

Dale shrugs. He and Cindy have their system, he says. She picks to the left side of the boat, he picks to the right side; that's the way they've always done it, and that's the way it will always be.

TRUTHFULLY, I am only half disappointed that I won't be getting up in the middle of night to walk on slippery rocks lugging heavy bags of wet dulse. For there is still the adventure of figuring out how to cook the stuff. And Nancy and I have landed in the perfect foodie haven to experiment: The Inn at Whale Cove, with its collection of rustic cottages and a superb dining room run by chef Laura Buckley.

Laura tells us that three Boston ladies happened upon this breathtaking cove in 1903. While the Roosevelts were establishing summer homes on the nearby Canadian island of Campobello and rich New Englanders were flocking to the posh resort town of St. Andrews by-the-Sea in New Brunswick, these gusty gals bought twenty acres here, built cottages and carved out many of the local hiking trails. Soon, their trust-fund gal pals were adding summer homes to the colony, including Pulitzer Prize–winning author Willa Cather and her partner, Edith Lewis. (The Cather cottage is available to rent, though, like most things on Grand Manan, barely advertised.) As Laura says, the remote island offered the "Cottage Girls" the freedom to drink, smoke, hike, skinny-dip and wear men's clothing.

Sadly, we've happened here fifty years too late for that fun, though Nancy is making her own party with martinis on the front deck of our cottage, trying to spot right whales, or so she says. I suggest that she's simply getting in condition for our next visit, to her home province of Nova Scotia, and that we lay off the cocktails and get back to figuring out how to cook dulse. She says something about leaving me to that adventure now that I can't go dulsing in the middle of the night.

Well, I admit dulse is an acquired taste, but there are ways to improve it. I came armed with advice from Willa and Ross Mavis, hosts of the TV show Tide's Table, who offered a few tips when we stayed at their luxurious spa in Saint John, New Brunswick, the Inn on the Cove. They suggest creating your own flakes by frying dulse in a dry frying pan for a few seconds, then crunching up the leaves with your hands. Ross says he spikes any dish with the flakes—pasta, soups, chowders—when he wants "that fresh briny taste and flavour of the sea."

Roland and Flora, a charmingly chatty couple whom I visit for an afternoon, recommend eating it the way islanders do, by popping it in the microwave for forty-five seconds at high power. The result is a tasty salt-and-veggie, potato-chip-like snack. Flora also adds dulse to her chowders, while Roland sprinkles flakes over his fried eggs—or just about anything where he would normally use salt.

Locals at the Saturday morning farmers' market tell me they add dulse to stir-fries and salads. Fried in olive oil, the seaweed takes on the flavour of bacon and makes for an incredible dulse, lettuce and tomato sandwich. Indeed, the ones I make for our lunch catch Nancy's attention. "Hmm," she says. "Bacon. Not bad."

At Keyser's Kafe at the wharf on Grand Manan, chefs Michael and Gordon make a sumptuous seafood chowder with dulse, to which Nancy delivers the highest compliment: "You can't really taste the dulse." Michael, who moved here from Hamilton after meeting his partner Gordon, likes to gather and dry the seaweed himself. He says he prefers his dulse crispier than islanders dry it, but I suspect that he'll use any excuse to spend time on the beach. "When you're lucky," he tells us over a beer on the sunny café patio, "you can see porpoises, seals, whales and ospreys."

By the end of the week, I'm ready to try a dish of my own, a rather bold adaptation of a traditional island dulse-and-potato soup recipe, to which I add sautéed onions and garlic, substitute milk for 18 percent cream and, where a spoonful of dulse is called for, pour in a cup and a half of sautéed crispy dulse that I've broken into flakes with my hands. The first taste hits me like the Groundhog Day gale of 1976 that flipped over rocks and tore off the dulse roots, ruining the dulsing season for the entire next year. I take the soup off the burner and prepare to toss it.

Then, as often happens with my cooking experiments, Nancy pulls herself away from her martini, wanders by my cooling, abandoned soup. The Seafood Goddess reheats it, adds a dash or three of pepper, a half cup of milk, a few squirts of lemon, a shot of wine and pronounces it fabulous. With only $2 of dulse, the chowder tastes like it's packed with $20 of seafood. And she finds the perfect things to accompany it for our evening picnic on the cottage deck: a crusty French loaf, a cold bottle of crisp Riesling and a sunset over Whale Cove.

# New Brunswick

## Keyser's Kafe Dulse Fish Chowder

This warming soup is perfect for fall and winter meals and a local Grand Manan favourite, adapted by chef Gordon Kinghorne for his wharf-side restaurant.

| | | |
|---|---|---|
| 6 | medium to large white-fleshed potatoes, peeled and cubed | 6 |
| 1 1/2 | medium onions, chopped | 1 1/2 |
| 1 1/2 lb | raw pollock, cut into 1-inch/2.5 cm pieces | 750 g |
| 2 tbsp | butter | 25 mL |
| 1 1/2 tsp | dulse flakes or finely chopped dulse | 7 mL |
| 1 | 13 oz/384 mL can 2% evaporated milk | 1 |
| 1 3/4 cup | 18% cream | 425 mL |
| 1 1/2 tsp | salt | 7 mL |
| 1/2 tsp | black pepper | 2 mL |

Rinse the cut potatoes to get rid of excess starch and place along with the onions in a large stockpot; cover with water. Bring to a boil; cook over high heat until the potatoes are pliable but not mushy. Remove from heat. Drain the water, leaving enough in the pot to just cover the potatoes. Purée one-quarter of the remaining water and the potato-onion mixture in a blender; return the mixture to the pot.

Stir in the pollock, butter, dulse flakes, milk and cream; bring to a gentle boil, then reduce heat to a simmer. Season with salt and pepper.

*Makes 6 to 8 servings.*

Credit: Chef Gordon Kinghorne, Keyser's Kafe, Grand Manan, New Brunswick.

## Inn on the Cove Salmon and Dulse Pasta

As Ross Mavis says, "There's nothing quite like the briny flavour of dulse to jazz up this fettuccine and salmon luncheon dish." You can make this pasta quickly with either fresh cooked Atlantic salmon or a tin of sockeye salmon. This dish can be made in less than 10 minutes if you use fresh pasta.

| | | |
|---|---|---|
| 1/2 lb | fresh whole-wheat fettuccine | 250 g |
| 1 tbsp | butter | 15 mL |
| 1 tbsp | chopped fresh oregano | 15 mL |
| 1/2 cup | sour cream | 125 mL |
| | salt and freshly ground black pepper | |
| 1/2 cup | cooked salmon, fresh or tinned | 125 mL |
| 2 | green onions, chopped | 2 |
| 1 tbsp | freshly squeezed lemon juice | 15 mL |
| 1 tbsp | dulse flakes | 15 mL |

Cook the pasta according to package instructions, drain and place in a large glass bowl. Toss with the butter and oregano. Stir in the sour cream. Season with salt and pepper.

Divide the pasta among individual plates. Break the salmon in rough chunks over the pasta. Sprinkle the green onion and lemon juice over each portion. Top with dulse flakes.

*Makes 2 to 4 servings.*

Credit: Chef Ross Mavis, Inn on the Cove, Saint John, New Brunswick.

# Nova Scotia

# TWO FISHERMEN AND A FARMER

*This could be the start*
*of a beautiful relationship*
*with the scallop.*
—Chef Eric Ripert

It is a bit surreal motoring out to sea with a man whom fisheries officials told me does not exist. Yet, Duncan Bates looks real enough standing at the wheel of his twenty-eight-foot converted lobster boat, even stubbornly so as we chug past a gleaming white private cruise ship moored offshore in Chester. Oddly, the Miami Vice–style craft looks more at home in this former fishing village than Duncan's aging haul, one of the few working boats left in a harbour now bobbing with sleek racing yachts. On the steep shoreline behind us, two-hundred-year-old sea captains' houses have been gussied up to their gables by moneyed Americans who summer here. Ahead of us, on one of the many outlying islands, is the white, sprawling Cape Cod–style home of Canadian financier Christopher Ondaatje. As we round the north shore of the basin, John Risley's monster mansion screams into view, a red-brick statement of grandiosity even on this ritzy shoreline. Fisheries departments certainly know this man exists—he has built a $640-million fortune with his Clearwater Seafoods, which pretty much owns Georges Bank, Canada's most valuable scallop fishery.

"It's gorgeous, isn't it?" Duncan says. He's definitely not referring to Risley's garish spread but to his own small slice of water estate, a five-acre scallop farm that forms a V on the sheltered side of the uninhabited Snake Island, about three kilometres off the mainland in Mahone Bay, on Nova

Scotia's southwest coast. Great blue herons nest on the island, and he has seen deer swim from the mainland to this splendour of sand beach and forest.

At 8 A.M. on this dreamlike day, sunlight drenches the ocean. A soft breeze stirs the surface. Duncan cuts his motor and we glide to a buoy that he catches with a grappling hook. "I've been ten years learning how to make this farm work commercially," he tells me as he ties up his boat, "but this is my passion. This is such an opportunity to work out here, I refuse to ever give it up. And that's what will make this work, the guy who won't give up."

I must confess that I had nearly thrown in the towel just trying to find a scallop farmer in Nova Scotia. Several calls to provincial and federal fisheries departments throughout the Atlantic provinces yielded the same bad news: A few people had set up operations but had not been able to make them work. They told me the most prominent had gone out of business a few years ago—an experimental farm in Chester run by Acadia University professor and scallop expert Mike Dadswell.

I tried another tack, asking if anyone dived for scallops commercially, an environmentally friendly means of fishing them. Some restaurants in Canada claim to sell diver scallops, but that's misleading. Nova Scotia issues only recreational licences and prohibits divers from selling their catch. Diver scallops should more properly be called "dry scallops." They are caught by traditional means but shipped fresh, without being frozen or processed with sodium tripolyphosphate, a common fish preservative that also allows processors to pump water into the scallop to increase its weight—the reason why many frozen or fresh wet scallops shrink so much in the frying pan.

Dry scallops are clearly better, but it still seemed that the only viable system of delivering the tasty treats to my plate was via dredging, a fishing practice so harmful that, in 2006, the United Nations urged countries to ban it. People who work with scallops think they're cute, but the hard-shelled creature is no white pup seal. Hollywood stars aren't exactly clamouring to have their picture taken with the dull brown mollusc. The folks advocating the ban were provoked by reams of scientific studies that showed dredging and trawling severely damages the ocean floor, ripping up crevices, seaweed, eel grass, sponges and coral that provide habitats for a range of species. John Risley, objective man that he is in this matter, promptly responded that dredging does no harm, and Canada lined up with a handful of countries opposing the ban, which eventually fell through. Today, Nova Scotia remains the epicentre of scallop fishing in Canada, landing about $70 million annually.

The bad news about dredging had placed me in a moral quandary, which I blame on my partner. I did not fall in love with the scallop until Nancy brought me to her home province of Nova Scotia for the first time. Initially, I was not a happy traveller. Upon landing in her landlocked hometown of Windsor, I quickly realized we were miles from the coast and, hence, a place to buy fresh lobster right off the boat.

To save me from sinking into a major sulk, Nancy whisked me two hours down the Bay of Fundy coast to Digby, a tiny fishing town that is famous well beyond its size for one thing—its scalloping fleet was once the largest in the world. And the boats, according to many, still land the finest scallop meats. That quality may well have to do with the massive Fundy tides, the highest in the world, which funnel nutrient-rich waters to a range of sea creatures, from whales and porpoises to the doughnut-sized mollusc. But the boats also play a role, plying these inshore waters for shorter periods—one to four days—then returning to port with a fresh catch, rather than flash-freezing it at sea as offshore trawlers do. The meats do freeze well, but I was about to discover what they taste like mere hours out of the water.

In a restaurant with a prime view of the harbour, which is just about any in Digby, Nancy ordered a pitcher of Nova Scotia's favourite beer, Alexander Keith's India Pale Ale, and a plate of fresh scallops. The puffy, slightly browned marshmallows arrived deep-fried, a method of cooking that I have come to consider a grave injustice to the sea meat. But even that rough tavern treatment could not destroy these tender treats. To the uninitiated, a scallop is like no other seafood. It lacks any trace of fishiness, being more like the tenderloin of chicken, the most succulent portion of the breast. The texture of these fresh scallops was sublime, with the spring of a ripe strawberry. And the flavour popped—a sweet decadence that I imagined could go well with maple syrup or maybe even a dollop of chili-infused chocolate sauce.

This was not supper so much as a seafood dessert. Just one turned my mood. The second made me deeply happy. By the third, I was ridiculously giddy and my sudden bright mood had nothing to do with the pitcher of Keith's. The tiny creature is not only among the most nutritious of seafood, it also packs a happy punch—tryptophan, a nervous-system freedom fighter that alleviates depression, anxiety, irritability and impatience. No wonder scallop chowder is a staple in Nova Scotia kitchens. Without it, the entire fishing industry might well be cowering in bed rather than heading out to sea on brutally cold days.

After that, Nancy and I made many blissful visits home (or so I have come to think of it now that I have found my proper place in her family—in the kitchen). Once, we circumnavigated mainland Nova Scotia in search of the best scallop recipes. Every chef we spoke to lamented the practice of dredging, but, well, there was no alternative was there? And then they went to work serving up dishes that made us wonder if they had lain awake nights dreaming up such concoctions.

At the Domaine de Grand Pré winery restaurant outside Wolfville, sautéed scallops swam in a tangy yellow curry with shiitake mushrooms. In town at the excellent Tempest, a single scallop the size of a cupcake arrived atop a sautéed slice of purple Peruvian potato with an eggplant-and-red-pepper purée. But no one, it seems, loves the scallop more than Claude AuCoin, executive chef of the Digby Pines Resort, a proud old hotel and golf resort minutes from the harbour. Here, AuCoin orders in scallops daily, and he makes the most of it. "Some days, they arrive still fluttering, and they're super firm," he told us. "After a few days, the texture starts to turn and they become soft in the mouth and the taste looses its pizzazz." He led us back to the kitchen to show off his stash—they were plump wonders with not a drop of the milky liquid that oozes out when scallops have been sitting a few days.

AuCoin took a large scallop (a ten to twenty count of meat per pound is best for individual servings; the smaller twenty to thirty counts are better for pastas and chowders) and placed it in olive oil in a very hot cast-iron pan, then seared each side for a flash of time, thirty seconds. "I like the middle to be pink and moist or it gets chewy," he said. "When it turns white on the sides, you know it's done."

To AuCoin, the bivalve is a cheeky chameleon that can dance with any number of spicy partners—butter and garlic, chili and curry, coconut and ripe mangoes. For an all-scallop tasting menu, he once whipped up a batch of smoked scallop ice cream. For us, he skewered three scallops, rolled them in nori, sautéed and sliced them and, then, to remind them of their home in the sea, sprinkled their upturned white faces with dulse flakes—the prize seaweed from the Bay of Fundy. As an encore, he served up an eye-popping presentation—a fetchingly fat scallop on a roasted red beet, surrounded by a spicy orange purée of carrot and cardamom.

Finally, after wrenching ourselves from Digby, we waddled west, to Halifax and FID, an exquisite French-Asian fusion restaurant. Here, shockingly, two whole sautéed scallops arrived at our table with the gonads attached. This was strange, a surprise even to my Nova Scotian partner who had only ever eaten the meats, the golf-ball-sized adductor muscle that closes the shells. Our waiter informed us that in Asia, the prized delicacy is nearly always served with the gonad attached.

Our server-turned-adventure-eating-guide also told us that the creamy half moon curled around the adductor was the male gonad—it tasted of smoked oyster. The electric orange was the female—her flavour was sweeter, closer to the dense roe of a lobster. But, as it would turn out, consuming the ovaries and testis was not to be my most extreme eating adventure with the scallop.

MY GHOST FARMER lifts a line from the water, feeds it into his hydraulic winch and starts hoisting up pearl nets. Dripping forests of algae come up with them. "The farm practically creates a reef down there," Duncan tells me as furry green globs splatter his boyish face and tussled brown hair. I can see now why he carefully stowed away his wire-frame glasses and pulled on foul-weather gear on this hot clear day. He works the whirring hydraulics, steadily, carefully. His overalls hang off his slim frame, making him look even younger than his thirty-seven years, more like a bookish graduate student.

With about a hundred pearl nets aboard, Duncan sets up a workstation on a table at the back of the boat and starts transferring two-year-old scallops from the fedora-sized pearl nets into larger, barrel-shaped lantern nets that he uses for the final year of grow out, when the scallops pack on weight. The process of transferring scallops from smaller to larger nets to reduce the numbers in each is what aquaculture boils down to, he says, thinning—reducing stocking density as the scallop grows. Each fall, he buys about a hundred thousand wild spat from a farm in Cape Breton, which are caught near wild beds (scallops spawn into the sea and the larvae will latch onto onion bags stuffed with old fishing gill net). The spat arrive here a year later, each the size of a fingernail, and go into the pearl nets at one hundred to a net. In the spring, Duncan thins them to twenty or twenty-five a net, reducing them again in the fall to twelve or fifteen a lantern net before harvesting the two-and-a-half- or three-inch scallops for market over the next year.

He puts me to work threading a string of fishing line to close the openings of the lantern nets he has filled, a task I perform too zealously. "Ah, maybe a little looser," Duncan instructs. Every extra second he has to spend with a net can add hours to his week. He has about five thousand nets on his farm, hanging from twelve-hundred-yard-long lines. He can empty and refill about a thousand nets a day. "It's pretty repetitive, I guess," he says, as if that's all there is to this.

Duncan's a brainy, understated guy and it takes a little prompting to get him to explain that there's a precise formula to his work that's taken him a decade to perfect. "Yeah, it's a complex game," he admits. "Mussel farming is dead easy by comparison."

He estimates that some forty to fifty species of sea plants and animals can slime up his nets—reducing water and nutrient flow to the scallops—so he has studied their growing seasons, timing his thinning and re-entry of nets into the water to avoid the worst of the fouling. He's had to figure out precise hanging depths of his lines—scallops grow better in twenty to seventy feet. He's also constantly adapting his equipment to speed the process of working with three hundred thousand scallops a year. And then there's the scallop itself, which, as Duncan says, "is a finicky creature that's pretty easy to kill."

Apparently, they don't like to be crowded in the nets. They don't like dirty nets. They don't like to be shaken by waves. They don't like sudden changes in water temperatures. They don't like to be out of the water for too long during thinning. And maybe they don't like you looking at them the wrong way—they have more than a hundred eyes lining the inside rim of their upper and lower shells, for spotting predators.

Japanese fishers invented the fussy art of scallop farming in the 1950s, adapting the equipment from pearl aquaculture. Duncan studied the craft as a biology student at Acadia University, in Mike Dadswell's class. Yes, that's the same Mike Dadswell who fisheries told me went out of business and, apparently, all of scallop aquaculture on the East Coast with him.

Duncan laughs when I tell him that story. "I pay them about a $1000 a year in lease fees, but for some reason they would rather not pay attention to me."

Duncan spent several summers working on Dadswell's experimental farm and couldn't get scallop farming out of his system after graduating. He took a job with the Canadian Wildlife Service, then travelled through New Zealand for three months before returning home to tell Dadswell that he wanted to be a scallop farmer. The two worked together for the next twelve years, with Duncan "putting in the sweat equity." Three years ago, the professor, approaching sixty, gave Duncan the farm. "Duncan said he was willing to go through the pain of growing it up into a commercial operation," Dadswell told me when I called to ask him directly why, as various fisheries departments had told me, scallop farming wasn't working out. "But it is working," he corrected me, pointing to Duncan and a handful of other small farms in the province. "And the Japanese and Chinese proved it will work. They have a multibillion-dollar scallop industry that's fifty times larger than the wild fishery on Georges Bank. But in Nova Scotia, the wild fishery's the big thing. They've kept their thumb down on scallop aquaculture."

On my callback to Nova Scotia Fisheries and Aquaculture, staff there confirmed there is no policy in place to encourage the sector to grow and, clearly, zero promotional support for farms that do exist.

This is odd, for scallop farming, like oyster farming, is environmentally friendly. Duncan cleans the fouling off his nets with a pressure washer and grows his animals without feed, chemicals or drugs. Like oysters, scallops feed naturally on phytoplankton, actually cleaning the water as they filter. And the spat set from Duncan's farm are even starting to restock Mahone Bay, which was once the centre of the scallop fishery in Nova Scotia, until it was fished out and the fleet shifted to Digby in the 1920s.

"This is about as organic as you can get," Duncan tells me. "I feel like I'm actually contributing to the ecosystem here."

What Duncan can't best the wild fishery on is price or quantity. Just one of John Risley's nineteen trawlers plying Georges Bank will return from a fishing expedition with more scallops than Duncan can produce in a year. Recently, Duncan solved some of his marketing woes by helping his distributor, Pec-Nord, develop an upscale niche market to sell Duncan's scallops live. It wasn't easy. Naturally, the pernickety scallops don't like to travel—a shipment of live scallops will last four to five days out of the water in winter, just two to three in summer. And they're fussy about the containers they're packed in—once out of the water, they don't like to sit in it. They prefer drained ice or refrigeration, with a damp cloth covering the shells. But Pec-Nord, with its shellfish processing facility in Lunenburg, developed a system to get Duncan's scallops from water to some of the best restaurants in Canada within twenty-four hours. When they arrive at Toronto's Starfish and Bymark, the chefs do little more to the scallops than open them, remove the digestive sac and mantle and serve them raw—gonads and all. As Starfish's Patrick McMurray would later tell me, diners are astonished by the dish. "People say, 'A scallop raw, with the roe attached, are you kidding me?' Then they discover the gonads are like fresh caviar, without being salted. You get that intense fresh egg finish."

Now, for whole live scallops, Duncan can command 130 percent over the market price of fished meats, and he can't keep up to demand—his stock usually sells out by May. Still, with his limited harvest, he admits that he's making only artist's wages, just $30,000 a year, and he has to pay boat and fuel expenses out of that.

After we stop work for the day, Duncan sticks a butter knife—his version of a shucking knife—into the hinge of a shell and pries open a scallop. "Do you want to try one?" he asks.

My adventure with the scallop is about to take a more extreme twist. A red tide may be on, Duncan tells me. That's a naturally occurring algae bloom that produces a biotoxin in shellfish, paralytic shellfish poisoning (PSP). The Canadian Food Inspection Agency (CFIA) has detected elevated levels in scallops at the Lunenburg facility that ships Duncan's. Shellfish affected—such as oysters, lobsters, clams and scallops—are not harmed by PSP and will clear the biotoxin after the algae stops blooming. But it's another story for humans eating shellfish with PSP. We can suffer nasty stomach cramps, diarrhea and, at worst, respiratory failure. And, for some reason, the biotoxin concentrates in the gonads of the scallop, while the adductor muscle, or meat, remains safe to eat.

The good news is that the CFIA and the Department of Fisheries and Oceans (DFO) monitor Canada's coastal waters stringently, closing harvest waters at the hint of a bloom. The only incidents since it started testing were the result of people harvesting shellfish illegally from waters the DFO had closed—good reason to buy shellfish only from a reputable source.

Duncan tells me he was out this morning at 5 A.M. to harvest thirty scallops, which he sent to the CFIA. His farm is one of its test sites. And he's almost certain there's no PSP in his waters. But even if it shows up elsewhere on the coast, he may not be able to harvest for several weeks, putting a serious squeeze on his already tight cash flow. He takes this possibility in stride. He's pleased the testing is so stringent. "The systems are in place to make things safe," Duncan says.

He gives me a tour of the Placopecten magellanicus—more commonly referred to as the sea scallop, one of some three hundred species worldwide. This one is found along the east coast of North America. The tip of his butter knife points out the adductor muscle in the deepest pocket of the shell, the orange gonad (or roe) that curls around it, the black digestive sac tucked in by the adductor, the mantle with its frilly gills that circle the edge of the shell and, on the inside lip of the shell, a ring of a hundred or more stunning pin-sized blue eyes that may well be staring up at me.

"For a shellfish, they actually have a lot of personality," Duncan says. As well as their well-developed eyes, scallops are the only bivalve that can swim, opening their shells to let water in, then closing them to force the water out the hinge end, creating a jet stream that can propel them up to five yards in a zigzag pattern away from predators. When Duncan scuba dives to fix gear, he says he can feel the scallops watching him from their nets, while those in the wild will flit away like flying saucers.

"The nets protect farmed scallops from predators," says Duncan, "so they tend to have thinner shells. They pour their energy into producing bigger meats."

Then, with one flick of the wrist, Duncan threads his knife under the mantle and pulls it back, gutting the animal and leaving the pristine—and safe—adductor for me to try, raw.

I stare at the white meat. Maybe I'm just squeamish about eating a raw scallop. Although the adductor, unlike the roe, is safe to eat even if from PSP-affected waters, I would rather wait for the CFIA's tests to come back. Duncan tells me that a lab extracts a portion of the scallop's gut and feeds it to a mouse. If the mouse dies, toxin levels are considered too high, and they immediately close scalloping waters.

"When do the test results come back?" I ask.

WHILE DUNCAN AWAITS the fate of the mouse, I get an opportunity to see the effects of dredging up close. Vance Hazelton, a fisherman and president of the Full Bay Scallop Association, has offered to take me scalloping for the day.

"We'll head out pretty early Monday morning," he warned me over the phone.

"Sure," I said, figuring that meant about 4 A.M.

He told me to meet him at the Digby wharf at 1:50 A.M. The boat would leave at two.

The DFO had recommended Vance to me—apparently he's a likable ambassador for the industry. He's also a survivor. When the DFO introduced transferable fishing quotas (licences to catch a given quantity of fish) as a conservation measure, Clearwater bought up most of the offshore quotas to fish Georges Bank, while other companies did the same on the Bay of Fundy. Some fishers sold their boats but hung onto their quotas and now fish by phone, selling their share of the total allowable catch to working boats who can then fish over quota. Vance is one of the few independents left who actually fishes with a boat.

When I called him, he told me that the inshore boats—half the size of the offshore trawlers—have far lighter dragging equipment than their offshore counterparts, and so do less damage to the ocean floor. He said he also focuses on quality, fishing for bigger scallops, as well as cleaning and icing them properly on board. He sells to Birch Street Seafoods, which in turn sells to the Digby Pines.

When I arrive at the wharf, I have no trouble finding Vance's boat. It's the only one with its working lights on, preparing to head out to sea. The crew—Chad, who looks about twenty-five, and Sandy, who looks about seventy—are readying the boat for takeoff. They ignore me as I step aboard, as if to speak would somehow remind them of the ungodly hour.

"They're a green crew," Vance tells me as we motor out of the harbour. Catches have been low in the Bay of Fundy, so it's hard to get help, even with the moratorium on cod fishing and other fisheries declining.

Chad and Sandy sleep in bunks below deck while I keep Vance company in the wheelhouse. We're heading to the centre of Fundy—just over twenty-two kilometres from Nova Scotia, twenty-one kilometres from New Brunswick—to fish in about 240 feet of water.

There's no moon. I can barely see the water. Rain pelts the windshield. But it's warm and cozy inside the wheelhouse. And Vance can keep a conversation going for longer than Duncan can fill nets.

The site we'll work in the morning is so close to a closed scalloping area that Vance says he would not be able to fish it without his Global Positioning System. He keeps watch in his captain's chair with his arms crossed. The fifty-four-foot boat steers by automatic pilot, which, unfortunately, can't see other vessels or whales or make coffee. Vance switches on his computer and opens files tracking the tows he's made over the past few years. On the screen, the tows appear as tiny fish hooks, a different colour for every year. They fill the screen.

Vance has short boxy hair, a slight paunch and a deep scar on his right cheek caused by two rounds with skin cancer. He started working on his father's boat summers when he was eleven, even though being on the water made him seasick. At age twenty-two, he became the youngest owner in the Digby fleet. Back in the 1980s and 1990s, he says a captain could clear as much as $90,000 a year after boat, fuel and crew expenses. "Sea sickness is the worst feeling in the world, especially when you know you're not coming back to shore for three or four days, but you couldn't make that kind of money on land, so I put up with it." He had this boat built when he was twenty-eight, a sister of his father's. He named it Branntelle, a combination of the names of his son, Bradley, his wife, Ann, and his daughter, Chantelle. A son who arrived later, James, now eleven, has never been fishing with Vance. Bradley now works in the Alberta oilfields, and Chantelle is a nurse. And that's just fine by Vance. He doesn't want any of them taking up fishing. Over the past few years, his quota has dropped from ninety thousand to thirty thousand pounds, and scallops from $9 a pound to $6.50. "It's not a good livelihood," he says. "The money's not there now."

On top of sagging prices, the environmental news about dredging has pretty much knocked out whatever pride Vance had left in his work. "Oh!" he hoots when I ask him how other fishers view him, "we're the scum of the earth."

I figure Vance is about fifty-five, but he tells me he's just forty-five, too young to retire, too old to change careers. He feels trapped. For the next two hours, he lets fly a litany of complaints about the DFO's regulations, jabbing his chin out with every point. He can't land scallops on shore without a monitoring company to verify the catch. A black box on his boat sends satellite signals to the DFO to ensure he doesn't fish in closed areas. "They treat us like criminals."

He concedes that the DFO has to impose some regulations to prevent overfishing but believes it's going overboard with red tape and, worse, favouring lobster fishers. He desperately wants to dredge a lobster fishing area near Yarmouth. "There's twelve- and thirteen-year-old scallops there," he says. "Their life span is fifteen years. They're just gonna die if we don't get them. And there's nothing to show we do damage to the lobster fishery."

On the topic of dredging, as it's called offshore, or dragging, as it's called inshore, his defence varies wildly. One minute he says, "Overall, we're not doing long-term damage. The bottom is very resilient." The next minute, jabbing his chin forward, he says, "In the Bay of Fundy, at this point, to be natural is to be towed. We've been doing this for a hundred years. It's not a pristine environment."

At five in the morning, when Vance has exhausted me with his tirade, we start to fish.

The boat heels, and the eighteen-foot-long drag with its massive steel nets heaves out of the water. Sandy works a hydraulic winch that will release the catch into a trough on the deck. It's his first time running the equipment. Vance places his hand on the winch lever over Sandy's, teaching him to feel the hitches, the grinds, the release point. Sandy is a tiny man with scraggly grey hair. He stares at the massive drag apparatus looming over the deck as if staring at nothing. His blue eyes are shot through with fear.

During the ride out, Vance told me that he knows of three people who were killed in the Digby fleet in his years of working the water—one fell overboard, a steel block flew off the dragging equipment and hit another in the chest. The story of the third somehow got lost in our blur of talk.

Sandy presses the gear forward, the steel nets open and the catch crashes into the trough.

On the Bay of Fundy, draggers pull up three kinds of ocean bottom—soccer-ball sized rocks; old crushed scallop shells that have been pitched overboard during decades of shucking at sea; and, Chad's favourite, a haul of lemonweed. "Just smell that," he says, sucking in air. "The whole boat smells of lemon."

With the catch in the trough, we go to work picking scallops from the bottom debris. There is no easy way to do this. I have to either brace my knees against the edge of the trough and strain my back fishing across the three-foot-wide mouth or climb right into the trough and scramble along on my legs like a chicken. We fill two plastic laundry bins full of scallops.

Then three short warning blasts sound and Chad yells at me to jump clear. Vance turns the boat sharply, a length of heavy chain rips across the deck and the drag plunges back into the water. The boat slows noticeably when the drag equipment hits bottom.

Then Chad leaps onto the gunwales of the boat, grabs two chains with a grappling hook, jumps back onto the steel cover of the hold, hooks the chains to the trough, and steps away as Sandy hauls on the hydraulic winch. The trough lifts up and tips its load of debris back into the ocean. When the trough crashes back onto deck, Chad reverses his frantic footwork.

Superstition number one: It's bad luck to wear black-soled rubber boots on a boat. I'm guessing red or yellow is better for spotting someone who falls overboard, usually headfirst.

Superstition number two: It's bad luck to have bananas on board. That one's obvious, with decks already slick enough from rain and sea spray.

Superstition number three: It's bad luck to whistle into the wind. I don't know why, but the whistling can get on your nerves. See superstition number one.

For the twenty minutes of the tow, which drags an eighteen-foot-wide swath of the ocean floor for 1.1 nautical miles, we work at a steel-clad table in the shucking station on the port side. Red tides in the Bay of Fundy are so common that it's illegal to land meats with the roe on. We shuck the adductor muscles into five-gallon buckets. The roe, guts and shell we pitch overboard through a slat window above our worktable.

Chad is dark-haired and handsome, befitting his soap-opera name. He gives me a lesson in shucking, which he pronounces "shocking"—appropriate, as it takes a shocking length of time for me to fill my bucket.

First step: Stick a knife between the shells at the hinge end and scrape the knife forward along the top shell to cut off the adductor muscle. (Except I often miss the muscle.)

Second step: Slip the knife under the rim of the mantle (the gills and ring of eyes) and flick—the digestive gut and roe should come off with the mantle and land overboard. (But the mantle can break and then you have to dig out the guts.)

Third step: Slide the knife back to cut the adductor muscle from the bottom shell, letting the adductor drop into a plastic bucket and the shell into the sea. (Try to do this fast and you cut away half the adductor, pretty much wasting your efforts.)

Another load comes up. When we're back to shucking, Chad tells me that Paul Gidney is the local shucking legend, a Canadian and international champ who started competing at age sixteen. He has won the Digby Scallop Days championship for the past twenty-four years straight. His fastest time—a hundred scallops in three minutes and forty-seven seconds. Back when scallops were plentiful in the Bay of Fundy, boats hauled their catch into shuckers who worked on stationary boats in the harbour. One day, Gidney shucked out 750 pounds.

Another load comes up. Today our catch will be about 250 pounds. It takes me four hours to fill a quarter of a bucket—about 6 pounds. I'm inept, yes, but the meats are also small. This time of year—late May through to August—the scallops are spawning and they pour their energy into that, losing about 30 percent of their meat size. In the fall, they start packing on glycogen-rich protein. October through January, the meats are at their best, fat and sweet for eating.

The thought of fishing scallops during spawning puts me in a bad mood. Shouldn't they be out of season? Or maybe it's another load crashing in to the trough that clenches my teeth.

Surprisingly, the rocks are easiest to pick through. The lemonweed often has one or two spiny sculpins that can puncture a glove. Usually the fish we haul up are dead. Not the sculpins. They growl at us. But the haul of crushed shell is the worst. We use old shells to scoop through the sludge to find the live ones.

Another load. In Fundy, at least, there is little bycatch of other species—the odd cod, dogfish and the godawful ugly monkfish. This is either a good sign or, more likely, a very bad one. Mike Dadswell had told me that dredging has turned Georges Bank and the Bay of Fundy into virtual monocultures of scallops. "You do wonder what it's doing to the bottom," Chad admits. "Some people say it's like an airport strip down there, just gravel drag-ways. But hopefully the bottom can come back."

On the plus side, dragging is actually good for scallops. They love nestling in the ploughed crevices, and a century of hard fishing hasn't knocked them out yet. One study even argues that the ocean bottoms scallops like best, gravel on shallower continental shelves, are frequently ripped up by ocean storms—the study showed there was little difference between a scallop ground on Georges Bank that had been closed to dredging for a few years and one that had remained open.

Then again, maybe the barren bottom of the closed ground shows that the bottom is not so resilient? Fundy has been dredged for so long, no expert I spoke to would hazard a guess as to what the bottom might have been like before, or what species it might support again. The DFO's current strategy is to contain dragging to traditional scalloping areas.

Another load comes up. I'm the only one happy for the low catches. Vance blames the thin yields on natural cycles more than overfishing. And the scallops are notoriously fickle when it comes to spawning, sending out a huge spat set one year, making for a big fishery when they grow to market size four or five years later. But another year, maybe Fundy's huge tides sweep away their romantic efforts.

Another load comes up. More and more, I'm picking the close side of the trough, letting Chad do the chicken walk down the inside. It's 9 A.M. We've been working four hours.

Vance brings us mugs of hot coffee and the box of doughnuts I've brought from Tim Hortons. As we stuff down doughnuts, Chad tells me this is one of the best scallop boats to work on—Vance treats his crew well and keeps a clean boat. "Some boats you wouldn't want to eat back here, it smells so bad."

Vance hoses down the decks several times throughout the day. He also washes the meats we've shucked in fresh sea water, bags them in cheesecloth and stores them below deck on ice.

Another load comes up. Chad, just getting into the grove of the day, starts yakking up a storm. He has friends who've fished lobster and haddock, but when they come out on a scallop boat, they can't handle it. "You need a proper attitude to work on a scallop boat," he says.

"What's that?" I ask.

"Crazy," he shouts.

Turns out he works on a mink farm but has taken time off to have his tonsils out. While off sick, he's crewing for Vance, who's having trouble getting deck hands. He lives with Vance's daughter. They're expecting their first child.

Another load comes up. How many scallops have I shucked now? Two hundred, five hundred? Each one is different. The female gonad ranges from pink to orange to fire red, the male from grey to milk-white. The mantle might be white, black or even orange—a startling backdrop to the ring of cobalt blue eyes.

Then Sandy's story finally comes out. He has crewed on fishing boats all his life—cod until that industry collapsed, halibut and haddock until those fisheries went flat. He expects to make $500 on this week-long trip—after his share of food and boat expenses. He's hoping scallops hold out. He may look seventy, but he tells me he's just forty-eight.

At noon we stop for lunch, though the boat continues dragging. Vance has sautéed some of our precious scallops in garlic and butter, especially for me. Chad and Sandy shovel the stew down with folded pieces of white bread. The dish is tasty, but I've been up to my elbows in them all morning and I can't decide whether I feel worse for the scallops, the bottom of the ocean or the crew. Then, twenty minutes later, the length of the drag, we're back at work.

We fish through the afternoon (no, that's not true; Chad and Sandy work, I can't make it without a nap). When I wake up, I think of exercising my writer's prerogative and hanging with Vance in the warm wheelhouse, but the work at the back of the boat is so damn hard I feel too guilty abandoning Sandy and Chad and so I take up the scallop shucking knife again.

Another load, another load, another load.

We stop for supper at five o'clock, for the length of a drag, twenty minutes. At nine, Vance starts hosing down the deck and I think we're done. But that's just a mid-evening cleanup. We fish until eleven, when, finally, Vance pulls up the dragger one last time and we head back to Digby.

We arrive at 2 A.M. Vance pulls alongside the wharf, stopping just long enough for us to shake hands and for me to scramble over the dredging equipment and catch the ladder. It's low tide. Twenty-odd steps loom above me in the dark. The boat is chugging back to sea before I reach the top rung.

They'll stay out until Friday morning, fishing eighteen-hour days.

THE MOUSE DIED. Duncan breaks the news as we motor out to his scallop farm to harvest a few pounds for dinner. He quickly adds that his farm is clear, although the CFIA found traces of PSP, or red tide, in scallop samples from the Lunenburg plant. A change of the plant's processing waters and three safe tests in a row and Duncan says all should be fine.

Mike Dadswell has come with us today. The professor is a dark-haired, barrel-chested man who looks rather like a crusty sea captain. On the way out, he tells me about another student who started a farm, in Digby, with about seventeen scallop fishers as investors. After seven years, they had one million scallops in the water, with a goal of hitting ten million. Then the scallop fishery took a downturn and the fishers faced a decision—keep their money in the wild fishery or in aquaculture. The majority chose the wild fishery and the project collapsed.

I tell Mike that, after my fishing adventure, I couldn't imagine anyone choosing to fish if they could farm scallops.

"Well, you can't farm scallops in the middle of Fundy or Georges Bank," Mike points out. "The tides would sweep the farm away." There are other strikes against farming. Prime sheltered coastal waters face competition from coastal developments wanting a pristine view. The meats cost more. And then there's what Duncan calls the plain stubbornness required to start up a farm.

Mike is pessimistic about scallop farming taking off here. Duncan, more optimistic, thinks it will ultimately prevail.

When we arrive at the farm, the two immediately go to work thinning. It's a reunion of sorts, as Mike hasn't been out on the boat with Duncan for a few years. Now Mike's the one asking questions and Duncan's giving directions. But it's clear Mike misses the work.

"It takes two Beatles songs to describe how we got the farm going," says Mike.

Duncan laughs, knowing the punchline, but lets Mike tell it.

"It's a long and winding road. And with a little help from your friends."

Although I'd like to be helping out, there isn't room around the worktable for three, and, well, it's another perfect summer day on Canada's prettiest ocean bay. I soak up the sun until lunch, when I go to work laying out the picnic I've packed—sandwiches and cold beers. Unlike on the scallop boat, we eat lunch for the length of time it takes to eat lunch.

Duncan tells Mike about his plans for expansion. He has his system fine-tuned now, and he's ready to grow. He's confident. "If someone had given me a pile of money ten years ago," he says, "I would have lost a pile of money. Now I've got everything working." In the fall, he'll triple the size of his operation, buying three hundred thousand spat and eventually harvesting three hundred thousand a year, with a corresponding jump in income. The challenge will be making it through the first year, until he can sell the larger harvest and afford to hire help.

Mike nods. Everything sounds fine. "If you can grow a good garden," Mike says, "you can grow good scallops. Duncan and I used to have a race to see who could pick the first red tomato. Duncan beat me every time."

Later in the afternoon, Duncan hauls up a lantern net and harvests a couple of dozen scallops. Mike doesn't exactly invite us back to his place for dinner; it's a given that we'll come, a ritual he and Duncan once had—work followed by dinner and a shot or two of rye to ease what they call "marine back." Mike, the scallop specialist, seems as eager to cook the beasts as to study them. He once thought of opening a restaurant by the wharf to showcase all the recipes he has collected. "Seafood is best eaten within one hundred yards of the ocean," he says.

His rustic cottage-style house sits atop a hill in Chester, its deck overlooking the harbour. Duncan's wife, Becky, and Mike's wife, Terri-Lee, join us, and we sit in a row of Adirondack chairs, drinks in hand, as Mike whips up a feast.

Becky, who has a steady warm presence, works as an occupational therapist. A few months later, Duncan will email to tell me that they are expecting their first child. He's thrilled.

Terri-Lee, who loves to laugh, tells me that she was walking past the house one day when she smelled Mike's scallops cooking on the barbeque. She stopped. He invited her in. As Mike says, it was seduction by scallops.

That dish is yet to come. Now Mike sets a plate of raw meats before me, with dipping sauces, one of Worcestershire, one of soy. Nancy, my land-loving East Coast partner, is not here. Her aversion to boats means she is missing the boat on this, and I am missing her. You might be thinking the Food Writer from Toronto is squeamish about eating seafood raw, but that's not the case at all. I just wish she were here so that she could sample first.

I take a tentative bite—the raw meat actually tastes like it has been lightly grilled, only the flavour is more intense. The chill of the sea-cool meat teases out the natural sweetness while somehow tempering it—cooked scallops can sometimes be cloying. I dip one in Worcestershire, another in soy, but decide that raw scallops go best with nothing—except maybe a glass of cold white wine.

Next off the barbecue is Mike's specialty—Tancook scallops, named for one of the larger outlying islands protecting Chester Basin. He douses the meat and gonads with butter, chopped garlic, wine, Parmesan cheese and breadcrumbs, then grills and returns the scallops to the half shell to serve. The meat is plump, the roe huge. With farmed scallops, the eating season reverses—meats are larger in fall and winter, but the roe is larger in summer. And, as I discover when I bite into one, the slightly grilled roe, less than an hour from the water, is divine.

After Mike slips meats wrapped in bacon onto the grill—the dish that lured Terri-Lee—he decides we should also have fresh corn on the cob, and he heads off to his garden to pick some.

While we feast and drink, the sun sets over Chester harbour. The sleek racing yachts tug at their moorings, wanting to play in the evening breeze. I crack some lame joke, wondering about what the poor wealthy people are doing tonight. Duncan's response is sudden and startling.

"I hate money," Duncan says. "I hate everything about it. I hate what it does to people." He takes a long swig of his rye and Coke. "But I guess you can't exactly get by without it."

The moment passes before I can think his comment through, and then the evening is winding down and Duncan is sending me home with his own recipe for raw scallops and a couple of dozen live ones in my beer cooler. I try to pay for them but he won't let me. We don't say goodbye. I tell him I'll be back next summer and that I'd like to help out on his boat for a few days. And he says that would be great.

I AM BACK on the Windsor Road—the Chester Road if you're travelling from Windsor. I can't remember how many times I've criss-crossed this slim province in the past week—from my in-laws' home in Windsor, to Chester on one coast, to Digby on the other. The road winds through dense dark bush, twists around rocky hills.

Maybe I am driving too fast, thinking too hard. I imagined my quest to meet farmers would yield some sort of equation: good farming = good food. Now Vance and Duncan have gone and complicated things. Now I have somehow gotten myself stuck in that equation. If I ever eat another wild scallop, good as they are, I will be eating Vance's mental torment when his dragger pulls up another mile of ocean bottom. I will be eating that ocean floor. If I can ever get my hands on Duncan's live scallops back in Toronto, I will be eating the stubborn passion he's poured into his farm, but also the lonely struggle he's had in trying to make things work.

A scallop was no longer just a scallop.

And so maybe I am driving too fast, maybe I am thinking too hard about Duncan's passion and Vance's angst and John Risley's goddamn mansion. But the raccoon is suddenly in my headlights and it's too late to swerve and there is the dull thud.

Sickened, I slow down. I shift into second gear to haul the Jeep up a steep hill. But the raccoon's death turns out to be a gift, a sacrifice, for as I crest the hill, and the road curves sharply, a horse appears in my headlights, a red horse running down the middle of the road.

"Geezus," I scream and hit the brakes.

The horse stops. I stare at the horse. He stares at me. He has exactly the same markings as the horse I had when I was thirteen years old. Red. A white slash of lightning on his nose. Two white socks on his hind legs. The same sleek build.

I called him Rebel. We used to ride meals to my father when he was working in the fields. My father would talk as he ate, and I would listen. And I came to understand that this was my work on the farm, delivering meals, listening to his stories.

Then the accident flashes through my mind. The truck coming up behind us and Rebel galloping. We're running for home. Now the truck is beside us and the driver is grinning, reaching for his air horn. Geezus, no. The blast scares Rebel into a dead run and I cannot stop him. The driver hits the gas and pulls away, winning his race.

The road to our farm looms and I know I cannot stop Rebel from turning, cannot stop his hooves from slipping on the hot summer pavement.

And suddenly we are down, Rebel sliding across the road on his side and me sliding across the road on my back. If the driver had stopped, he would have seen the scorching pavement slick with our blood.

Now, Rebel runs out of my headlights and disappears into the dark. Not Rebel, I tell myself. Rebel didn't make it. My father had to put him down the next day, while I was in the hospital, with the skin ripped off my back and a fractured skull.

It's a ghost, my second ghost in Nova Scotia? I drive after the horse, pick him up again in my headlights. No, it really is a horse, trotting back down the middle of Windsor Road toward me and in the worst possible place, at the top of the hill on a curve.

It's my chance to save him this time, but how? The horse has no halter, and I have no rope to lead him. I can't see a house light in either direction. My cell phone won't pick up a signal. And a car or truck could come blasting up the hill from either direction at any moment. I angle the Jeep across the road and turn on my four-way flashers, hoping a car will see me before the horse and slow down, hoping they'll see me and slow down.

One, two, three cars come toward me and I flick my headlights frantically, managing to slow and stop them all. But no one knows the horse. And no one knows what to do. Slowly, the cars drive on, past my Jeep and my horse. Than, finally, a local stops. She thinks she knows the owners of the horse and offers to drive to a nearby house to alert them. She asks if I will stay and babysit the horse. From the side of the road, Rebel calmly watches her drive off. And so now it's eleven at night on the Windsor Road and I am babysitting a horse.

He trots down the road. I drive after him. He turns and trots up the road. I turn and drive after him.

My journey is taking a very weird turn. My research will take me to Newfoundland, then across the West to meet farmers, yet somehow it feels like I am travelling home, back to my family's farm. What next?

Rebel, trotting ahead, stops and looks back at me. Then he veers off the road, gallops into the bush and disappears.

# Nova Scotia

## Tancook Scallops

This recipe requires whole live scallops, with the roe attached. Live scallops may be hard to find; ask your fishmonger if he or she can bring some in. Although the roe tastes much better when the scallop is live rather than frozen, you could use frozen. Mike made this over a barbecue, even though his recipe outlines how to make it in the oven.

| 24 | whole live scallops | 24 |
|---|---|---|
| 1/2 cup | wheat cracker (such as Breton) crumbs | 125 mL |
| 1/2 cup | minced garlic | 125 mL |
| 1/2 cup | butter | 125 mL |
| 1/2 cup | grated Parmesan cheese | 125 mL |
| | salt and freshly ground black pepper | |
| 1/2 cup | dry white wine | 125 mL |
| | juice of 1 lemon | |

Preheat oven to 425°F (220°C).

Shuck the scallop by placing a shucking knife between the shells at the hinge end and prying open. Remove the bottom shell (the shell with the least depth) from the scallop. Place the tip of your knife under the digestive sack (the black sack near the hinge of the shell) and under the mantle (the ring of eyes) and flick the knife; this should remove both. Drain the top shell of any liquid, reserving the liquid, and place the shell and meat on a baking sheet. Sprinkle the cracker crumbs over the scallop meats.

Sauté the garlic in the butter and reserved scallop liquid in a frying pan over low heat. Drizzle 1 tbsp (15 mL) of the melted garlic butter over each scallop. Sprinkle scallops with Parmesan cheese and season with salt and pepper.

Bake the scallops for 5 minutes. Remove from the oven and drizzle 1/2 tsp (2 mL) wine and 1/2 tsp (2 mL) lemon juice over each scallop. Return the scallops to the oven and continue to bake, watching closely, until they are crispy and brown but some liquid remains in the shell, about 10 minutes.

*Makes 6 servings, with 3 to 4 scallops per person.*

Credit: Mike Dadswell, Chester, Nova Scotia.

# Duncan's Scallop Ceviche

This wonderfully refreshing summer appetizer calls for fresh scallop meats rather than frozen. Ask your fishmonger for dry scallops, which will be fresh and also not pumped full of water. The scallops need to be marinated at least 3 hours, but preferably overnight.

| | | |
|---|---|---|
| 1 | red onion, peeled | 1 |
| 2 lb | fresh scallop meats, cut into four wedges | 1 kg |
| | juice of 10–12 limes | |
| 12 | cherry tomatoes, halved | 12 |
| 5 | stalks celery, coarsely chopped | 5 |
| 2 | avocadoes, pitted, peeled and cut into 1/2-inch/1 cm pieces | 2 |
| 2–3 | hot chilies, finely chopped | 2–3 |
| 1 | bunch cilantro, finely chopped | 1 |
| 2 tbsp | white vinegar | 25 mL |
| | plain taco chips | |

Blanch the onion by placing it in boiling water for a few seconds, to soften. Coarsely chop.

Place the scallops in a large glass bowl. Add the lime juice and red onion to the scallops; stir. Refrigerate, covered with plastic wrap, for 3 to 6 hours or overnight, to marinate.

Just before serving, add the tomatoes, celery, avocado, chilies, cilantro and vinegar to the scallop mixture, stirring to combine.

Serve with taco chips for dipping.

*Makes 6 to 8 servings.*

Credit: Duncan Bates, Chester, Nova Scotia.

## Nancy's Sexy Scallops

These scallops make a great wintertime appetizer. For a homey presentation, serve them right in the pan you cooked them in. Of course, you can also serve 3 to 4 scallops per person on individual plates, but the frying pan will keep the scallops warm.

| 3 tbsp | olive oil | 45 mL |
|---|---|---|
| 1 tbsp | red pepper flakes | 15 mL |
| 1 tbsp | sea salt | 15 mL |
| 12 | large scallops | 12 |
| 3 | cloves garlic, minced | 3 |
| 1/2 cup | 18% cream | 125 mL |
| 1/4 cup | dry white wine | 50 mL |
| 1 cup | chopped cilantro | 250 mL |

Heat the olive oil in a cast-iron frying pan over medium heat. Sprinkle the pan evenly with the red pepper flakes and sea salt. Sear the scallops on one side to brown, about 3 to 4 minutes. Add the garlic; flip scallops over and brown the other side for 2 to 3 minutes. Add the cream and wine and simmer for 2 to 3 minutes to reduce the liquid slightly. If the scallops are too large, halve them once they are cooked. Top with cilantro.

Serve with thick slices of baguette for dipping in the sauce.

*Makes 3 to 4 servings.*

Credit: Nancy Lyons, Toronto, Ontario.

# Mains

# Newfoundland and Labrador

# FOR THE LOVE OF COD

*It is the peculiarity of many Newfoundland fishermen
that they do not want to go fishing provided that
they could get other work to do. Maybe one day they will find
other work because the fish stocks will have been destroyed.*
—Adolph Nielsen, cod hatchery specialist, 1896

My visit to an experimental cod farm in Newfoundland and Labrador coincides with the fifteen anniversary of the moratorium on cod fishing. As anniversaries go, this is a sombre one. Radio talk shows mark the occasion by inviting fishers to call in with comments. They are all irate. They complain that the cod have returned yet the federal government won't lift the moratorium. They hint at dark conspiracies as to why. Others complain that the cod have not returned in sufficient numbers and the government isn't doing anything to stop massive foreign vessels from vacuuming up the fish just beyond Canada's 320-kilometre exclusive fishing zone. They complain that a ten-day summer recreational fishery allows everyone with a floatation device to catch the fish, while they, professional fishers, must pay for licences and for dock inspectors to monitor their miniscule bycatch of cod hooked while targeting other species. They complain about the price of snow crab.

More emphatic is the silence—a generation of young Newfoundlanders has simply moved on, leaving remote communities to find work in other regions, bleeding their home province of its vitality, its future. For the rest of Canada to understand the devastation the July 1992 cod moratorium wrought here, we would have to imagine Alberta running out of oil, Ontario's car manufacturers folding. Yet, Newfoundland's connection to cod runs even deeper. The fate of the fish and the people who settled in remote ports to catch them has been inextricably bound for some five hundred years. In a July 7, 2007, *Globe and Mail* column marking the anniversary of the moratorium, proud Newfoundlander Rex Murphy declared that the outports—the very "soul of Newfoundland"—are "effectively dead." Locals call the moratorium Newfoundland's 9/11.

But away from the public outcry—perhaps too far to receive adequate financing and support—one feisty fish farmer has not given up on cod, nor on the dream that Newfoundland's coastal communities might flourish yet again. For the past half dozen years, Jennifer Caines, a former bird biologist and scallop farmer, has been raising cod on an experimental farm in Fortune Bay on the south coast of Newfoundland. Her partners in the caper are a man she calls the Codfather, who scrapes together government grants and industry support, and a group of researchers who supply her with fish raised in a university hatchery. The provincial government may also become a major player, helping fund a quasi-commercial farm as a way to kick-start an industry, but their announcement has been "forthcoming" for nearly two years.

I grew tired of waiting to see what might unfold and so called Jennifer to inquire about her work. She told me she would be harvesting the first crop from her ocean pens at the end of the summer. Then, in a breathless stringing together of sentences, she said she hated to see them go—"They've been with us for so long"—but is also eager for the public response and impatient to see her work continue on a commercial scale. On her "good days," she believes cod farming might take off in a way similar to British Columbia's salmon sector, which employs about three thousand people and generates revenues of $600 million a year, or the emerging cod industry in Norway, where the government pours oil revenues into developing a more sustainable fuel—aquaculture. Other days, she questions whether all her work might be for nothing. As for the fish and how she is raising them, she has few doubts. Although she wouldn't say her farm-raised stock are better than wild, she does say that the fillets are thicker, the flesh firmer, the colour whiter, the meat sweeter.

"We have the chance to produce a really good-quality fish and to do it right environmentally," she told me over the phone. Then, barely into her next sentence, she invited me to the farm to see for myself. She recommended a bed and breakfast in town and then offered one last lure, sure to hook any food lover. When I arrived, she would put one of those big fat experimental fillets into the frying pan for me to try.

APPROPRIATELY NICKNAMED "The Rock," the rugged island of Newfoundland juts up out of the frigid North Atlantic, across the Strait of Belle Isle from the mainland portion of the province, Labrador. When Nancy and I arrive in the middle of June, there is still plenty of ice bobbing in the ocean, and two massive icebergs have parked themselves outside the St. John's harbour. Turns out we have timed our trip perfectly to coincide with the annual spring parade of ten-thousand-year-old bergs that break off Greenland and drift south past the eastern coast of Newfoundland.

We have also arrived for prime eating season. The taxi driver ferrying us through town turns out to be a gourmand. He tells us where to buy fresh lobster and snow crab. The capelins—tiny sea-snack fish that attract humpback and minke whales up from the Caribbean for summer feeding— are also starting to run. Much of Newfoundland's rich culinary culture is based on such wild foods, as the island's short cool summers and rocky terrain make land-based farming difficult. By eating "in season," our epicurean cabby means hunting and fishing seasons—he bags moose and caribou for his freezer, fishes for brook trout. "Oh, I'll try to catch a cod or two in the summer fishery," he says, "but they're hard to get." He shrugs. He is surrounded by an ocean that is becoming more barren by the day. After the fifteen-year moratorium on fishing cod, the stocks still haven't recovered. Atlantic salmon hasn't been fished commercially since 1985. Now halibut and haddock stocks are also declining.

The Ocean Sciences Centre at Memorial University of Newfoundland is a sea-anemone-shaped building that sits on a cliff high above the North Atlantic. Here, scientists are looking to aquaculture as a way of meeting our increasing demands on our increasingly exhausted oceans. Their research supports aquaculture initiatives such as blue mussels, Atlantic salmon, halibut, steelhead trout, sea cucumbers and sea urchins, but the project that has scientists buzzing is Atlantic cod.

Danny Boyce, the tall, affable business manager of the facility, has offered us a behind-the-scenes peek at the Atlantic Cod Genomics and Broodstock Development project, an $18-million effort to decode the fish's DNA. The goal is to create an elite broodstock, Secretariats of the sea, fish with superior flesh quality, that grow quickly and can resist the stress of fish farming and diseases. A team of researchers here and another in New Brunswick are developing two streams of breeder fish, starting with wild cod from local waters, to ensure farmed fish remain genetically similar and therefore reduce the genetic impact of escaped fish on wild stocks. So far, Boyce says the scientists here have identified thirty or so families of Northern cod, and each has significant variations—some are high-performers and some, frankly, are reproductive duds. To develop stronger and healthier fish, researchers cross the super families with other hotshots, tossing the genetic losers from the breeding program. "This is not about genetically modifying fish," assures Boyce. "This is about selecting traits using traditional breeding methods, not unlike how we've been breeding cows for centuries."

During a PowerPoint presentation, Boyce constantly compares cod to cows. It's a bit disconcerting, though he means to reassure us, to normalize what seems a rather scary new frontier: farming the sea. But Boyce doesn't see a huge distinction between aquaculture and our traditional means of working the ocean—fishing. He says five hundred years of exploiting cod in Newfoundland has hugely altered the fish's genetics: "Cod stocks have declined by 90 percent since the 1960s, and they're just not coming back, for whatever reason." The cod caught now are half the size they used to be. And researchers are discovering that many cod families, reproductively speaking, are simply "bad performers."

Boyce suggests that the distinction between wild and farmed blurs even more when you consider various enhancement projects to build up depleted fishing stocks. Pacific salmon were introduced into the Great Lakes in the 1900s to replace depleted Atlantic salmon. Pacific Rim countries, including Canada, raise about five billion "wild" Pacific salmon each year under similar conditions as farmed—fish are born in hatcheries, fed in freshwater pens for a year and a half, then released into the ocean. Called fish ranching, this is less intensive than farming, where fish are held in pens right up to harvest, but may have a greater impact on ocean ecology. In ranching, all the fish are "escapes." They can introduce any disease or parasites present in the pens directly to wild stocks. They also compete for food and breed with vulnerable wild salmon. Each year, about 20 percent of the salmon caught in Alaska (along with a wasteful bycatch of other fish) was actually raised on fish ranches, yet sold to consumers as wild.

Boyce's point is that we must face reality. Aquaculture now accounts for 30 percent of the seafood we consume globally, a figure that will rise to nearly half by 2030, according to the United Nations. As Boyce says, "There's a global shortage of seafood. If you want to eat seafood, here are your choices: It has to be farmed." Although Canada is still a small player, ranking well behind Norway, Chile and the United Kingdom, its aquaculture sector has been growing at a rate of 15 to 20 percent a year. And Boyce sees enormous potential for Newfoundland, with its cold, pristine waters, twenty-nine thousand kilometres of largely uninhabited coastline, and a local culture that views the ocean as a place to work rather than for recreation. The cod project, he says, has already played a small role in reversing the talent drain from Newfoundland by attracting researchers to the Ocean Sciences Centre. As for the end result—farmed cod—Boyce says he would even prefer eating it to wild. "In Canada, fish farming is scrutinized to death. I feel safer knowing where all the feed ingredients came from. I know the waters the fish have been swimming in. It's all tested. With wild fish, you don't know where they've been swimming or what they've been eating. And I'd rather eat a fish fresh off a farm than one that's been sitting in the hull of a boat for days."

Boyce outfits us with lab coats and rubber boots before leading us down into the cool, dank basement—the hatchery. We tread through a foot bath—biosecurity—then enter a massive warehouse with about forty-four swimming-pool-sized fish tanks. He throws back the lid of one that holds full-grown broodstock. As I lean in for a look, a huge fish leaps out of the water. Startled, I jerk back just in time to escape kissing the cod. Boyce laughs, "They do that. They're curious."

He pushes back the lids on other tanks where thousands of robust offspring dart about in fresh sea water that circulates through the tanks. Compared with the wild, these wee fry live a life of comparative ease. In the sea, a female will spawn about one million eggs, but odds are only one will survive to adulthood. In this lab and later on the experimental farm, the likelihood of growing up to become a big fat cod is considerably greater. Raised on lab-grown algae and rotifer (microscopic sea animals), then pricey fish meal—dried pellets of wild fish that are packed with vitamins and minerals—the young grow to about a third of an ounce, finger length, in about 120 days. Before being shipped to the farm in Fortune Bay, the fingerlings must be disease-free; they're also vaccinated against the more common diseases that afflict wild cod. About 80 percent will survive the next thirty-two months as they grow out on the farm to between six and eight pounds—harvest weight.

"The day they leave the hatchery is very exciting," Boyce says. "It's like graduation day, after watching kids grow up." He pauses. He is actually a bit misty-eyed. He laughs off the well of feeling but admits he gets emotional just talking about this project. Boyce has a wavy thatch of red hair and a spray of freckles that makes him look more teenager than middle-aged. He grew up in Bonavista, the cod capital of Newfoundland, where John Cabot reportedly landed in 1497. In *Lament for an Ocean*, author Michael Harris describes the tragic politics of cod since Cabot's discovery of an ocean coast that was "swarming with the fish." For the next five hundred years, Europeans and Newfoundlanders exploited that seemingly inexhaustible resource until they had exhausted it. Boyce remembers the day the federal government announced the moratorium on fishing cod. Some thirty thousand people were thrown out of work—among them his neighbours, friends and family. Now Boyce's heart beats with the bright hope that he can bring the cod back, if not in the wild then farmed. "Everyone knows some sad cod story," he says. "This is politically popular research. It's emotional research. The hope, the want, the hurt here is high."

THE CODFATHER is waiting for us at the end of the tour. He suggests lunch at a patio on George Street in St. John's, a two-block stretch that is packed cheek by jowl with bars.

He is a small man, surly and, by his own account, not the most optimistic spokesperson for cod aquaculture. "You probably don't want to hear what I have to say," he had warned me on the phone earlier when I asked to meet him. "I've pretty much had it with cod farming."

We order Quidi Vidi beers from a St. John's microbrewery and fish and chips—cod, of course. Since my culinary coming of age happened after the moratorium, I cannot remember ever eating the Atlantic version. And what the waiter sets in front of us is not very good. Jonathan Moir guesses the fillets are "twice frozen"—caught outside Canada's 320-kilometre fishing zone and frozen at sea, then shipped to processing facilities in Russia, where it is thawed, processed, refrozen and shipped back. He doesn't have to point out that a farmed fillet could arrive on our plate just hours out of the water. It's just one more thing to set him off. "Yeah, they call me the Codfather," he says, "though I wished they'd call me the codpiece."

As an aquaculture consultant and entrepreneur, Moir describes himself as the guy who's "always been there" for cod farming in Newfoundland, holding things together between projects. And there have been a few.

Shortly after the moratorium, Moir convinced the provincial government to transition fishers into cod farmers. He wrote a training manual, conducted seminars. But the early farms were beset with problems. The fishers-turned-farmers caught juveniles in the wild, raised them in pens near shore and fed them fresh bait. The wild fish didn't feed well, and the lack of properly formulated fish meal resulted in watery fillets of poor quality. Eventually, the government ended its own program by prohibiting the practice of catching juveniles, saying it contravened the moratorium.

Undeterred, Moir helped build a commercial hatchery to supply juvenile cod to fish farms. In 1996, the hatchery reared twenty thousand fish and set a goal of producing ten million annually. "We were ahead of the world," says Moir. Then, in 1997, a fire destroyed the building. It has taken more than ten years to rebuild and still needs another injection of cash to complete. Moir shrugs. "The building was inadequately insured. The fire put a nail in the coffin of the industry for the next decade."

Now he's involved with two companies that are industry partners in the cod genomics project. They are subsidiaries of North Atlantic Sea Farms, recently rescued from bankruptcy by the Barry Group, which owns the lion's share of fish processing in Newfoundland. The other partners are New Brunswick's giant Cooke Aquaculture, the largest independent operation in North America, and GreatBay Aquaculture in New Hampshire. The latter two already have commercial cod farms up and running, while Newfoundland has yet to go beyond the experimental stage. That, too, sits in Moir's throat, like the slab of wet, bland, twice-frozen cod.

With strict environmental regulations and expensive feeds, the days of small family-run fish farms have long passed. It's increasingly tough for even large local companies to keep a stake in the industry. In British Columbia, foreign-owned companies control about 90 percent of that province's salmon production. Each new application for a farm must pass through more than twenty Canadian government agencies to secure approval. Properly formulated cod fish meal costs about $1600 a ton, and a farm can use twenty-two tons *a day*—a feed bill can run into the tens of millions of dollars a year. As for launching a new commercial cod farm in Newfoundland, Moir estimates that it will cost about $8 million, and it's tough to secure that kind of cash on The Rock.

"Banks won't touch aquaculture," Moir says. "And Bay Street thinks Newfoundland is where money goes to die." As for government support, he concedes that the province hasn't much to invest but believes the federal government is overlooking a huge opportunity. "Norway takes money from its oil revenues and pours millions into aquaculture [making it one of the country's largest industries]. Here, aquaculture is a funding nightmare." Still, for all his pessimism, Moir admits that he can't turn his back on cod farming. "Someone has to champion it. After the moratorium, I knew the cod weren't coming back, so what are we going to do? What's the alternative?" He stares at me hard, letting the question hang in the air.

Perhaps it's not the best moment to question him about environmental issues that have plagued fin-fish farming. But just about every environmental organization in Canada has slammed salmon farming, and cod is raised in much the same way. The first crush of bad news came with the 2004 study by professor Ronald Hites, published in the noted journal *Science*, which claimed that British Columbia's farmed salmon had average PCB levels of 32 parts per billion, compared with 4.8 for wild salmon. Other studies have shown some wild salmon testing higher, though that didn't whip the media into a frenzy. Hites's findings have since been refuted as wild exaggeration— the statistical differences between contaminants found in farmed and wild salmon are insignificant and well below Health Canada's allowable limits of two thousand parts per billion. As Boyce had told me earlier, what really matters is not whether the fish are farmed or wild but what waters they've been swimming in; for instance, farmed salmon raised in the pristine waters off Newfoundland will have fewer contaminants than a wild salmon swimming off an industrialized coastline or in a polluted river.

But environmental organizations have stuck by other concerns—that farmed salmon pass on disease and parasites and that escapes can genetically pollute wild stocks; that an overload of feces and undigested food creates a dead zone under farms; that farmers contaminate surrounding waters by feeding antibiotics to overcrowded, stressed fish and by cleaning nets and equipment with toxic anti-fouling treatments. And then there is the real kicker: Does it even make sense to catch wild fish to fatten farmed carnivore fish such as salmon or cod?

With every issue I raise, Moir looks as though he might explode. "Do you eat beef?" he asks. He points out that salmon and cod have the best feed conversion rates for farmed animals—about one and a half pounds of feed for every pound gained, compared with five to one for grain-fed beef cattle and pork. It's also far superior to wild salmon, which consume from five to fifteen pounds of wild fish for every pound gained.

He swats his hand through the air. He refuses to get *too* worked up over what he perceives as old issues that the media won't let go of. He concedes that the industry, in its bumbling pioneering days, made its mistakes, but it's made enormous strides since to become one of the most regulated and safest food-producing sectors in the country. And he contends that Newfoundland, the new kid on the block, has adopted the toughest aquaculture regulations in Canada. The environmental movement clearly did its work in forcing governments to improve regulations and farmers to improve fish husbandry practices. But what drives Moir crazy is what appears to be an ongoing institutionalized opposition to fin-fish farming within environmental organizations. "You don't get that rhetoric in places like Norway, Chile or the UK. There, aquaculture is a source of pride. But in Canada ..." Moir shakes his head. He drains the last of his beer and gets up abruptly. He tells me that I can make up my own mind when I see the experimental farm in Fortune Bay. It's Friday afternoon. He says he's heading down to his sailboat to repair a broken window.

BEFORE LEAVING FOR THE FARM, we spend a few days on the "Cod Trail," a route of our own making that takes us to Bonavista to see a replica of Cabot's ship, *The Matthew*, and a former cod processing facility, now a museum. Another trip takes us to Dildo, site of the world's first cod hatchery. What's so amazing is not just that locals can say the name of their village without snickering but also that, back in the 1880s, Newfoundlanders knew their most precious resource was disappearing. With catches falling off drastically, the government, in 1889, invited Norwegian fish expert Adolph Nielsen to establish the hatchery. By historical accounts, his work was a tremendous success; at the peak, Nielsen produced some 185 million hatchlings a year, which he released into the ocean to replenish stocks. More incredibly, in 1896, the government decided that cod were doing just fine and cut off funding to the hatchery. Now it's also a museum.

In St. John's, our quest turns to sampling the fish prepared by the city's top chefs (and there are more than a few, what with offshore oil money flowing in). I must admit that I am a bit nervous about trying cod again. In this matter, my partner, Nancy, is no help. She says there is very good reason to be afraid. Growing up in Nova Scotia, she ate salt cod regularly and remembers it as salty, dry and heavy.

But, as it turns out, the problem was not with the fish but how it was treated. Newfoundlanders salted cod to preserve it indefinitely without refrigeration, but, as Michael Harris points out in *Lament for an Ocean*, quality problems plagued their fisheries. Merchants often shipped fish that wasn't fully cured. That and loading the fish with pitchforks, which pierced the fillets, eventually closed Newfoundland's fish out of premium markets. Rather than improve their techniques, rather than processing fewer cod well and selling them for a higher price, merchants simply switched to markets eager to buy cheap cod, leading to a close trading relationship with Caribbean countries—boats hauling the salted fish south brought back dark Jamaican rum, fondly called screech here.

In the kitchens of Newfoundland, the prized catch was treated little better. After desalting cod for twenty-four hours with multiple soaks in fresh water (or not), locals figured the best treatment for the lean delicate fish was tossing it into a frying pan with a heap of fat and cooking the bejesus out of it when just eight minutes would do. Then they topped it with scruncheons—fried pork fat. For a fish that often kept fathers and sons out in dangerous seas for days, this culinary approach seems more retribution than recipe.

The moratorium has actually been kind to the cooking of cod, according to chef Bob Arniel, who had a turn in the spotlight coaching actor William Hurt for his role as a chef in *Rare Birds*, a Hollywood movie shot in Newfoundland. On less star-studded days, Arniel runs a gourmet catering business from his home in St. John's, practising what noted Canadian food writer Anita Stewart has dubbed Nouvelle Newfoundland cuisine—fresh local ingredients used in international dishes. When I called Arniel to inquire about cod, he told me this: "The perception that cod is rare has made chefs do more interesting things with it." Then he invited us around for a demonstration.

Yet, when we arrive at 10 A.M., he decides to prepare an old Newfoundland favourite—cod tongues and cheeks. I wish these were simply peculiar names, but they are as he says—the tongues and cheeks cut from the fish's gargantuan head. Suddenly, I am feeling the effects of my research into the province's cod-for-rum trade, conducted a little too assiduously the night before on George Street. Arniel's kitchen banter does little to quell my roiling stomach. He says large cod have better fillets but more gelatinous tongues. Arniel prefers smaller tongues—"better texture." As for cooking them, there is only one way to do it. "The tongues are coated with a thin skin that crisps up when you fry them. And you have to fry them or the tongues will just melt."

With a wry smile, he dubs the dish Newfoundland foie gras. Traditionally, it's fried or even deep-fried in pork fat and served with scruncheons, but Arniel, thank God, gives it a lighter twist. Along with the cheeks, checker-sized morsels of meat, he dips the tongues in milk, dusts them in flour, then sautés them with pine nuts. He also makes a concession to breakfast—serving points of toast with cod roe, a bright orange and briny confection.

And, so, this is my morning challenge: I slip a fried tongue onto my fork; I bite it in half. Inside the crisped skin, the meat is soft and dense, yet mild, rather like a pâté. I manage another. I'm not sure about a plateful of these rich treats, but a snack of tongues is rather yummy.

Now on to the cheeks. These scallop-sized bites, crispy on the outside, are meatier than the tongues but not at all fishy. The texture and taste reminds me of chicken nuggets—gourmet nuggets, that is. These I could feast on.

On our subsequent eating romp across St. John's, we fall hard for the fish. As Arniel had told us, it really is a beautiful creature: pure white with thick flakes that break off into juicy tender bits. And it has substance—namely protein (nearly 52 percent)—and almost no fat. Fresh, it has no fishy smell, and the taste is so mild it can be dressed up in any number of guises. And so it appears at Restaurant 21, poached with a Tabasco-spiked molasses that reminds us of Newfoundland's Caribbean connection; at The Cellar, chef Chris Brown turns it into a jazzy New Orleans number, either blackened or baked with a savory stuffing. At the Inn by the Bay in Dildo, chef Todd Warren spikes his traditional cod cakes with oregano or savory.

As Arniel says, cod is a great chameleon. "And it's wonderful anytime you can get it fresh."

Alas, without farmed cod, there will be fat chance of that back home.

As THE CROW FLIES, the experimental cod farm on Fortune Bay would be a two-or-so-hour drive from St. John's, but there is no coastal road connecting these communities, so we must take the Trans-Canada Highway north and west, then a highway south, a gruelling, seven-hour grunt through a never-changing landscape of scraggy evergreens that somehow find a foothold on this ancient metamorphic rock. After two hours of driving, I beg Nancy to shoot me. She replies that she does not have a licence. This is moose country. The moose population on the island is pushing a hundred thousand. And it is just past calving season, when the mammas turn their attention to new calves and drive off their yearlings. So this is Nancy's job—keeping a lookout for forlorn young bucks springing out of the woods and onto the road. After six hours of this, Nancy begs me to shoot her.

And, then, as we near the coast, the bush thins, the road twists, a rock face splits open and the tiny village of Pool's Cove springs into view. Nancy gasps, and I actually hit the brakes. Below, about forty pretty homes hug the curve of the cove and overlook what has become so rare in Newfoundland—a thriving little harbour. *This place has energy* is my first thought.

I barely have the car in gear again before a blue Tracker hurrying toward us stops. The driver frantically waves as she rolls down her window. She calls out our names. We call out hers, albeit with a huge, astonished question mark. But, yes, the driver is Jennifer Caines, the manager of the experimental cod farm.

"There aren't too many tourists who wander down here, so I figured it must be you," she laughs. She and her husband, Doug, live five minutes back up the road and she motions for us to follow her.

When we arrive, Jennifer bounds out of her Tracker to shake hands. Her voice dances with the Irish lilt of Newfoundlanders. With her dark, wavy hair and high, emphatic cheekbones, she reminds me of actress Meryl Streep in yet another of her many guises—this time a forty-something biologist on a mission to grow cod and, we soon learn, to save this magical place. "My father was a schoolteacher, but my mother grew up here, so we spent every summer here as kids," Jennifer tells us as she leads us to a deck that wraps around the front of the house.

Our jaws drop. Jennifer laughs: "It's something, isn't it?"

That "something" is the view: a sprawling ocean bay ringed by moody barren cliffs and dented with rocky coves. A steep wooden walkway leads down a hill to the Caines' boathouse and dock. Eagles swoop through the cove. Dolphins play in the distant waves. Just then, the setting sun turns the cliffs a fiery red, the water a pale orange.

Perhaps to clamp up our drooping jaws, Jennifer fetches us beers and tells us the story of their cove—once known as Turnip Cove. It was home to three or four fishing families, but the houses were hauled away to larger communities during Newfoundland's infamous resettlement of the 1960s. Folks hadn't much choice: either take the government money to move or stay on without services. Jennifer says there has been an unofficial resettlement going on ever since, with schools, government offices and medical services closing in remote communities.

Over the next few days, as we tour the bay by boat, Jennifer will point out other abandoned coves—"Doug's mom lived there.... Doug's grandmother was born there." Eerily, nothing remains save the odd chimney, a set of cement church steps. Now Pool's Cove is the only inhabited village on the bay, yet virtually every inlet has a name and, for Jennifer, a memory—

"There's the Elephant Stacks.... Doug and I went camping there once.... We used to picnic there.... There's Courting Rock."

Doug arrives later that evening. At fifty, he has the beefy shoulders of a boxer, tight curly hair and eyebrows that slant upward in a perpetual smile. But he seems wary of us, and it takes a few days for his story to unfold. He grew up here, one of eight kids, son a fisherman with health problems, family on welfare. He and Jennifer became friends as teenagers, when Jennifer's parents summered here. Doug became a lobster fisherman, then went to work on the offshore oil rigs. Jennifer did a master's and taught at the university. After marrying, they decided to move back to Pool's Cove and start up a scallop farm. "It's like watching anything grow," Doug says. "You get hooked." They poured their heart into the farm for nearly twenty years. Doug served as mayor of Pool's Cove. But with a shortage of spat, the scallop farm faltered, and, as mayor, Doug grew tired of chasing make-work projects to revitalize the town. Then, just as they were about to return to their old careers, the Codfather came calling. He asked Jennifer to run the cod farm and Doug to manage five salmon sites moving onto the bay for Natures Sea Farms.

Eight years ago, Jennifer and Doug bought this land, built their dream home and moved into the cove of ghosts. They were unable to have children, but Doug is immensely proud of how their work has helped the local community: "There's about twenty-nine kids on that school bus now, and many of them are sons and daughters of our employees." Three locals work for the cod farm, twenty for the salmon farm plus another hundred in its processing plant in Hermitage Bay, an hour away. "I'll tell you one thing," Doug says, "if I had stuck with the offshore, I would be retired now, but this would be a different town had Jennifer and I not moved back."

THE COD FARM, a fifteen-minute boat ride from the Caines' dock, is located off yet another abandoned outport, Lally Cove. Jennifer's speedboat has two 150-horsepower outboard motors and she drives at a good clip with her Irish setter, Tanner, sitting on her lap, his ears flapping back in the wind. As we approach, Jennifer cuts the motor and Tanner leaps onto the bow of the boat.

The farm is a low-lying series of steel platforms surrounding five netted pens situated in what would have been the harbour of the old fishing village.

Where there were once diesel-spewing boats there is now thick silence. On the shore, rocky cliffs plunge down to the green valley of the cove; the ocean laps at a sand beach; eagles nest in the trees; the air is fresh, the water shockingly clear. I suggest that there could be few more beautiful places to go to work and Jennifer laughs. It's not so serene in the winter, she says, when the platforms are covered in ice and a snowstorm's blowing in.

She ties up the speedboat and Tanner leaps out, trotting off in search of his favourite treat: fish pellets.

The platform configuration is practically ancient now—many modern farms have round, three-hundred-foot net pens secured to a floating ring—but Jennifer says this works well for the purposes of an experimental farm, as she and her employees need more access to the fish.

She walks ahead, chatting about her work as she tours us through the farm. She wears rugged foul weather gear atop pink rubber boots decorated with a floral pattern.

The pens, she says, are fifty feet deep, which allows the fish to swim at different temperature levels, depending on the season. One net contains new arrivals, another the two year olds, the last the three year olds slated for harvest in the fall. Her employees spend the better part of each day feeding the fish. A good part of her work is weighing the cod and charting their growth. She has discovered that fingerlings do better when they arrive here in spring rather than in August—"they get that burst of summer growth." A goal is to get the fish up to market weight in two years rather than in three, and so Jennifer is closely monitoring the performance of various families coming from the genomics project. "They're stronger, better fish," she says, "but there is still too great a disparity in size." And this, she says, is something the genomics folks need to work on, for bigger cod get the bigger share of food and may also develop a taste for smaller ones. "Some cannibalism can go on," she says, "and you don't want that."

Jennifer pulls back a tarp on the last pen—a recent innovation to protect the usually bottom-dwelling cod from sunlight. Initially, we see nothing through the clear water, even though there are about twenty-five hundred cod in this corral. Then, suddenly, a mass of sleek, two-foot-long torpedoes swirl up from the bottom. Beyond the monster head, the cod are beautiful creatures, with snow-white bellies, a sharp white stripe running along their grey-green sides and a distinctive barb on the chin, a barbel.

"They have really quirky personalities," says Jennifer. "They'll swim like that, right on top of the water. They can be sensitive at early stages of development, but by the time they get here, they're really tough. They're bottom-feeders, scavengers, so they eat almost anything in the wild. Lots of bacterial problems salmon have don't bother cod." Of course, an advantage of feeding pellets to these pampered fish is that they don't pick up the bottom-dwelling worms that can be a problem in wild cod—which explains the traditional tendency to overcook the fish.

As we continue our amble, Jennifer tells us that this site corrects many of the problems created by the first generation of fish farms. While those farms tended to locate in shallow water with poor currents, these nets sit in deep water—about 115 feet—with a strong tide to flush away fish feces and any uneaten fish pellets, which can create a dead zone below the farm. But dispersed into surrounding waters, this so-called waste (unlike animal waste, fish feces does not have E. coli) becomes valuable organic matter that provides nutrients for other species. This makes sense to me, considering that Newfoundland's once vibrant oceans were once jammed with cod, which, I presume, did not leave the water to go to the bathroom. Now, Cooke Aquaculture is experimenting with multi-trophic aquaculture projects, such as growing mussels alongside salmon pens to absorb the nutrient production of the farm, a fundamental principle of land-based organic agriculture.

Another innovation is using underwater cameras to assist in feeding: When operators see that the fish have stopped eating, they stop feeding, which minimizes the loss of the pricey pellets and reduces nutrient overloading on the ocean floor. And Newfoundland regulations demand that fish farms lie fallow for at least one year between production cycles, to give the bottom a chance to rejuvenate and also break any cycle of disease that may have established.

Jennifer's experimental operation doesn't have to grapple with density issues, as the entire site has only twenty-two thousand fish, but lowering stocking is key to reducing stress, which makes fish prone to disease, including parasite infestation—such as lice in salmon and cod. Both occur naturally in wild fish but can spread more readily on farms where fish swim in close proximity. To combat lice, farmers can add the pesticide SLICE to the feed. But the safest method is preventing the buildup in the first place through good fish husbandry practices. Jennifer says the challenge with stocking densities is finding "that sweet spot," which is healthy for the environment and the fish and good for production: "You listen to what the fish tell you." For instance, on Doug's salmon sites, although the industry typically stocks about fifty thousand salmon per pen, he has found that thirty-seven thousand is the sweet spot. "But you need a certain density to get a good feeding response," says Jennifer. "The greater the density, the more aggressively the fish feed. And cod actually like to be together." And this, too, makes sense, I suppose, given that the fish travel in massive schools.

In six years of running her farm, Jennifer says she hasn't had any problems with disease nor has she used any antibiotics. In all of her sampling of fish, she has discovered just two individual louse and has not had to treat her fish. "Fish husbandry practices have vastly improved over the past decade. People don't believe it, but there are very few antibiotics used in fish farming now, and what is used has to be prescribed by a veterinarian."

She and Doug also use pressure washers to clean nets and equipment rather than anti-fouling chemicals. In the winter, when they have to cut ice around the farms, they run chainsaws without oil lest any enter the water. "You have to be careful," says Jennifer. "For instance, cod won't go into a white net. So I spent weeks researching colourfast dyes to use on the dipping nets. You make one mistake, an innocent mistake, and the residue shows up in the cod and you don't want that."

During our tour, Tanner has raced up and down every platform, sniffed out every corner of the farm but still hasn't found a spill of pellets. Now he is at Jennifer's feet, whining. She tries to put him off, but he is persistent. His mother, we learned, was a hunting dog owned by Jennifer's brother, who was killed in a hunting accident. His dog stayed by him until he was found. Tanner doesn't hunt; instead, he uses his hunting skills to get his way. Jennifer finally gives in, heads to the feed storage bin and returns with a handful of dry, brown pellets.

I ask to try some, in the interests of research, see what these cod are eating. Jennifer shrugs, pours a few into my palm. But I wait for Tanner to eat his first.

We are back at the pen with the fish that will go to harvest in the fall. Jennifer admits that she hasn't worked out how to round them up, as cod don't naturally swim against a current like salmon do. But she'll figure something out. Part of her work is developing procedures that cod farmers can use on a commercial level and adapting the equipment from salmon farming as much as possible, to reduce costs. "Fish farming," she says, "is about coming up with thousands of tiny innovations."

Tanner has lapped up his salty pellets in one go. Now, as I muster the courage to try mine, he parks himself at my feet. The pellets smell and look like dog food. I am having second thoughts.

I ask Jennifer about the netting system used on fish farms. This is a hugely contentious issue. One environmental organization, SeaChoice, an umbrella group that includes the Coastal Alliance for Aquaculture Reform, concedes that management practices on salmon farms have improved, but now they want the industry to adopt closed-container systems at sea and on land, to prevent escapes and transmission of disease and parasites to wild stocks. The Canadian industry is resisting—such systems are vastly more expensive and require energy to circulate and regulate the temperature of the sea water. And it says there is no proof that such costly systems are required. After studying and monitoring the impact of fish farming for the past few decades, the Department of Fisheries and Oceans has not found evidence that fish farming has adversely affected the population levels of wild stocks; indeed, many of its studies show that wild salmon typically have more lice than farmed and that disease is more likely to be transmitted from wild to farmed fish, though it could also be that lice building up on salmon farms subject young wild salmon in the area to higher infection rates.

Jennifer is tired of the constant attacks on fish farming, but she is also a deeply pragmatic woman. She readily admits that fish farming does have an impact—it only stands to reason. Everything we do on the ocean has an impact—fishing, recreational boating, dumping city sewage and industrial waste, allowing agricultural chemicals to run off. "We're paying the price for our industrialized society, for dumping PCBs and toxins into the water for decades." But she believes fish farms leave a relatively light footprint and that farmers have a vested interest, along with environmentalists, in working to keep our oceans clean. In other words, they would do well to join forces and tackle bigger issues.

And she will go so far as to say that farming can even have a positive impact—for one, escaped fish, as long as they're indigenous to an area. "First," she says, "you don't want to lose expensive fish, so we do everything we can to prevent this. But a lot of people think it would be a bad thing for farmed fish to survive and reproduce. The five hundred years of fishing here have greatly altered the fitness of cod as a species. Farmed cod are very fit, strong individuals. These would probably enhance the fishery."

But Tanner has had enough of our talk. He starts to whine. Jennifer nods at the pellets in my hand, tells me it's high in protein, low in fat, mostly herring caught in South America, dried and mixed with a formulation of vitamins. Not exactly dog food. The supplier, EWOS Canada, is among a group of salmon food suppliers and farmers in British Columbia that have developed organic standards for the industry. Such farms have been recognized in Europe, but the Pacific Organic Seafood Association's attempts to be accredited by the Certified Organic Association of British Columbia have raised severe opposition from SeaChoice and other environmental groups.

Now Tanner starts pawing at my running shoe. He looks up at me with big black pained eyes. How could I torture him like this? I peer at Jennifer. If these fish pellets were packed with pesticides, antibiotics and industrial pollutants, okay, maybe she might let a journalist eat them, but surely not her Tanner. I pop one in my mouth. It is dry as dust, salty, fishy. Yes, it pretty much tastes like fishy dog food. Not that I've tasted dog food; I'm just guessing.

But the cod seem to thrive on it. And about now, I have had enough fish pellets and enough of politics. What I would really like is to try one of those fat, juicy fillets.

ON OUR LAST EVENING on Fortune Bay, Jennifer and Doug cook up a feast of seafood, a bounty that we've rarely had on visits to East Coast fishing villages. Usually there is one local catch. Tonight we're having lobster, salmon and cod.

Yesterday, after a tour of Doug's salmon sites, he carried a ten-pounder out to the pickup, dropping the back gate and using it as a carving table. As we watched, he demonstrated various filleting techniques, but what really impressed us is that he wore a white T-shirt, yet somehow managed to slice up that salmon without getting a single drop of blood on that crisp white cotton.

Now he heads down to the dock and hauls up a net full of lobsters his brother caught on the bay earlier. "Those are the guys I answer to," says Doug, "the local lobster fishermen. If I harm the fishery, I hurt their livelihoods. The last thing I want to do is give them a stick to beat me with."

Doug plunks the lobster into a pot of boiling water. Jennifer has dressed the thick fillet in maple syrup, brown sugar and butter. "You'll really want to get that recipe," he nods to me. He is proud of the way he farms, proud of his salmon. Doug wraps the fish in tinfoil and takes it out to the barbecue.

The Caines' kitchen is huge and sits at the heart of the house, with the living room wing and bedrooms on one side, the dining room and offices on the other. The centre work island overlooks the ocean and, at this time of the evening, light from the setting sun floods in through the massive picture windows. Doug admits he and Jennifer are foodies and spend most of their time here.

There is plenty of room in the kitchen for all of us to work together and we do. Nancy opens the wine, while I make a Greek salad and cut garlic and onions for Jennifer. She lightly dusts the cod fillets with a mixture of flour and corn flour before slipping them into a hot frying pan—"you have to fry cod at high heat for it to hold together." She is also sautéing the cheeks and tongue and baking the chitlin and pea—the male and female gonads. "I'm not doing anything fancy," she says. "You said you wanted to taste the meat."

Doug returns and suggests a toast, "to good food, good conversation." Doug has finally come around to trusting that I am actually listening and not rushing to conclusions. Now he feels confident enough to share his concerns about aquaculture. He, too, admits that you can't farm fish without affecting the oceans. He believes the most severe effect is on the bottom directly under the farm, but he also says it's local and temporary and a pretty small area. In total, the eighty farms in British Columbia cover about one square kilometre of ocean. Each of Doug's sites on this bay is about the size of a football field, and the five are separated by kilometres of water. The public reaction to salmon farming, he suggests, is out of proportion. "But don't get me wrong," he says. "The regulations are tough, and we need them to be tough, and we can work with them. We have to ensure food security. We can't leave it in the hands of industry and expect it to police itself."

And perhaps, he concedes, we can't leave the policing entirely to the government. He thinks third-party inspectors, such as organic certifiers, would be good for the industry. Now, all salmon farms are painted with the same black brush. There is no way for consumers to differentiate between farms, to support better farms with better practices.

And then we get to his worst fear—that his good work and good name could be tainted by less scrupulous operations setting up on the bay, that Newfoundland might bend its tough regulations to accommodate large multinationals offering investment and jobs. "We have a real good fishery on this bay and locals look after it," says Doug. "People who don't come from here won't have the same interests in preserving it. Now, if something goes wrong, we can't blame it on anyone but ourselves. It's ours for us to use or destroy."

Jennifer elbows Doug, reminding him the salmon is on the barbecue. There is time to talk over dinner and later, when we sit out on the deck late into the night. And we will have still more conversations in the future, when the Newfoundland Aquaculture Industry Association names Jennifer and Doug growers of the year for 2007, and, on a sadder note, when the industry partners decide to sell the cod site she manages and relocate the experimental farm to Bay Bulls, closer to Memorial University. The project will continue, but without Jennifer's passion or the benefits to Pool's Cove. But right now, that news is in the future and the table is heaped with lobster, platters of salmon and cod, a treat even for Jennifer and Doug. "I can't be bringing home the experimental fish," she laughs.

I must confess that I have always preferred farmed Atlantic salmon to wild Pacific, something foodies consider a travesty. Yet, when I admit this to my foodie friends, they usually agree. But up until this evening, guilt usually trumped my temptation and I often passed on the fish. Now, I am not only eating Doug's salmon but feeling rather smug. I am saving not only a wild salmon but also up to three hundred pounds of wild fish from ending up in that wild salmon's gut. So let me tell you about guilt-free flavour—it's dreamy, the texture velvety, the flavour buttery and luscious.

As for Jennifer's cod, I can say that she is good for her word. This fish is all that she promised: The fillets are plumper, whiter, firmer, sweeter. And I will go even further than Jennifer and pronounce this cod better than wild—at least better than any we sampled on our trip. Although the wild fillets were good, they were also thin and lacked zest, perhaps a good feed from a full ocean? They needed the jazz of sauces and spice, whereas these farmed beauties are veritable steaks with tender flakes that break off in large scallops and a deep, clean flavour that makes me think of the farm, the clear water, the sharp ocean breeze and not at all of the dry, salty, fishy pellets that went into them.

But the gonads, yikes. In our rush to dig into our seafood smorgasbord, then into seconds and thirds, we have forgotten the gonads in the oven, and they're Jennifer's favourite part of the cod. When Doug hauls them out, they are blackened and hard. He shrugs and eats his anyway. I try mine, but the burnt things require a steak knife to saw through and they taste like overcooked liver. I'll leave them for another time, or for Tanner.

# Newfoundland

## Jennifer's Cod au Gratin

This recipe is a variation on an old Newfoundland favourite, comfort food
for a howling winter night. For the sauce, an aged sharp white cheddar is
best.

| | | |
|---|---|---|
| 2 lb | cod fillets | 1 kg |

**For white sauce:**

| | | |
|---|---|---|
| 1/4 cup | butter | 50 mL |
| 1/4 cup | all-purpose flour | 50 mL |
| 2 1/2 cups | 2% or homogenized milk | 625 mL |
| 2 tbsp | minced onion or green onions | 25 mL |
| 1/2 tsp | salt | 2 mL |
| 1/4 tsp | black pepper | 1 mL |

**For cheese topping:**

| | | |
|---|---|---|
| 1 tbsp | butter (or margarine) | 15 mL |
| 1/2 cup | breadcrumbs | 125 mL |
| 1 cup | grated cheddar cheese | 250 mL |

Preheat oven to 375°F (190°C).

Place cod fillets in a single layer in a lightly greased shallow casserole
dish.

For the white sauce, make a roux by melting the butter at low heat in a
saucepan and gradually adding the flour to form a paste. Gradually add the
milk, stirring to remove any lumps. Stir in the onion, salt and pepper.
Heat, stirring constantly, until the sauce has thickened to a creamy
consistency, about 5 minutes.

For the cheese topping, melt the butter in a saucepan over low heat. Stir in the breadcrumbs. Remove from heat and stir in the cheese.

Pour the white sauce over the fish; top with the cheese mixture. Bake, covered, for 35 to 40 minutes.

*Makes 4 servings.*

Credit: Jennifer Caines, Pool's Cove, Newfoundland.

## Cod Cheeks with Pine Nuts

You might have to go to Newfoundland and Labrador to try this recipe, as cod cheeks, fresh or frozen, are difficult to find elsewhere. But it's worth asking your fishmonger if he or she could bring some in. Chef Bob Arniel buys his at the Bigood's supermarket or Belbin's Grocery in St. John's. He lightens this traditional favourite by substituting pine nuts for scruncheons. This makes a fun appetizer for four, with about three cod cheeks per person.

| | | |
|---|---|---|
| 1 lb | cod cheeks | 500 g |
| 1 cup | 2% milk | 250 mL |
| 1 tbsp | Worcestershire sauce | 15 mL |
| 1 cup | all-purpose flour | 250 mL |
| 1 tbsp | kosher salt | 15 mL |
| 2 tsp | black pepper | 10 mL |
| 1/4 cup | clarified butter | 50 mL |
| 1/2 cup | pine nuts | 125 mL |
| 2 tbsp | freshly squeezed lemon juice | 25 mL |
| 2 tbsp | chopped fresh parsley | 25 mL |

Soak the cod cheeks overnight in the milk and Worcestershire sauce.

Drain the liquid and dredge the cod cheeks in the flour seasoned with kosher salt and black pepper. Melt the clarified butter in a sauté pan over low heat. Increase the heat to medium-high; sauté the cod cheeks on one side, about 30 seconds to 1 minute. Add the pine nuts. Flip the cod cheeks to sauté on the other side for another 30 seconds to 1 minute. Be careful not to let the nuts brown; stir or remove them if necessary.

Finish the cod cheeks with a drizzle of lemon juice and a sprinkle of parsley. Serve immediately.

*Makes 4 servings.*

Credit: Chef Bob Arniel, Chef to Go, St. John's, Newfoundland.

# *Manitoba*

# GOING WHOLE HOG

*Man is more nearly like the pig than the pig wants to admit.*
—Marilyn Nissenson and Susan Jonas, *The Ubiquitous Pig*

In Manitoba, which has become a pork-producing powerhouse in the past thirteen years, thousands of little piggies go to market every day. But this evening, one very special piggy is going to Government House, the official residence of Lieutenant Governor John Harvard.

For farmer Ian Smith, the Victorian mansion is just one of the four stops he'll make on his Friday-night delivery run. He actually tells me about three other customers first: his two vets—"One even has his own hog operation, but he buys from me. He says, 'We haven't had pork like this for years'"— and a single mom—"It's cheaper buying direct from me than from the supermarket, and she knows what the product is."

Still, as Ian turns his 1988 pickup into the circular drive, he can't quell the kick of excitement in his stomach. As he says, "It's not every farmer who delivers pork to the Lieutenant Governor."

Harvard's wife, the first lady of Manitoba, Lenore Berscheid, answers the front door. She chats with Ian long enough to get to a sense of him—"He's a great, humble, dedicated guy," she tells me later—then she directs him to the kitchen, where he carries two boxes of wrapped chops, roasts, hams and bacon.

Government House doesn't serve pork at official functions, out of respect for Muslim and Jewish guests, but Berscheid buys Ian's meat for family and staff dinners. "The men in the family like to have a ham sandwich," she says, "so we cook up one of Ian's hams."

However, Berscheid herself has a major problem with pork or, rather, the way it's produced on massive industrial operations. Her chief concern is animal welfare. "I haven't been an activist in this cause, but I wish I were," she says. "That we treat the animals in this way, in this day and age, is absolutely untenable."

She heard about Ian through her support of the Winnipeg Humane Society (WHS). In 2002, that organization became the first animal-welfare group in Canada to certify farmers who raise animals according to humane standards set by the WHS. Ian was one of the first farmers to gain certification. "I didn't really have to change anything I was already doing," he says. For doing things the way he's always done them, the way his father did things, Ian was named WHS's Humane Farmer of the Year in 2005.

Still, Berscheid admits that her "revulsion" for Manitoba's pork industry is "too foregone" to really enjoy Ian's meat. "I just don't like to eat pork, even though Ian treats his animals very nicely. And I do hope his methods spread."

Across town at Fusion Grill, food impresario Scot McTaggart has a different problem with pork. He has turned his tiny dining room into a pulpit for preaching the virtues of locally produced foods, harkening back to the province's culinary halcyon days when small mixed farms and market gardens supplied exquisitely fresh produce to Winnipeg's plethora of ethnic restaurants. "Taste a tomato from Manitoba," he says. "The long, hot prairie sun and cool nights makes for a perfect balance of sweet and tart." Fusion's menu features farm-raised bison, elk and wild boar; grass-fed beef; and northern pike and pickerel from Canada's largest freshwater commercial fishery, based on Lakes Manitoba and Winnipeg. But there is no pork on the menu. McTaggart says it has become too much like wheat, an inexpensive commodity. "It's too common to cook."

There is more bad news from a restaurant that really knows farming, LuxSolé Restaurant and Tapas Lounge, a trendy Winnipeg bistro started by four farm boys, brothers Chris, Eric, Eugene and Lawrence Warwaruk, in 1999. The first thing they did when the restaurant turned a buck was buy back their family's repossessed farm. They've since made it their mission to support small Manitoba family operations, buying lamb directly from their Uncle Julian, trading timothy hay from their farm for bison. Unlike most other restaurants, which buy only prime cuts, making it nearly impossible for smaller farmers to be suppliers, LuxSolé buys animals nose to tail, the whole hog—well, except for hogs. In a province that produces over eight million hogs a year, the brothers have had trouble finding a small, quality supplier of pork. "Look," Eugene says, "I can't tell you what to write, but it's such a bad-news story." Factory hog farming, he says, has been devastating for Manitoba's environment and for farmers.

By the time I drive out to Ian's farm, about an hour northwest of Winnipeg, along flat gravel roads that zing arrow straight through the Prairies, I am beginning to feel a little of what it must be like to be Ian Smith. While enduring the isolation of raising pork in his old-fashioned way, he must also suffer the ill will mounting against the industrial system. And then I run headlong into Big Pork's attitude toward Ian.

I have stopped off in Argyle, Ian's hometown, where he went to public school and where his grandfather donated five acres to build a community centre. The town straddles the prime meridian, marking the central point of Canada. It used to be a thriving little agricultural hub. When Big Pork argued for tax breaks to expand the industry here, it promised to reverse rural depopulation in Manitoba. It has delivered exactly the opposite. Where there were once fifteen farms raising pork in this area, there are now three. Ian's is one of them. There isn't much in town now—a corner store, a curling rink and the Prime Meridian Café, which triples as a post office and liquor store.

The Prime Meridian has an inviting picnic table on the front sidewalk, so I stop for a beer. I'm organizing my notes when a big burly farmer drives up in a half-ton truck. He pushes the tractor cap up from his eyes, nods at my notebook.

"You're not from around here," he says. "What brings you all the way out here?"

"I'm from Toronto," I smile. "I'm here to write about pork."

He tells me about an operation up the road, tells me that I should go and see it. "They have about six thousand hogs."

I mention that I'm writing about a smaller farm, one that's raising pork a little differently. "He's from around here," I say. "You probably know him, Ian Smith."

"Huh," the farmer grunts and heads inside. He returns a moment later with his mail. "You know the difference between Argyle and Toronto? Most times I come for mail, I don't run into anyone. And that's just the way I like it."

When I turn into Ian's gravel laneway, I sense that very little has changed on this low-lying quarter section since he bought the 160 acres from his parents, Malcolm and Audrey, in 1994, or, for that matter, since his folks moved here in 1953. Although most small mixed farms disappeared decades ago, this one, against all the economic and social pressures to modernize, somehow endures. The lone new building—an implement shed—covers an assortment of aging tractors. Small fenced pastures and three outlying buildings—almost too small to be called barns but neatly painted red and white—house some 180 pigs, 75 chickens, 13 cattle and 3 riding horses. Until 1988, Malcolm still used horses to clear manure and haul straw.

As I get out of the car, Ian's dogs—Jip, an old black mutt, and Gismo, a young yappy Jack Russell that looks like a runt pig—race to greet me.

Ian follows, pushing open the screen door on the back porch of his small white-board house. At age forty-three, he still has the appearance of a college boy, handsome and fit with soft brown eyes and close-cropped hair. He greets me with a gentle handshake and a wide smile. He's amazed, he says laughing, even after all my phone calls to set up the trip, that someone from Toronto would bother coming all this way to see him.

"But, well—" the slightest of stutters shakes his voice, "you're just in time to feed the pigs." He turns and strides to the barn, shoulders and head hunched forward, leaning into his next step, as if his mind is already on the chores.

I follow, feeling oddly at home. Ian's tidy little farm brings to mind my mother's stories of the pigs her family kept on their farm just outside Alliston, Ontario. They had three sows—she pigs—who had free-rooting roam of a pasture by the barn. After Christmas, my grandfather sent the sows to a neighbour's farm to be serviced by a boar—a he pig. In spring, the mammas tucked into the barn to have their litters—eight to ten piglets, cute pink, hairless things that look an awful lot like cute pink, hairless babies. My mom and her seven siblings loved pigs. They were the cleanest of the farm animals. They didn't foul their straw beds but did their business in a gutter that ran through the centre of the barn. That was easy enough to shovel out, and the nitrogen-rich manure improved the sandy soil of the potato and turnip fields. The kids didn't like potatoes and turnips nearly so much, for they spent their Thanksgiving weekends, three whole days off school, digging up seven acres of potatoes. But the pigs! Often there was a runt that couldn't compete with the bigger piglets for milk. Lucky runt, for he ended up in the house being bottle-fed by my mom's sister, Alice. One spent the whole summer living in the kitchen and back porch. Pigs are easily litter-trained. They're social animals and love to cuddle and play ball and fetch sticks. Like a dog, that little runt followed Alice everywhere, including down the lane to collect the mail. She called him runt or pig. On a farm, it's not good to get too attached by naming an animal, for by late summer little pig was big enough to join his siblings in the barn. And by late fall, he was fat enough to be butchered. That, too, took place on the farm, with my grandfather tying the pigs by the hind feet to a crossbeam, slitting their throats to let the blood drain out. After quartering the carcasses, he salted and cured the meat for winter hams and roasts, and sent the head and feet to a butcher in town to be scraped clean and made into sausages, which my grandmother boiled, then preserved in jars. "And, oh my, those sausages were good," my mother told me, "fried up and served with mashed potatoes and mashed turnips."

In E.B. White's fantastical children's story *Charlotte's Web*, a spider manages to save the runt pig from the frying pan. Lucky Wilbur. But in his essay "Death of a Pig," White confronted what he called the "tragedy enacted on most farms" of raising a spring pig only to be butchered in fall. The "smoked bacon and ham," he wrote, "provide a ceremonial ending."

Ian's farm is a little larger, but the pigs lead a similar life—well cared for while they're living and delicious after. His thirty-odd sows and their two boar boyfriends live together, free to make pig love when they want to—as long as they provide Ian with a steady stream of piglets year-round, averaging two and half litters each. During the four years of a sow's breeding life (when the libido slackens, "it's down the road for her," says Ian, "to become sausage"), they have the run of a fenced-in field with a massive mound of straw to root and snuggle in, and a pond for cooling off—essential since pigs can't sweat—plus a good layer of mud protects their pink skin from sunburn and pesky insects. A roomy lean-to provides shade in summer and shelter in winter.

Sows and boars can grow to be massive beasts—eight or nine hundred pounds, though Ian's younger hogs average four to five hundred. Like humans, pigs establish hierarchical social structures. Alpha sows will pick on underlings who maybe haven't filled out as much at the loin, while every boar considers himself the centre of the universe and can be downright nasty. But, also like humans, pigs behave better when they're happy, can breathe fresh air and aren't overcrowded. Ian says a sow can be shy when she returns to the herd after birthing, but will work things out. On this hot day, the big porkers wallow together in the pond like gentle hippos. Still, Ian suggests I hang back when he enters the pasture to feed them, for then the alpha breeders charge in to be first to the seven-foot-long trough. Put off, the meek trail after Ian as he fills another feeder. When the alphas barge in on that, Ian moves to a third trough, doling out more grain. With the food democratically distributed, the big bullies realize they will go hungry darting back and forth trying to control all eight pork barrels, so finally settle at one trough to eat their first-class rations, letting the others settle at theirs.

Inside the farrowing or birthing barn, an exhausted mamma lies on her side in a seven-by-two-foot farrowing crate, which is the reverse, really, of a baby crib. It keeps her from rolling on her newborns, who sleep in an adjoining pen, entwined in a heap under a heat lamp. When we enter the barn, they wake up and squeeze through the bars to suckle her teats. After about a week, when the little ones are big enough to get the heck out of the way when big mamma sits down, Ian will move the sow to one large pen that she'll share with her piglets. Yes, he admits, one or two might still get crushed, but that's the price of mamma's freedom.

Four sow families live in the barn in separate pens, each about ten by twelve feet. The piglets run beneath the fences' lower bars, playing tag with neighbouring litters, streaming like pink clouds around our feet. The socialization is important, Ian says. When the pigs are weaned—at about five weeks—he'll regroup them by size so that they can compete equally for food, then move them to the finishing barn to fatten.

But there's one last chore here—Ian scoops up a runt from the new litter, slips a bottle of milk from his pocket, gives it a suckle. The starter milk is expensive—$80 a pail, which will feed three or four runts for about three weeks. Ian will feed this one four times a day. "But what are you supposed to do," he says, "just let it die? I don't know." Before he goes to bed, he'll slip out to the barn to give the runt another bottle.

We move onto the finishing barn, where Ian fattens about three hundred pigs a year to the market weight of 240 to 250 pounds, in about six months. It's a short life but not a miserable one. Six to ten pig pals live together like teenagers, in a seven-by-fourteen-foot pen, playing tag in the clover straw, eating and drinking all they want, sleeping in. During the summer, they poop where it's hot, sleep where it's cool; in winter, they poop where it's cool, sleep where it's warm, making the task of cleaning up after them easier. I think it would be nice if they could run outside, too, but Ian says the extremes of Manitoba's hot and cold weather are hard on them. So are the coyotes. And, the barn has plenty of natural light, and it's well ventilated. It smells but does not stink. The odour is almost pleasant, of pungent black earth, dry and musky.

As Ian does the chores, he moves calmly, quietly, rhythmically. He fills feeders, scrapes manure into the barn's centre gutter, to be carried by a conveyor to compost in a pile outside. He shakes down a fresh bed of clover and barley straw that the pigs love to root in. But now, curious creatures, they cock their heads to watch Ian's every move.

They know he'll be here at 6 A.M., after he finishes watching Report on Business TV while simultaneously listening to the sports news on the radio. They know he'll be back at 3:30 in the afternoon, after working in the fields. As he is every day, seven days a week. "Pigs like routine," Ian says. He hasn't had a day off since his father died in 2001.

"Do you like pigs?" I ask as we walk back to the house. Ian has invited me for dinner. "I mean, do you have a special feeling for them?"

Ian considers my question seriously, as he does everything I ask. "Not really," he says. "A lot of guys around here go deer hunting. I don't. I could never kill a deer. I guess I have more of a special feeling for cows." He raises eight or so calves a year and sends them to market—he eats beef, but not his own.

"We would make a good pair," I say. "I grew up on a beef farm. I could sure take a cow to market. But I think I'm kind of getting a thing for pigs."

Ian laughs, holding the screen door open for me. Inside, his mother, Audrey, is setting dinner on the table—they eat every day at five o'clock, on the hour.

Audrey, at seventy-three, has a bad back and arthritic joints and is considering moving into a retirement home, but she's reluctant to leave the farm. Ian is single. She worries about Ian getting a hand caught in the baler, being kicked by a cow, lying in a field hurt somewhere with no one knowing. When he climbs the ladder to the top of the grain bin, she holds the ladder until he ties it off. "What if he falls?" she asks me.

"She worries about everything," Ian says.

We eat at the tiny kitchen table—Audrey and I at either end, Ian in the middle. I can't imagine how the whole family once squeezed around it—Audrey, her husband, Malcolm, Ian and his two brothers, Brian and Blair.

As the middle son, Ian wasn't in line to take over the farm. "My brothers were more interested in machinery, driving the tractors and stuff," Ian tells me. "I was always left behind to work with Dad, to work with the livestock. But I preferred that." His brothers both became truck drivers, and Ian says they don't think much of the way he farms, staying small and raising pigs naturally. "They say if I were going to be successful, somebody else would be doing this, too." They have never bought a pig from Ian.

Ian passes me a platter of meat. It's pork, of course. A dark pink ham. This is a moment of truth. Certainly, it is a very good thing to raise a pig humanely, but as the culinary glutton I am, I wonder, does it taste better than ham from industrially raised pigs?

"People tell me it does," Ian says. "They say it has a deeper flavour. And it doesn't have that pork smell."

Now Audrey is worrying again. "I'm not much of a cook," she says.

She cooks like my mother, simply, with the freshest of ingredients. There are mashed potatoes, boiled peas, a yellow-bean relish—all ingredients from the quarter-acre garden behind the house, where Ian also plants watermelons, muskmelons, corn, lettuce and onions. Audrey says she boiled the ham for an hour and a half and that's all.

I take a bite. It's dense and thick, with a deep satisfying tang. It's nothing like wet vapid supermarket ham. I try a piece dipped in Audrey's pickled beans, and it sends me dreaming of summer picnics. Still, I wonder, is the flavour in the meat or the curing?

Later, as we're clearing the table and washing dishes, Audrey has a question for me. "I hope you don't mind me asking," she says, "but are you married?"

THE NEXT MORNING, after a frenzied dawn commute from Winnipeg, I turn into Ian's laneway at one minute to seven. Audrey already has my eggs in the frying pan. Breakfast is at seven, *on the hour*, Ian had warned me the night before. I slip into my seat just as Audrey slips two sunny-side ups onto my plate, eggs that Ian says were sitting under a chicken's butt just moments before. Also on the plate are two strips of Ian's bacon. I wish there were three or four, but the two lone slices turn out to be more than enough, for they are not at all like their grocery store brethren, shrivelled salty strings. Even fried up crisp, these are thick, succulent planks laced with juicy fat.

"The bacon's amazing," I say.

"Could be the way it's butchered," says Ian, pushing his bacon into his runny yolk of egg. "We're heading there this morning. You can ask them."

It's Tuesday, Ian's market day. After breakfast, he hitches a horse trailer to his pickup, backs the trailer to the loading ramp at the finishing barn, and throws open the barn door. There, in the alley, is one unlucky pig, eyes big, eyes bright. She is a beautifully plump pink confection on four thin legs. And it seems as though she can see straight into my strange dark human heart, perceive that I would rather pack the trailer full of pigs than take a single sacrificial one. But Ian doesn't twist his heart up turning her into Miss Piggy. He walks behind her, shooing softly, and, brave pig, tottering on her high-heeled hooves, clacks right up the loading ramp. Ian bangs the trailer door shut.

On the forty-five-kilometre drive to the butcher—Ian lives in the Interlake Region between Lakes Manitoba and Winnipeg—he tells me there used to be 120 independent hog farmers in this area when he was growing up, each of them raising three hundred or more hogs a year. Now he estimates there are just ten or so independents left, plus a few massive corporate operations with thousands of pigs. For most urbanites, rural depopulation is an abstract term. For Ian, it's deeply personal. Consider the statistics this way: there were once 120 or so farmers' daughters for Ian to meet and now there are practically none.

Pork farming, Ian says, changed virtually overnight. In 1996, with massive factory farms facing ever stricter environmental controls in the United States, Europe and in Quebec and Ontario, Manitoba invited Big Pork to move here, even though the vast majority of the province drains into Lake Winnipeg, already suffering from nutrient overload. But Manitoba offered plenty of what pigs like best: cheap grain; good, fresh water (finishing pigs drink up to two gallons a day); vast open spaces to establish intensive livestock operations; and a huge competitive advantage over the United States of a low

Canadian dollar, which then hovered at US$0.72. To lure giant meat processors, Manitoba plunked down a bag of incentives: millions of dollars in grants, tax breaks and free land; changes to the planning act that made it practically impossible for local municipalities to resist or regulate factory farms; and an end to the provincially controlled single-desk auction selling system, giving big processors what amounted to alpha control of the trough by letting them buy pigs directly from farmers. Of course, the new system made it nearly impossible for small independent farmers to supply big processors. As Ian says, no processor is going to send a transport truck out to a farm for fifty pigs when the truck can hold two hundred. Big Pork pushed big farmers to grow even bigger, and companies such as PIC, Puratone and Elite (a division of Maple Leaf) set up corporate-owned barns on independent farms, filling them with their own pigs and supplying the feed. The farmers became little more than managers, what Ian calls Wal-Mart farmers.

By 2001, Manitoba's *Farmers' Independent Weekly* estimated that just 11 percent of the 1379 producers who remained (down from nearly 3000 before 1996) sold 82 percent of Manitoba's eight million hogs, 90 percent destined for the export market. And, not surprising, after Big Pork and its meat processors moved into Manitoba, the price of pigs plummeted.

"Those guys are like motorcycle gangs," says Ian. "It's like, you stay off my turf and we'll set the price and we'll both be happy. How can the price of hogs be the same thirty-five years ago as it is today? Somewhere along the line, someone's making big bucks, but it's not the farmer. Farmers are like puppets. We're dangling on the strings of big industry controlling us. They're calling the shots and we do the dance for them."

Ian says he never considered taking the bait to go big. "If the government or agricultural people say, try this, I do something else." That "something else" was virtually dropping out of the system, to sell directly to customers.

We turn off the highway into the gravel parking lot of Interlake Packers, a family-owned operation in St. Laurent, where Ian takes his pigs to be killed and butchered. He backs his trailer to an off-loading ramp, opens the door. Inside, brave little pig is now scared. Nothing is familiar here, not the long alley leading inside the holding barn or the empty pen at the end. Where are the other pigs? Ian climbs into the trailer behind her. "Ha, c'mon, get," he says, in exactly the same tone he uses to speak to me—always soft, always calm. But, obstinate pig now, she won't go. Ian has a pig swatter, a square of canvas nailed to a hockey stick. But Ian uses the swatter to extend the reach of his arms, to shoo and direct, not to swat or smack stubborn pig. When he realizes that she really won't go, he leans down, places his shoulder against her rump and leans on her. Finally, she gives in, trotting down the alley and into her new pen, right across the hall from a giant set of sliding doors that leads to the killing floor.

Minutes later, pig is knocked out by a stun gun and hung up by her hind legs to bleed out. Then she's dipped in a scalding tank and run through a dehairing machine. After her intestines and organs are removed, the carcass is cut in half, washed again, weighed and placed in a cooler. At 5:30 the next morning, the butcher and sausage maker take over and the bountiful pig will yield about six lovely five-pound hams, six roasts, fifty pork chops, eighteen pounds of bacon, three pounds of ribs and six pounds of sausage—all cut and packaged according to how the customer wants it.

"If the customer wants inch-thick steaks for the barbecue, they get inch-thick steaks," says Eddy Schon, general manager for the packer. "If they want pork loin roasts instead of chops, or pork belly instead of bacon, they can have that." His company processes about thirty pigs an hour, compared with more than seven hundred at big processors. The Schon siblings took over the business from their father. Eddy's brother, Rick, runs the sausage department; his sister, Monica, handles the books; while Eddy oversees the thirty-person shop. They have modernized enough to become one of the largest of the independent packers in Manitoba, but they still follow what Eddy calls "the old practices that take longer." They cure bacon, hams and sausages in a cooler before sending them to the smokehouse, where they smoulder over maple or oak shavings Eddy gets from a local cabinetmaker. The hams stay in for ten to twelve hours, the bacon and sausages for four to five. The big processors, Eddy says, simply spray on liquid smoke; they also increase the weight of the hams by injecting them with water. "They start with a twenty-pound ham and it becomes thirty pounds. They sell their hams for ninety-nine cents a pound, but it's half water. Whereas we lose weight on our finished hams."

Rick doesn't add fillers—wheat and soy—to his sausages either, or water that can extend a 1000-pound batch to 1200. He makes the links—breakfast, garlic, farmers and smokies—according to recipes handed down from his father, "with some modifications of my own," he says.

They're proud of their work. Says Eddy: "People who taste our sausages say they're the best they've ever had." Indeed, on Friday nights, there's a lineup at Interlake's store, with city folks heading to cottages on Lake Manitoba stopping in to buy sausages and chops for weekend barbecues.

But while good custom butchering definitely plays a role in taste, according to Eddy, flavour starts with the meat. "I've found Ian's meat to be more tender," he says. "It has more taste. Ian's pigs are old-style. It goes back to the way we used to raise them." What pigs Ian can't sell directly to customers, Interlake buys for its own custom-butchering business.

Back in the pickup, driving home, I ask Ian why he thinks his pork tastes better than what comes out of the industrial system. He rules out breed: He fattens pretty much the same kind of pig as the mega-producers, a cross between four whites—the Yorkshire, Landrace, Duroc and Pietrain. His feed of barley, corn and soybeans with mineral and vitamin supplements is virtually the same. "Oh, some use peas for protein," he says, "but I like soybeans." He also follows the Canadian Quality Assurance standards for pork, which bans growth hormones or animal protein and demands specific withdrawal times from antibiotics and other medications before slaughter so that no residue shows up in the meat.

A key difference is that he raises pork naturally, but *natural* is a fuzzy term, with no official body to define it or inspect a farm's practices. Essentially, "natural meat" stakes out a middle ground between regular producers and organic. Going organic would mean using organic feed, which would double the price of Ian's pork. "There's a limit to what the consumer will pay," he says. Unlike organics, Ian still applies chemical fertilizers and pesticides to his crops, but limits those chemical inputs as much as possible; he grows clover that he ploughs down as green manure to improve his soil and for weed control. Ian will treat his pigs with medication but only when they're sick. He does not add it to the feed, as industrial producers do.

The major difference, of course, is that Ian raises his pigs humanely, according to Winnipeg Humane Society standards or, as Ian constantly reminds me, the old-fashioned way his father taught him. He's happy with the WHS certification program, but he has a problem with the way animal-welfare activists promote an alternative to industrial meat. "Their radical way isn't working," he says. "I don't hear meat eaters condemning vegetables."

And I agree, their message often makes consumers feel guilty for eating animals that have been bred for that purpose. Or they seem more concerned with livestock than the people who care for them, like Ian. Still, when it comes to farm animals, the activists certainly have cause for grave concern, which we should heed.

In Canada, farm animal welfare is covered under Canadian Food Inspection Agency (CFIA) regulations, the Criminal Code and provincial animal-welfare organizations. The CFIA is primarily concerned with the humane transportation and slaughter of animals, as well as the reporting and controlling of disease; animal-welfare organizations target the inhumane treatment of animals outside normal farm practices. And that's the catch, for normal farm practices have changed drastically over the past few decades with the onslaught of factory farming, to a "new normal" that Winnipeg Humane Society executive director Vicky Burns calls "institutionalized cruelty."

I tell Ian about the boar station I visited when I first arrived in Winnipeg.

"The boars seem to have it pretty good," I say.

Ian laughs. "I bet."

Like most large hog operations in Manitoba, the Puratone Boar Station in Stonewall is what the industry calls a high-health barn, another misnomer in conventional agriculture lingo. Ian is surprised they even let me in. Like all employees and the rare guest, I had to shower before entering; pull on overalls, boots, T-shirt and even underwear and socks provided by the barn. I also had to shower upon leaving. I was not permitted to visit another barn seventy-two hours before or another high-health barn for seventy-two hours afterward. The tight biosecurity is to protect the pigs from humans—or humans carrying disease between pigs—not vice versa. It's not that pigs are frail creatures, but cram hundreds and even thousands together in a tight space with rudimentary sanitation facilities and see how quickly disease spreads.

But back to the boars. There are only 136 living here—the average station holds 200, larger ones 500. This barn is well ventilated, with heat in the winter and a cooling misting system in the summer. Staff pressure-wash high-traffic areas every day, clean and disinfect the barn once a week. "We have to keep the boars happy," says Krystal, a senior health technician. "We're constantly catering to them." That's because a happy boar produces more sperm, and that's his singular purpose here—the station collects and sells doses to sow barns for artificial insemination.

Still, this is hardly the glamorous life of a play boar. For the two to four years of their stud span, the six-hundred-pound boys live in three-by-eight-foot pens, and the only time they get out is for their once-a-week love session.

And there is pressure. Isn't there always? Kirk, a sluggish boar with upright ears, hasn't exactly been firing blanks, but he's on his sixth week of passing what Krystal calls bad semen, with low density or mobility or too many damaged or dead cells. Two more weeks of dealing duds and it will be on the truck for him, to a rendering plant.

Krystal opens Kirk's pen, and, with a heavy sigh, he lumbers down the alley to the collection pen. Kirk is a GPK4. There are other Puratone branded "breeds" here—GPK2 and EBX—plus the Duroc. Using semen from these "latest in genetically updated boars" enables sow farms to quickly adapt to breeding trends, toward a leaner pig with greater feeding efficiency. But breeding fat out of the pig may have compromised the robustness of the modern pig, admits Arian de Bekker, a partner in Shamrock Swine Genetics, the company that runs the boar station. "Lean pigs," he says, "are more stressed."

But Kirk certainly doesn't need to hear that today. He waddles into the collection pen and stares at his mounting stand, a plastic-coated dummy about the size of a child's rocking horse. Usually, boars don't need much to stimulate them—a round shape reminiscent of a sow will do. But today, Kirk is having trouble mounting. Krystal, a perky and pretty woman, makes seductive sow noises, barking and oinking. She blows on his nose. After about ten minutes pass, she even starts making excuses for Kirk—he's in a different pen, usually mounts from the right rather than the left. But I'm thinking this stud's days are numbered.

Finally, Kirk heaves himself onto the dummy and unravels the oddest penis I've ever seen in the animal world. It is nearly a foot long, pencil thin and twisted like a corkscrew, designed to thrust through a sow's vagina right into her cervix, where it locks into the pattern of the pads there. With one rubber-gloved hand, Krystal grabs a donation cup the size of a Tim Hortons' travel mug and, with the other, grabs the end of Kirk's penis. The latching on simulates the sow's "lock" on the penis and Kirk immediately stops thrusting and starts ejaculating. And ejaculating. And ejaculating.

Boars, one farmer told me, have the best love life in the animal kingdom. They can ejaculate for up to forty minutes, passing about three billion sperm in one session. Technicians add an extender to the semen—a combination of protein, sugars and antibiotics—so that one donation can impregnate up to twenty-five sows. The extender also helps keep fresh boar semen viable for up to five days, as it can't be frozen like most other types.

And still Kirk goes on, Krystal still hanging on. "It's certainly an odd job," she admits. She tells me she has a science degree, and left her job at a horse farm to work here. She likes pigs. "They're very vocal animals. I think they have a lot of personality. The mood of the people collecting is really important. If they're aggressive or mean, the boar won't donate. If the boar's unhappy or depressed, the dose is low."

Kirk seems pretty happy now. At long last he finishes and slides down from the dummy. Good boar. Some boars, Krystal says, linger. "They want you to keep holding onto it, but I say no."

Sows, of course, don't have things nearly so good. On our drive back from the packers, Ian turns into the New Haven Colony, a Hutterite community a kilometre from Ian's farm. The community of a hundred owns five thousand acres and a sow barn as large as any corporate operation. The Hutterites are pacifists who immigrated to Canada in 1918 and have established several hundred closed communities across the Prairies. They eschew modern dress and outside social interactions, yet, paradoxically, embrace the latest innovations when it comes to farming—massive tractors, fully loaded pickups (albeit with the radios removed) and, in this case, high-tech sow and finishing barns that house ten thousand pigs.

We drop in on Dave Wollmann, the general manager of the colony. He and his wife have seven children and live in a modern bungalow attached to a long line of bungalows. Dave has known Ian since they were teenagers, when he used to sneak out of the colony on Saturday nights to watch *Hockey Night in Canada* at Ian's. The colony helped put out a fire at Ian's barn in 1977. Now the community invites Ian and his mother to its annual Christmas concert. "I'm not saying anything about the way they raise pigs," Ian had told me earlier. "You have to be neighbours here."

Dave gives us a tour of their village: the two-room schoolhouse, the honey-making operation, the shoemaking shop, welding shop, community garden and communal kitchen and dining room, the computerized feed mill with its giant vat of tallow—rendered pig fat that's poured on pig feed to keep the dust down. He won't show us inside the high-health barns, but he tells me they use a liquid-manure system, typical of 90 percent of the hog operations in Manitoba.

In this "new normal," sows spend their entire lives in crates too small to turn around in. They are artificially inseminated and kept in a constant state of reproduction, to yield, on average, 2.4 litters a year, about fourteen pigs a litter, of which twelve usually survive. For delivery and nursing, sows are moved to even smaller farrowing crates. The piglets are rushed into weaning, in three weeks or less.

Although pigs love straw for rooting, there is no straw in this system. Instead, sows and finishing pigs spend their entire lives standing and sleeping on slatted concrete floors, which allow their dung to pass to a subfloor below. They live over their raw sewage until the subfloor is flushed—two or three times a week—with thousands of gallons of water. Without vigilant ventilation, dander, dust and noxious gases such as ammonia can build dangerously. Workers in liquid-manure system barns can suffer skin, intestinal and lung ailments. And animal welfare is a major concern, according to the director of University of Manitoba's swine research unit.

In an interview, Dr. Laurie Connor told me that autopsies on finishing pigs raised in confinement barns—and remember, they spend just six months here before slaughter—showed they had lesions on their lungs. "It's a sign of poor air quality and, for humans, that's a concern." And for pigs, too, she says. "It can affect performance and also behaviour. You can get more fighting and tail biting and poor dunging behaviour. If pigs are dirty, that can be a sign of high ammonia." She also says gestation crates are a "huge concern"—the European Union has moved to ban them—as is the "barren environment" of cement floors.

Confining sows and frustrating their natural tendency to root and nest in straw, pushing pigs to wean prematurely, then crowding them into massive barns with questionable air quality can cause stress, making them vulnerable to pneumonia and salmonella-based diseases. These so-called high-health barns control disease by isolating herds from each other and treating pigs with steady doses of medication in their feed. The stress? Well, I'm guessing we can taste that in the meat.

Ironically, Connor's latest research compares a liquid-manure system with a straw-based one; in the latter, both sows and finishing pigs run free in large pens on straw beds, which sounds an awful lot like Ian's old-fashioned set-up. Of course, Connor's challenge is to show the industry that the straw-based system works, economically.

As Dave winds up the tour, with a gracious offering of his colony's prized sausages, I put the question of animal welfare to him. "Sure, it's okay to have sows run loose and have bigger pens," he says. "But how many pigs do they have? What's the size of the farm? How much life and freedom can you give an animal in an industrial food system?"

Dave's question is easy to answer: Very little, for an industrial system measures every square inch of freedom in dollars and cents. A tougher question is this: If we don't like this new normal of animal care, how do we turn back?

SOME DAYS it's not easy being a food writer. Like today, because I still want to put this issue of taste to the barbecue test, grilling Ian's humanely raised pork side by side with industrial. And pity the poor family I am staying with in Winnipeg and also my guinea-pig partner who has flown in for this June weekend to celebrate the end of school for our friends' six children and their various graduations from public, junior and high school. You might see where this is heading. Our hosts are wonderful people and close friends, but how can I resist all these captive appetites? And so I offer to host the last-day-of-school afternoon barbecue.

In the morning, I drive to Winnipeg's south end and Crampton's Market, a seasonal outlet that sells fresh local produce and natural meats, including Ian's pork. Erin Crampton, the twenty-eight-year-old dynamo who bought the store when she was twenty-one, spent two years looking for a local natural producer of pork before finding Ian. "I have a gut check on meat," she tells me. "My dad and I both do. We eat pork from a store and, two hours later, you don't want to be near us. We get bad stomachs. There's a barn smell in that pork. But with Ian's, it's not only tastier and smells nicer, it's easier to digest."

Crampton believes North Americans spend too little money on food and far too little time thinking about it. "People are willing to spend $1000 on a couch, but not on good food, and it's all going to come back and bite us on the butt. The way we raise meat now is unsafe and it's unstable. In ten years, we'll see."

Ian's pork sells here for about twice the price of industrial pork in Winnipeg grocery stores—$5.49 a pound for ribs, $4.99 a pound for bacon, $5.59 for pork loin chops—though that's just slightly more than the cost of industrial pork at grocery stores in Toronto. As the old saying goes, we have been living high off the hog on cheap pork—choice cuts literally higher on the hog, such as tenderloin, chops and roasts.

Consumers can actually pay less for natural pork—about $1.48 a pound cut and wrapped, with smoking extra—by buying a half or whole pig directly from a farmer such as Ian, taking the "lower on the hog" picnic hams and sausages along with choice cuts. A side weighs about ninety-seven pounds, but pork freezes particularly well and lasts up to six months in the freezer. Ian and his mom go through two halves a year.

Today, with eleven people to feed, I buy ribs, bacon, pork chops and sausages from Crampton's, then identical industrial cuts from a grocery store, including the "world-famous" sausages from Winnipeg Old Country Sausage. As an appetizer, I fry bacon and set it out on the picnic table—Ian's sets off a feeding frenzy among the kids, and I dearly wish I had a pig swatter to save some for the adults.

First test, Ian's sausages easily beat out the Old Country links. My youngest food critics have this to say: Ian's aren't as spicy, they taste real, and they're meaty.

And now for the ribs and chops—the truest test, for they are without spice or curing to alter taste. I put nothing on the chops and only the slightest sprinkling of steak spice on the ribs, which one normally slathers in dry rubs and sauces to lend flavour, tenderness and moisture.

Raw on the grill, the meat looks dramatically different. The industrial pork is a pale pink, the colour of uncooked chicken; the chops have virtually no marbling. Ian's chops are beautifully marbled, the fat is bright white, and his ribs and chops are the colour of café au lait.

The industrial ribs, with very little fat or meat between the bones, grill to a dry, tasteless leather. But Ian's ribs set off another feeding frenzy among the kids and provoke moans of approval from the adults, for they are tender, juicy and meaty. They don't need spicy rubs or rib sauces. Nancy pronounces his ribs the very best she has ever tasted. And the rest of us agree: There is a deep, satisfying flavour to this pork.

But that causes a problem when it comes to the chops. The under-twelve set actually prefer the industrial ones; they're used to the bland white chicken taste. To them, the industrial chops taste "like pork," while Ian's are "different" and even "strong." Of course, everyone over twelve loves Ian's chops for exactly the same reasons.

But this disagreement is really quite easy to solve: For seconds, the kids get the industrial chops; we adults lap up Ian's. Then, for dessert, I tell the kids how industrial pork is raised.

As THE FIRST LADY of Manitoba had hoped, Ian's methods of raising pork are catching on in the province. Several months after our backyard picnic in Winnipeg, ten chefs got together for a Naked Pig picnic on Centre Island in Toronto to celebrate the arrival of natural Manitoba Berkshire. Pork, properly raised, is the sweetest of meats, and the Berk is like candy to these chefs, who let loose with playful new recipes: pork belly stuffed with black truffles and mushroom duxelle, chili, quesadillas, potato-salad dressing made from rendered pork fat, and even dessert—bacon, peanut butter and chocolate truffles.

David Chrystian, the wunderkind chef at Chez Victor in Toronto's Hôtel Le Germain, is now promoting the premium pork to fellow chefs and quality butcher shops. For Chrystian, the Berkshire restores a nobility to serving pork in restaurants. And it's not because the Queen keeps a purebred herd at Windsor Castle; rather, farmers raising Berkshire for the Manitoba brand must do so naturally and humanely, as Ian does—free ranging on straw, even allowing the sensual swine the bliss of old-fashioned rutting.

At Chez Victor, Chrystian serves succulent Berkshire ham, bacon and sausage at brunch; for dinner, a loin chop with a raisin sauce, a divinely brazed belly over cassoulet—pork and beans for grown-ups. As a breed, Berk produces fatter, darker, richer pork than other breeds, with an inch-and-a-half fat cap and thick rivers of marbling running through the meat. The crisped fat caramelizes wonderfully and, as Chrystian says, "has a great mouth feel."

Still, although the Berk is a different breed from Ian's, a black pig to Ian's white, and has much more fat, the taste is quite similar, which convinces me more than ever that how the pig is raised is the crucial factor in the flavour. As Chrystian says, "All good cooks have to be aware of how things are raised and treated. Berkshire is grown ethically. That matters. The product tastes better. Pork you serve should be worthy of the table."

ON MY LAST DAY with Ian, my heart is heavy and I think his is too. I am pushing on to Saskatchewan, but I am sad to leave Ian to his lonely work. Plus, the runt pig died. He also lost a calf—he thinks in the clover, which stands eight feet tall this time of year. Yes, the free-ranging life has its perils.

We're in his pickup, making the rounds to his customers, closing the link between farm and plate. Ian says this is the toughest but most exciting part of his business. He enjoys meeting people, answering their questions and also being appreciated for his work. "Customers thank me," he says. "Not many farmers get to hear that." But his customer base is expanding slowly and mostly by word of mouth. He's built a website, developed a marketing brochure and spends hours returning calls and doing paperwork, but marketing is new for him, and he hasn't really had anyone to talk business with since his dad died. "Ian's a super honest, upfront guy," Erin Crampton told me earlier, "but he's a typical farmer, a producer first. Agriculture departments should be helping guys like these with marketing." Although companies such as Maple Leaf have massive marketing divisions, farmers selling directly to customers must rely on their own smarts, with little in the way of courses or support from agricultural departments.

One of Ian's biggest challenges has been cracking into the retail and restaurant trade. Terry Gereta, who started the superb restaurant Mise in Winnipeg, is one of the few chefs in town who delights in cooking pork—tenderloin with a maple and Crown Royal sauce, ribs in a Seagram's whisky glaze. Ian dropped off a sample that Gereta is still raving about months later: "The bacon was really incredible. The meat was a really different product—clean and nicer to handle and look at. And I saw the romance coming from

Ian. It was a story I could tell my customers." But Gereta has the same problem most restaurants and retail stores have: Customers only want the very top cuts, meaning he can use only about 25 percent of the meat. "Ian wants to sell the whole animal, and I can't take the whole animal. And that's the trick for farmers—staying small to do things right, yet be big enough to supply restaurants."

Back in Toronto, David Chrystian and the Manitoba Berkshire program are having the same problem. "There are chefs who are willing to do creative, wonderful things with pork hocks and shoulders," Chrystian says, "but customers have to be more accepting of a wider variety of cuts. I really hope the Spanish influence builds and we'll see chefs with recipes for ham and prosciutto, sausages, charcuterie." Meanwhile, their off-cuts are also stocking up in a butcher's freezer in Ontario.

Back in Manitoba, Ian is struggling to sell his annual production of three hundred pigs directly to customers. If he does, he makes about $203 on each, better than the $135 he would make from a processor such as Maple Leaf. But that still only translates into about $60,000 a year, before expenses. Still, when Ian does the math, he's excited. "My farm and machinery's paid off, and I keep expenses low." He's hardly getting rich, but that's not his goal. "My mom and dad raised three boys on this quarter section and no one had to take an off-farm income. I just want to keep this going." And he is doing better than if he took a job in the so-called high-health barns, where wages start at $20,000 and rise to $40,000 for a top manager.

Ian's first-ever customer is Sheldon and his wife, Kathy, who live in a subdivision on the edge of Winnipeg. They buy three pigs a year to feed three teenagers, "plus the friends who are always staying to supper," laughs Sheldon. He gets his pork chops smoked and says they're incredibly tasty with just a bit of steak spice. "Cut up a cube of pork belly," he tells me, "and add it to fried rice." He's a trucker and one of his runs is delivering tallow from rendering plants to industrial pig farms. "You'd think we'd learned something about feeding animals to animals from BSE," he says. He also buys his beef and chicken directly from farmers. "I like to know where my meat comes from."

Ian's newest customer is Danny's Whole Hog, the barbecue king of Manitoba. Three years ago, Danny started making barbecues large enough to hold a whole hog, then renting them out for pig roasts. It's become the ultimate Manitoba pork experience, one Winnipeg food writer told me. Last weekend, Danny sold ninety pigs—he has another eight hundred hanging in his freezer, his supply for the next few weekends. Now some customers are asking for natural pork, and Danny has asked Ian to be his supplier.

On our rounds today, Ian is meeting with a new customer, and I admit that I did some matchmaking. I take Ian to meet the boys at LuxSolé Restaurant and Tapas Lounge, and they immediately connect, as farmers usually do. Their anger at Big Pork spikes quickly. They blame the industry for wiping out a generation of farmers like Ian while replacing farm income with lousy-paying jobs (Maple Leaf rolled back wages 40 percent at its meat-processing plants) and devastating the environment (Lake Winnipeg is dying from nutrient overloading caused by runoff from intensive livestock operations, chemical fertilizers from grain farmers and the city's antiquated sewage system; the greatest damage has occurred over the past two decades).

But, finally, the conversation turns to how Ian raises his pigs, and the brothers immediately place an order for two. (When I phoned a few months later, they had bought several more and raved about the meat. "We have to be inventive to use it all up," chef Lawrence says, "but we make pork-pulled sandwiches and chorizo sausages, as well as roasts and chops and loins for specials. When we find a supplier like this, we want to support him.")

That night, Ian and I stay for dinner at LuxSolé and our talk turns to the future. Ian says that he knew staying single was a sacrifice he might have to make when he took over the family farm. He tells me about a few recent dates—women still getting over divorces ("you know how that goes"), another with five children ("well, c'mon now"), one who wanted to know how far his farm was from a shopping mall ("I knew right off that wasn't going to work"). He still holds out hope of meeting someone. "But you see how I operate, no weekends off, no holidays. What woman would tolerate this life?"

I don't have an answer to that. But, after spending a few days here, I can imagine there's someone out there who can tolerate a nice guy like Ian. But I have advice for her—buy a half a pig from Ian first, to show him you're sincere.

# Manitoba

## Braised Berkshire Cassoulet

This is David Chrystian's variation on a cassoulet, for a one-pot dish for a small dinner party. Cooking the shoulder with the bone in maximizes the flavour. Although David specifies Berkshire pork, I have tried this recipe with both natural and organic pork and the dish still works wonderfully.

Note that the beans need to be soaked ahead of time.

| | | |
|---|---|---|
| 7–8 lb | bone-in pork shoulder | 3.5–4 kg |
| | salt and freshly ground black pepper | |
| 6 | slices bacon or fresh Berkshire belly, diced | 6 |
| 1/2 lb | butter | 250 g |
| 4 | cloves garlic, minced | 4 |
| 2 | carrots, cut into 1-inch/2.5 cm pieces | 2 |
| 2 | onions, cut into 1-inch/2.5 cm pieces | 2 |
| 2 | stalks celery, cut into 1-inch/2.5 cm pieces | 2 |
| 4 | bay leaves | 4 |
| 1 | bunch thyme, chopped | 1 |
| 2 cups | dry navy beans, soaked in water overnight | 500 mL |
| 1 cup | diced dry wild mushrooms (black trumpet, chanterelle, porcini) | 250 mL |
| 1 cup | tomato paste | 250 mL |
| 4 cups | chicken stock | 1 L |

Preheat oven to 375°F (190°C).

Season the pork liberally with salt and pepper. Roast in the oven for about 15 minutes, or until brown. Skim any fat from the roasting juices with a metal spoon and discard. Reduce oven heat to 300°F (150°C).

Fry the bacon over medium-high heat. When cooked, transfer to a plate lined with paper towel to drain off extra fat.

Melt the butter in a large, heavy-bottomed pot over medium-low heat. Add the garlic, carrots, onion, celery, bay leaves and thyme; sauté to caramelize the vegetables. Stir in the beans, mushrooms and tomato paste. Season with salt.

Add the vegetable mixture and the fried bacon to the roaster. Pour in the chicken stock; season with salt and pepper. Roast, covered, for 3 to 4 hours, until the beans are very tender and the pork pulls easily from the bone. Remove the roaster from the oven. Allow the meat to rest for 20 minutes before pulling the meat from the bone.

Serve the pulled meat in deep bowls with the vegetables and beans, accompanied with a crusty baguette, hot mustard and dill pickles.

*Makes 6 to 8 servings.*

Credit: Chef David Chrystian, chef at Chez Victor, Toronto, Ontario, and for Manitoba Berkshire.

## LuxSolé Pulled Pork

Chef Lawrence Warwaruk of LuxSolé Restaurant and Tapas Lounge says his Kentucky barbecue–style sauce in a pulled pork sandwich with mayo coleslaw makes a truly wonderful summertime Manitoba picnic snack. But he assures me you can enjoy it in other parts of the country, too. The dry and liquid rubs can be made in advance; keep the liquid rub refrigerated until ready to use.

With a 5 to 6 ounce (150 to 180 g) serving per person, a 10-pound (5 kg) roast can serve as many as twenty people; use a smaller roast for a smaller crowd and reserve leftover dry and liquid rubs for another day. The liquid rub will keep for several weeks in the refrigerator.

| | | |
|---|---|---|
| 5–10 lb | pork shoulder | 2.2–4.5 kg |

**For dry rub:**

| | | |
|---|---|---|
| 1/3 cup | brown sugar | 75 mL |
| 2 1/2 tbsp | mustard powder | 30 mL |
| 2 tbsp | mild chili powder | 25 mL |
| 1 tbsp | garlic powder | 15 mL |
| 2 tsp | salt | 10 mL |
| 2 tsp | black pepper | 10 mL |
| 1 tsp | ginger powder | 5 mL |
| 1/2 tsp | ground allspice | 2 mL |

**For liquid rub:**

| | | |
|---|---|---|
| 4 cups | ketchup | 1 L |
| 1/3 cup | molasses | 75 mL |
| 1/3 cup | hot sauce (such as Frank's) | 75 mL |
| 1/3 cup | water | 75 mL |
| 2 1/2 tbsp | white vinegar | 30 mL |
| 1 1/2 tbsp | liquid smoke | 20 mL |
| 1 tbsp | Worcestershire sauce | 15 mL |

Place the pork shoulder in a roasting pan.

For the dry rub, in a small bowl or jar, combine the brown sugar, mustard powder, chili powder, garlic powder, salt, pepper, ginger powder and ground allspice.

For the liquid rub, in a small bowl or jar, combine the ketchup, molasses, hot sauce, water, vinegar, liquid smoke and Worcestershire sauce.

Rub the pork liberally with the dry rub, reserving some for later. Cover the pork with plastic wrap and refrigerate for 24 hours.

Preheat oven to 275°F (140°C).

Remove the plastic wrap from the pork. Add water to the roasting pan to 1/2 inch (1 cm) deep. Roast the pork, covered, for 6 to 8 hours, depending on the size of the shoulder. (If cooking the pork on a barbecue, cover the roasting pan.) Baste the pork several times with the liquid rub, reserving some of the rub for later.

Once the pork is cooked through, remove from the heat and drain the fat. Allow the pork to rest for 30 minutes, uncovered, before separating the meat from the bone. Cut the meat across the grain in 1 1/2-inch (4 cm) slices. When the meat is cool to the touch, pull the meat into strands. Add dry and liquid rub to taste—the meat can be as wet or dry as you like.

Serve in an egg-bread bun topped with a generous portion of mayo coleslaw.

*Makes up to 20 servings.*

Credit: Chef Lawrence Warwaruk, LuxSolé Restaurant and Tapas Lounge, Winnipeg, Manitoba.

# Saskatchewan

## GOLDEN FLAX TALES

*In 8th century France, King Charlemagne considered flax
so important for the health of his subjects that he passed laws
and regulations requiring its consumption.*
—FatsforHealth.com

Where to start the story of a humble Saskatchewan oilseed that's been called the darling of the plant world, a wonder food, a power food and, no kidding, a superhero of the supplement world with superpowers?

Let me start at the end.

It is the last day of my visit to Regina, the capital of Saskatchewan, and I am at Mutchmor Lodge seniors' home chatting to residents about, of all things, their bowel movements. Uh, when I said "the end," perhaps I should have made it plural, for *that* end is where flax flexes some of its greatest super-seed powers.

The lodge, along with the Santa Maria Senior Citizens Home across town, started offering Cecil Werner's Flax for Nutrition Golden Roasted Flax Seed in an attempt to unknot a painfully common condition for seniors: constipation. One University of Saskatchewan study showed that residents in seniors' homes spend about $40 a month on laxatives, which, with long-term use, can actually impair bowel function. And seniors are not the only ones grimacing. According to a whole whack of experts, Canada has become a constipated nation. Thanks to processed foods that are low in fibre, most of us suffer some sad stool story—too little, too infrequent, too painful, too hard. University of Saskatchewan nutritionist Wendy Dahl believes that the typical Canadian woman should double her fibre intake. And the University of Manitoba Inflammatory Bowel Disease Clinical and Research Centre reports that Canada has become a hotspot for bowel diseases, though no one quite knows why.

In trials at both of the seniors' homes, nutritionists had a hunch flaxseed would win the battle against blockage. The tiny kernel, about the size of a sesame seed, punches above its weight when it comes to dietary fibre, especially of the insoluble kind. Rather than being digested, insoluble fibre passes straight through the gastrointestinal track, albeit performing a couple of tricks along the way—absorbing water and forming a gel. The water increases stool weight and softens it, while the gel lubricates the passage for the stool, decreasing transit time—a fancy term bowel experts use to describe down time on the toilet.

Ah, but every superhero has an Achilles' heel, and for flax, that's taste and texture. The raw seed is too tough to chew and must be milled into a powdery flour to unlock its magical powers. But the ground seed is mealy and bland, even "yucky" as one resident emphatically tells me. Exposed to air, the oil in ground flaxseed quickly goes rancid.

For good reason, nutritionists worried whether residents would tire of eating flax or even refuse it, but this is where Cecil Werner gives the story a delicious twist. Cecil, who grows the crop on his farm just outside Regina, developed a roasting technique that breaks down the tough shell, making the seed easy to chew and digest, and also gives the oilseed a rich nutty tang. He built a sparkling new plant that now offers four variations of flaxseed: whole, milled, and milled with either blueberry or apple-cinnamon flavouring.

The seniors like Cecil's flax as much as the results that follow. And it seems there is nothing older folks like talking about more than a good satisfying movement. Thelma, ninety-two, who sprinkles a tablespoon or two of milled roasted seed over her cereal every morning, tells me she can now pass things "a lot easier." Ann, eighty-seven, stopped having problems after she started stirring milled flaxseed into her orange juice. "Sometimes I might miss a day, but next day I go and it will be a good one. It makes you a lot more regular."

And listen to John, eighty-one, wax poetic about the blueberry-flavoured roasted flax he's been heaping onto his hot porridge for the past few months. "Flax works like wax," he tells me, "like it waxes your insides so when you go it's real easy. I used to have stomach aches and sometimes it would hurt to go and it took a while. Now, the flax kicks in fast and it makes your stool real soft. Trust me, you take it for a month and it well help you, too."

Well, I can add my own testimonial to the chorus. Since discovering Cecil's roasted flaxseed a year ago, I've taken it religiously every morning— two tablespoons of the whole seed (I prefer the nutty crunch to the powdery consistency of milled) over a bowl of fruit and cottage cheese. On Sundays I take a break—but not from the flax. The buttery roasted flavour is like catnip. Rx warning here: You can get addicted. On my day of rest from slicing and dicing fruit, I slather a warm bran muffin with my own favourite constipator—peanut butter—then sprinkle on roasted flaxseed. And ten minutes later, my bowels—often finicky stubborn creatures before—go right to work and, *ding ding*, I'm as regular as a church bell.

Yes, flax has become my personal superhero, and I haven't even begun to tell you about its other even more impressive powers. Or how a Saskatchewan farmer came to the rescue of countless Canadian bowels, a tale as intriguing as flax itself.

So, perhaps I should start my story at the beginning.

IT'S SOMETHING OF A RITE of passage in my farming family to go west, to learn about farming from *real* farmers, settlers like Cecil Werner's father, who arrived in one of the harshest climates on the planet, ploughed up the ancient prairie grassland and cultivated it into the bread basket of the world within decades. Compared with the east's small hundred-acre family farms, immigrants staked out turf here by the section—640 acres. Everything about the Prairies—the land, the sky, the challenge, the possibility of success— loomed large, even mythical.

My father made the journey west twice during the Second World War, helping skeletal threshing crews bring in the crucial wartime harvest, before returning east to buy his grandparents' farm. My brother Graham made his pilgrimage after graduating from high school. He pushed farther west, to Alberta, to work on a beef farm, then returned home to set up a new feedlot on our farm. Years later, when I followed in their workboot steps, I spent my first night in Saskatchewan sleeping in my car. Stupidly, I was attempting to race through the province to get to the Rockies—when I drove straight into the spectacular drama of a Saskatchewan sky.

First, the horizon to the east, seen in my rear-view mirror, darkened to black slate, then erupted into a hellfire of lightning. That's when the horizon to the west kicked in with its theatrics—a glorious summer sunset that ripped the sky into ribbons of red, orange and purple. I pulled off the Trans-Canada Highway, parked on a gravel side road, and settled in for what locals call the cheapest entertainment around, an exhilarating Saskatchewan lightshow. The next thing I knew, I was waking up to a scene nearly as exalting—a flax field at dawn, in glorious bloom. I staggered out of the car, awestruck. In that shimmering morning light, the fields looked like a stack of designer colour swatches had fallen from the sky—sunburst canola, golden-brown barley, sea-green wheat and that surreal square of flax.

Flax is the most visually impressive crop on the Prairies, with most varieties producing a delicate lavender blue flower that, alas, drops off by noon. Still, a field can blaze that fabulous blue in the mornings for nearly two weeks, as each plant, self-pollinating, produces up to ten flowers until each of its ten seeds are fertilized. Prairie farmers don't grow flax for its beauty, though you might think so after listening to them go on and on about it.

Years later, when I called Cecil Werner to organize this trip to Saskatchewan, he recommended that I visit during the third week in July, when the flax is in bloom. He offered a delicate description in a voice that reminded me of the morning breeze whispering over the prairie so many years before. Yet his soft voice can hardly prepare one for actually meeting him. When I arrive at CanMar Grains, his ultra-modern $4.5-million plant just outside the Regina airport, a wide-shouldered, imposing man greets me. At sixty-three, Cecil is five foot eleven, wide-girthed and with a face chiselled from the sternest of homestead stories. Suffice it to say, he looks nothing like a health-food zealot. Then again, as he shows me into his corner office, he doesn't look much like a farmer either, though he tells me that he still pulls on the overalls and takes a turn at the combine every fall at his ten-thousand-acre operation.

I have made this trip west without Nancy (not enough seafood in the Prairies, she joked, though she had already taken weeks off work to help with my research). And so Cecil and I sit across from each other in his office, trying to make small talk about flax, which invariably involves chatting about bowel care. I tell him that on my cross-Canada tour of farms, I'm usually standing in poop rather than talking about it. It's hard to tell whether a joke goes over with Cecil. He is infinitely polite and restrained, which makes my sense of humour seem all the more flatulent. With his employees all taking flax, I suggest he must run a pretty regular office. He offers a muted "huh." We switch to talking about business, Cecil's métier.

This is the first flax-roasting facility in North America, he tells me, and quite possibly the world. Before this venture, he built a successful animal feed sales company. It was on a business trip to Asia that a customer suggested he try roasting flax, to appeal to the same Japanese market that snacks on some 140,000 tons of roasted sesame seeds a year. Cecil reasoned that if he could take just 10 percent of that business, he would be very successful indeed, so, at age fifty-nine, he sold his feed company and started anew. "A lot of people thought I was crazy," he admits.

While most men his age were hitting the golf course or an easy chair, he spent four years pulling together millions in financing, patenting the roasting process, building the 21,500-square-foot plant, hiring thirteen employees and flying to food tradeshows across North America and Asia to drum up sales. "I just felt I wasn't ready to retire," Cecil says of his late-in-life adventure. "I wanted to do one more thing."

Clearly, *doing* is Cecil's thing, rather than talking. And his venture is setting a sterling example of what modern farming in Saskatchewan might achieve. Now, of course, the agricultural picture is pretty bleak. Farmers here suffer the highest rate of bankruptcies in Canada. For the province to build a strong diversified economy and keep jobs here, Cecil says they have to stop simply exporting unprocessed crops around the world and start adding value to them, as his own roasting operation does. Consider the numbers—a farmer sells a metric tonne of flax for $400; Cecil wholesales his roasted seed for $7000; finally, retailers sell the same tonne for $19,000. No wonder farmers like Cecil want a piece of the processing pie that the east has long enjoyed. The big question is, can farming as we know it—independent family farms—survive this transition to a more integrated farming/processing economy?

Farmers in the Prairies have been hit with a series of drought years, but government policy over the past decade has been as scorching—a persistent reduction of agricultural subsidies (Canada ranks well behind both the

United States and Europe in government support for farmers), the cancellation of transportation subsidies for getting grain to distant ports and the restructuring of various farmer marketing co-operatives, such as the Canadian Wheat Board (CWB), seemingly with the aim of phasing them out. Cecil believes the CWB has stymied innovation by forcing farmers to sell directly into the wheat pool, rather than, say, keeping their own grain and processing it into pasta, as one group of farmers attempted. But, he also concedes, the government is doing little to help farmers diversify. The resulting economic shakeout, of course, favours big operations over independent family farms.

Murray Fulton, a professor of agricultural economics at the University of Saskatchewan, describes a new Prairie economy taking shape that looks an awful lot like the corporate takeover of pork in Manitoba, with a few large companies buying up farms and controlling food—from the field through to processing—and experienced, entrepreneurial farmers being reduced to little more than hired guns overseeing machinery steered by Global Positioning Systems working massive corporate farms. "It's nicer to have a distribution of power than having it concentrated, which tends to make systems much less adaptable," Fulton tells me. "Plus we need to have some control over quality—having food that is actually tasty and healthy. There's a trend as you get to larger corporations that taste and quality suffers." He also thinks agricultural policy in the Prairies should be more concerned with issues such as community and rural depopulation. "People doing the production under large corporate structures are going to be very lonely. They'll be doing this by themselves without a social component."

Cecil's company may prove to be the exception: a field-to-processing operation that started from a stake on a family farm and tenaciously focuses on quality and taste every step of the way.

Cecil suggests a tour of the plant. As we don hairnets and foot covers along with lab coats, he tells me that he pretty much did things backwards when he started up—going after an export market before developing a local one. He invited a potential customer, Japan's Nippon Flour Mills, to inspect construction of CanMar's plant, to make sure the food-grade facility met Japan's exacting standards. "I wouldn't say they have higher standards of quality than Canada," Cecil says, ever so diplomatic, "but they deliver on the administration of those standards."

Indeed, the plant is immaculate and also smells luscious, like fresh toast. At the heart of the operation is the $700,000 roasting tower, about the size of a railway car. Although flaxseed can be baked in bread and muffins for up to an hour at 180°C without any loss in its nutritional content, roasting may destroy flax's omega-3 and omega-6 essential fatty acids, a one-two punch in its arsenal of nutritional superpowers. Undeterred, Cecil sent samples to various roasting plants in North America until he found a technology that could roast flax at temperatures low enough to preserve the essential fatty acids, then he had the results verified at the University of Saskatchewan.

We arrive at the final station, where the flaxseed is vacuum-packed into 425-gram bags, then fed through a metal detector to catch any particles that might have somehow survived the journey through two $155,000 colour sorters that clean the flaxseed of any dust, weed seed, glass, stones or metal bits, to a guaranteed 99.999 percent. The Japanese inspectors suggested the metal detector. "The Japanese are very fussy," says Cecil. "They were over here three or four times to check for this and that. At the end of the day, we were glad they insisted on perfection. We wouldn't want someone to break a tooth on something."

Meeting Japan's exacting standards helped open the door to many more markets. A year after opening in 2005, Cecil's roasted flax was selling into South Korea, Hong Kong, Mexico, the United States and Britain. And now he's courting European countries, though that means raising the bar on quality yet again, this time at the farming level.

THE PRAIRIE HAPPENS SUDDENLY. One minute, Cecil is nosing his black Jeep Cherokee from the CanMar parking lot and the next we are turning down a gravel road, under a gigantic canopy of blue sky pegged down to a vast tabletop of cropland. And just as quickly, in true farmer fashion, Cecil relaxes once he's behind the wheel of his truck.

Cecil tells me that his grandfather emigrated here from Germany, via Iowa, in 1905, the same year the province joined Canada. He did his bit for nation-building, operating the steam engines and ploughs that broke up the prairie grasslands that once fed millions of buffalo just decades earlier.

His parents had what he calls a "small" mixed grain farm, eight hundred acres in Grand Coulee, now on the outskirts of Regina. In stark contrast to most modern grain farms, his parents planted a massive garden, raised pigs, chickens and ten to fifteen cows. They sold boiler chickens and cream to customers in Regina, butchered a cow and pig for their own use and sold the rest. "If we didn't make much money from grain farming," says Cecil, "we always had meat and vegetables from our garden. We were never rich, but we never starved." Some of his favourite memories are of harvest-time meals in the field, his mother bringing out picnics of roast chicken, corn on the cob, thick slices of homemade bread.

He was the second oldest of four children, but the oldest boy, which gave him a sense that this life could one day be his. He loved to horseback ride and had his own horse, Two Spot. "Yeah," he laughs, "she had two spots." Prairie communities were thriving then, with families every half mile and villages springing up around grain elevators that were close enough to reach by horse-drawn wagon. His father played the harmonica and called square dances at community halls. Cecil contemplated becoming a musician himself but didn't think a music career could support him, so took an agriculture degree instead. After graduating, he worked with the provincial department of agriculture, then joined a feed exporting business and discovered a knack for negotiating. He eventually bought the company and became its CEO, all the while continuing to farm alongside his father, ploughing whatever he made from the farm back into buying more land and more machinery. When his father retired, Cecil took over the family farm. "I used to come out to the farm at six at night and work until midnight and come out on weekends," he says. "The feeling of harvesting a good crop always stayed with me." He always intended to farm full time, Cecil says, but business started taking more of his time. "I was better equipped to do the marketing side of things, and a person is better off specializing." He finally turned the day-to-day running of the farm over to his younger sister and brother-in-law.

Along with barley and wheat, Cecil's father also planted flax but never thought of eating it, though he did feed it to the horses. "If one got bunged up," says Cecil, "the flax would unbung it." His mother also heated the seed into sticky mucilage and used it to hold her hair in place—the original Prairie hair-care product.

Though flax is an ancient crop, grown by the Greeks and Egyptians, and Hippocrates wrote about the seed's medicinal qualities as far back as 650 BC, the wonder food was better known in the Prairies as an industrial super crop. The straw stem was woven into linen fabrics and fine papers; the oil from the seed served as the oil base for house paints and stains, and linoleum flooring. The demand for flax peaked during the Second World War, waning with the rise of the plastics industry.

In the 1970s, researchers at the University of Saskatchewan's Crop Development Centre started cross-breeding flax to find varieties better suited to the province's growing season of short, hot, dry summers. The goal, plant breeder Dr. Gordon Rowland had told me earlier, was to produce a variety that would mature in about 105 days. But the centre also discovered that the farther north (or south) from the equator flax grows, with the accompanying longer days and cooler nights, the more essential fatty acids it produces, making Saskatchewan flax the most coveted in the world. About the same time, nutritionists got interested in flax in their quest for omega-rich foods, fish oil among them. That led to a slew of studies arguing the health benefits of the oilseed—that it can ward off heart disease, stroke and diabetes by lowering bad cholesterol and blood sugar. It can also ease painful inflammation caused by rheumatoid arthritis, reduce symptoms of menopause and lighten depression. University of Toronto nutritional science professor Lilian Thompson also found that, of sixty-six plant foods normally found in a vegetarian diet, flax contains seventy-five to eight hundred times more lignans—antioxidants that have significant cancer-fighting properties. Thompson followed up with a landmark study on women suffering from breast cancer, finding that consuming flax corresponded with a 50 percent reduction in the size of tumours and significantly halted the spread of the disease, within weeks.

The buzz about flax was on, and health professionals and farmers alike hitched their wagons to the oilseed's rising star. Now Canada is the world's leading producer of flax, and Saskatchewan, which grows 80 percent of that, is at the epicentre. And the story is about to get even better. The Flax Council of Canada, which represents the industry and growers, has launched Flax 2015, a $10-million marketing and research effort to make flax a major driver in the Prairies' emerging bio-food economy and also to boost farm sales of flax from $400 million to $1.6 billion by 2015.

Ever understated, Cecil offers his own anecdotal evidence of flax's health benefits as he eases his Cherokee to the side of the road. Since he started taking it, his cholesterol and blood pressure have both dropped. "And I'm not exactly in the best of shape," he admits. He has stopped along a desolate stretch of gravel road. "This is one of our fields," he says.

"This is your farm?" I ask.

But it is just as Cecil said, a *field*, a massive flat block of flax with no barn or house or fence in sight.

"In the 1950s, people started to specialize," Cecil explains. "Technology allows you to do more in a day, with bigger tractors, sprayers, combines. The trend was to buy your neighbour's farm, knock off all the buildings and clear off all the trees. Thirty years ago, the size of a field was 50 to 80 acres. Now, on our farms, the field size is a half section, or about 320 acres. With two pieces of equipment, you can seed a section in a day. That was unheard of, even twenty years ago."

Cecil is far too measured with his words to say something like this: that the 1950s hit the Prairies like a bomb. When the wartime economy retooled, government and businesses targeted agriculture to soak up the sudden excess. Ammonium nitrate, used to make explosives, became the basis of chemical fertilizers; poison and nerve gases led to pesticides. The new chemicals were so cheap and effective that most farmers could not resist spreading them on their fields. And someone must have borrowed the book on war propaganda for, almost as suddenly, a mind shift took place. It was as if farmers woke up one day with a weirdly fierce hatred of weeds. Those growing crops with chemical fertilizers and controlling weeds with herbicides, all of which made farming much easier, were soon viewed as good, progressive, intelligent farmers, while those growing crops by working with nature, by farming, were considered backward and even lazy. Not surprisingly, the progressive farmers expanded, the price of chemicals skyrocketed and chemical companies have done very well indeed. "The risk associated with grain farming now is humongous," Cecil says. "If you look at a farm of ten thousand acres, you have input costs of $100 an acre [for seed, chemicals, fertilizer]. That's over a million in cash out just to put your crop in." During a year of drought or low grain prices, he says, "you can lose a lot of money in a hurry. It seems we have to have a bumper crop or reach a crisis situation for grain prices to go high enough for grain farming to be profitable."

Today, the average farm size here is five to six thousand acres and increasing, leaving rural Saskatchewan littered with ghost towns.

We haven't bothered to get out of the Cherokee to look at the flax. It's a day or two away from coming into its splendid blue bloom and, well, the field just feels empty. "It doesn't feel like farming compared with when I was young," Cecil admits. "The combines are $350,000. You can't shut it down for an hour and have dinner. You can't justify stopping it. So you work shifts and grind away seven days a week. If you get involved in a big farm, you have to realize, it's a business."

Cecil concedes that industrial farming gave him incredible opportunity, allowing him to build a career while also farming. But now it presents him with a significant problem. Currently, flax is being touted for its stupendous cancer-fighting benefits—among others—yet farmers are growing flax with pesticides, which are consistently linked to serious disease such as cancer, according to the Ontario College of Family Physicians. And when it comes to regulating harmful chemicals, Canada lacks flax's stellar reputation. The World Health Organization rates four pesticides registered for use in this country as highly hazardous. Norway, Denmark and Sweden have all banned 2,4-D, one of the oldest and most widely used herbicides in Canada and once a component in making Agent Orange. Quebec, taking the lead, has banned more than one hundred pesticide products available for use in the rest of Canada. In Saskatchewan, not only do regulations lag, but crop farmers use chemicals extensively, applying 36 percent of all pesticides used in Canada, according to the environmental NGO Saskatchewan Eco Network. Farmers will argue that chemicals dissipate after being applied, but one University of Saskatchewan study detected that five of the most commonly used—including 2,4-D—had seeped into the air, surface water and pond water. At least in this regard, the province's declining rural population may be a good thing, helping limit human exposure.

Cecil has developed tougher standards for chemical use than the industry norm. As his own farm cannot supply the volume he requires at his plant, he contracts several farmers to grow seed, but they must do so according to guidelines he has established. That includes not spraying after the flowering stage, to prevent pesticides from coating the seed, which develops about twenty to twenty-five days later. He also restricts use of certain sprays, such as 2,4-D. Farmers must also store the seed in rodent-proof bins and grow only identity preserved AC Nugget yellow seed, which means the seed cannot enter the commercial system to mix with others. (Although brown and yellow seed have similar nutritional profiles and taste, Cecil says a differentiation is taking place in the market—yellow for eating, brown for industrial use.) For following his tougher guidelines, Cecil pays a premium to his contract growers—$10 a bushel, compared with the $6 flax normally fetches.

But now he has to develop even higher standards to break into the European market. "Various companies in Europe say unless it's organic, they won't touch it," says Cecil. He is a businessman rather than an environmentalist, but, increasingly, organics is making business sense. He is now contracting certified organic farmers to grow flax for him. "For a while, we'll do both," he says, "but ultimately we may go wholly organic. The consumer is king. It's all about what the consumer wants. If the consumer wants organics, our challenge is to produce it for them."

THERE MAY BE NO TOUGHER PLACE to grow grain in the Prairies than Palliser's Triangle, a swath of land extending from Manitoba through southern Saskatchewan and into Alberta. In 1863, British surveyor James Palliser deemed it too barren, dry and sandy for farming and, hence, human civilization. Ironically, the vast grasslands once supported millions of bison—and the Native tribes that followed them—until over-hunting and persecution led to their near extinction. Now the bison, as the North American buffalo is properly called, are making their way back to the Prairies with some nineteen hundred farmers raising the animals for meat. It's delicious and also healthier for you than beef, with less fat and cholesterol while packing more protein. Curiously, grass-fed bison shares other wonder-food characteristics with flax—it, too, is high in essential fatty acids, with a cancer-preventing agent, conjugated linoleic acid. The other thing bison and flax share, of course, is this land, which, seventy-five million years ago, was a vast prehistoric sea full of aquatic life that left behind a medicine chest of vitamins and minerals in the soil.

Alex Garlarneau and his brother, Robert, farm forty-two hundred acres in Palliser's Triangle, in Radville, some 130 kilometres south of Regina. The two brothers, along with their father, are organic pioneers, forming the first group of farmers to bring organic certification to Saskatchewan in 1987.

Many of the organic farmers I spoke to told me they converted for health reasons, usually after inhaling a good dose of grasshopper spray, which left them feeling dizzy and headachy whenever they handled chemicals. Others said they felt guilty loading the environment with pesticides, which kill not only pests but innocent bystanders—good micro-organisms, worms, birds and predator insects. And almost all had gotten fed up with big chemical companies prescribing more pesticides when pests and weeds build immunities and more chemical fertilizers when the soil, devoid of micro-organisms to turn plant matter into nutrients, simply wears out.

But the Garlarneaus are an anomaly. They have never used chemicals on their land. In 1981, Alex says, they saw a clear fork in the road—between high-input chemical farming and organics. They took the latter.

Although the Garlarneaus were already following organic practices, they understood that organics can mean everything and also nothing. Simply offering their word that their grain is organic would not stand up in distant export markets. Certification, on the other hand, is a guarantee of the farmer's methods. It requires joining a certification agency, growing crops according to its regulations and submitting the farm to an arduous yearly inspection of soil, crops and records to prove that the farm has followed those regulations. And now, every organic certifier must adhere to the Canadian Food and Inspection Agency's (CFIA's) new national organic certification standards. The extensive audit means that a consumer can, through the farm's certification number on a package, follow a paper trail back through retailer, processor, transporter, right to the farm.

That paperwork is a massive pain in the butt for farmers and another reason organics cost more, but the Garlarneaus persevered. Now there are more than a thousand certified organic growers in Saskatchewan, making up about 30 percent of all organic farmers in Canada, though they still represent less than a million acres of the sixty-four million under cultivation here. But Garlarneau Farms has built a tidy business alongside farming—cleaning, bagging and marketing grain for eighty-four other farmers, representing fifty thousand acres in organic production. They also grow flax for Cecil.

When I talk with Alex, unlike so many other bitter Prairie farmers, he's upbeat, energetic, inspired. He's also deeply proud of the way he farms. He tells me about a day that lives on in some infamy here—when Environment Canada recorded pesticides raining from the sky across the provincial border in the grain-growing belt, in Lethbridge, Alberta. "Every acre that goes organic helps the environment," Alex says. He excitedly tells me about local restaurants that bake bread with his grain, neighbours who drop by to pick up bags for home use. "In organics, it's about quality [rather than yield]. Customers pay a premium for quality and you have to deliver that."

Alex admits that growing flax without chemicals is more challenging. In the Prairies, farmers sow the seed in mid-May; many spring weeds emerge later, and flax doesn't compete well with weeds. It also likes nitrogen. And a bad year of grasshoppers can wipe out a crop. Yet, Alex says he manages to attain yields within 10 to 15 percent of chemical farmers, with only a third of the input costs, by ploughing down "green nitrogen" such as clover to improve soil quality (enhancing soil is a requirement of organic certification), and growing flax the year after heavy nitrogen crops such as legumes and kamut (an ancient grain enjoying a resurgence on organic farms). He uses about four or five tillers to control weeds. He anticipates insect cycles. "You know about eight months ahead if you're going to have problems with grasshoppers," he says. "We go out with shovels in August, when they lay their eggs, and see where they're going to hatch. They look for green so their offspring will have something to eat. If the grasshoppers are up, you have to keep the green weeds down through tillage. They won't go near a bare field. We have neighbours who spray for them, but we haven't been affected. Organics is a very proactive way of farming. Chemical farming is reactive. And those farmers are suffering. I have a neighbour losing $15 for every acre he's growing. There's no argument for conventional, but there's a mindset here that a weed makes a bad farmer."

Later, I chat to another of Cecil's contract growers, Earl Perkins, who made the switch fifteen years ago after thirty years of chemical farming—and getting a bad whiff of grasshopper spray. He admits there's a hefty learning curve and that the first few years were tough, but he is managing similar results to the Garlarneaus. He pegs his yield at 25 percent less than chemical farmers; he concedes that some years he has more weeds than his neighbours, but many years he's on par, and some years his fields are cleaner.

On the drive back to Regina from our farm tour, I consider what it might take for Saskatchewan to emerge as a bio-food region we could actually trust. Imagine a pristine frontier producing safe, healthy grains totally weaned off environmentally destructive chemicals. Yet, on an earlier stop, a chemical farmer who also grows flax for Cecil had told me that such a thing would be impossible—that we couldn't feed ourselves, let alone the world. That's a common argument of farmers here. They believe that as much as they hate weeds.

Later, I call Brenda Frick, the Prairie coordinator at the Organic Agriculture Centre of Canada, to hear her thoughts on the matter. Her organization, funded by federal and provincial governments and a few businesses and private industries, operates on a paltry $350,000 budget. Underfunding, Frick says, is a major impediment for the expansion of organics. Currently, chemical agriculture companies fund most of the private research as well as the so-called public research in university agriculture departments, which often attracts matching government money. She says that system of funding has created a pro-chemical culture at our university agricultural research centres. But just think, Frick says, where we might be if the money and energy that goes into the chemical system were put into the organic system. "Some tests show we're at par, some 20 percent less in yield. And that's without substantial research." At the Crop Development Centre, Dr. Gordon Rowland, for instance, told me he is trying to develop a faster maturing flax variety for organics—one that could be planted after spring weeds are tilled down. But developing a new variety costs money, about $3 million by his estimates. The good doctor admits the research centre uses chemicals to grow its experimental flax, but the flax he eats every day at home? That's organic.

Frick believes the way forward for the Prairies is to bring more people back on the land and to return to more mixed farming, producing a diversity of foods locally and selling more locally, as opposed to the extreme specialization that industrial agriculture has introduced here. Not only would that cut down on the environmental costs of transportation, but mixed farms are more self-sustaining than specialized farms, producing, for instance, their own fertilizer from cows and bison, rather than depending on chemicals. "Is it good use of our prime agricultural land to deplete our soil and undermine an environmental system in order to ship cheap $2-a-bushel wheat around the world?" asks Frick.

It's a question worth pondering, deeply, for Frick believes the potential for organics in the Prairies is huge. Cold, harsh winters kill off most pests, while dry summers cut down the need for fungicides, making conditions ideal for organic growing. And compared with many places, Saskatchewan is still a relatively clean environment. "Consider China and some other places," she says. "This agricultural land is still far superior to our competitors'."

I put the question to Cecil, but he seems worn down by the debate. "As a young man, I used to spend a lot of time thinking about where agriculture should be going," he says. "Many people say that in difficult times, do what you do best. I think that still applies."

AS WE CRUISE BACK to Regina on the Trans-Canada, Cecil asks me about my family's farm. I tell him about the hundred acres my father sold to developers and about the hundred-acre farm we moved onto when I was fourteen, which became home base for the eleven-hundred-acre operation my brother built. He and my father were to be partners but, a year after moving onto the new farm, my dad, inexplicably, disturbingly, at age fifty, became forgetful, moody. He suffered a series of emotional breakdowns, at least, that's what my mother called them. One day, he was admitted to the hospital, the psychiatric ward. It was not an easy thing to watch, and we had no idea how to talk about his sudden mood swings, so we talked about them like the weather—changeable, sunny one day, stormy the next.

My brother Graham pushed on, shouldering sole responsibility for the farm. He took a look around him, at the future of agriculture, and made himself into a modern, progressive farmer. Like my father, he used chemicals, and expanded, growing soybeans and corn, running a feedlot for beef cattle—big then at two hundred head—before specializing solely in crops. With seasonal help here and there, he farmed the eleven hundred acres on his own. He became what I call a farmer's farmer—on the evenings farmers drove around the township to compare progress, they measured the growth of their crops and cleanliness of their fields against my brother's. We were proud of him.

I tell Cecil about my own immersion in farming, the two springs I helped my brother on the farm when I returned to school to do my master's. For family reasons, it was a special time, for, as it would turn out, these were the last years we were able to keep my father at home. He had not been able to help my brother for years—he would forget to turn on the auger when unloading a truck full of seed, even as he watched the crop overflowing onto the ground. He lost his ability to drive the trucks and tractors, then to communicate beyond confused scraps of sentences. By now, his behaviour had become bizarre and even dangerous on the farm. We hid the keys to vehicles. When I was home helping out with spring planting, I was finally able to convince my mother that she could no longer care for my father, that it was time to place him in a nursing home. Working together on the land, my brother and I were able to heal some of the rifts that had wrenched open between us during those difficult years. I don't know why my brother and I turned our anger on each other. I suppose we did not know where else to put it. We each had our theories about what had caused my father's mental decline. My brother thought it was Alzheimer's. I suspected a farming accident: When we were clearing stones holding down plastic in a bunker silo, a miss-thrown rock struck his head, though that happened some years before his symptoms appeared. Now, after hearing stories of farmers reacting to pesticides, I began to wonder what role the chemicals we applied on our farm might have played.

Those springs working with my brother, I finally did what I think of as serious work farm. I drove the cultivator and planter and the five-ton trucks that carried water, seed, sprays and chemical fertilizers to the field. After a winter of books, I enjoyed letting my mind drift while planting arrow-straight rows, working from sun-up until sundown, feeling the spring warm and turn to summer. The days were long, but it was satisfying work.

Yet something nagged at me. I learned to handle sprays (the fine-print instructions told us to wear masks and gloves, though we never did). I learned to drive machinery and work hydraulics. I watched my brother figure chemical applications, wielding a calculator like an accountant. But I learned nothing about nature, about working with nature, what I would call real farming. My brother and I talked about market prices, yields and input costs but never about the quality or taste of the crops. Maybe I was looking for the impossible from my brother, some magical knowledge of farming with natural systems that I imagined my father once possessed and lost.

Well, I suppose I did not tell Cecil my entire family drama. The distances between places in the Prairies is vast, but not that vast.

HAVING STARTED MY STORY at the end and backtracked to the beginning, I should fill in the rest of my golden flax tale here, bringing me to my favourite part: eating. With a population of just under two hundred thousand, Regina is not a large city but, as the province's capital, it possesses a number of fine restaurants and many chefs who are eager to cook with local foods—bison, wild boar, wild rice, grass-fed beef, steelhead trout, pickerel, Saskatoon berries and, now, Cecil's golden roasted flax.

At the Northgate Bakery, a standby for more than thirty years, Dave Waverly started using the milled flaxseed in his buns, muffins, cookies and bread. He tells me that adding milled flax to baking allows both the flour and sugar to be reduced. And the roasted quality, clearly, gives a delicious kick to everything. "You can smell the aroma when you bake it," he says. "I love the taste." Oh, and customers, he adds, say they buy his baked flax products because they're good for them.

Later that day, I drop by the Chimney Restaurant for lunch with Cecil's son, Duncan. He oversees the logistics of running the plant, while Cecil works on international marketing and sales. Duncan, thirty-three, is also the fitness fanatic in the family, working out every day and downing a 425-gram bag of flax every week, heaping tablespoons into his morning smoothies. A few days earlier, he dropped off a sample to The Chimney, and today pastry chef Sia Gourgaris presents us with baklava—two tablespoons of flax per piece, she says, one tablespoon of milled seed and one of whole seeds. I usually find baklava too sweet, but the flax undercuts the sugary zing, adding a deep nutty flavour. "Walnuts, flax and honey," she says, "I think it works very well together." I agree.

Across town at Zest, a restaurant tucked inside the Saskatchewan Science Centre, chef Rob Fuller has become something of a flax zealot. When not cooking here, he lends his expertise to FarmPure Foods, a new and thriving bio-food company that creates gluten-free foods for those suffering from celiac disease—with flax being a prime ingredient. For my visit to Zest, Fuller whips up a four-course meal that uses Cecil's roasted flax in every course. "Natural flaxseed is pretty bland," he says, "but I like the flavour of roasted flax, the nutty roasty-ness of it. There's the health aspect, yes, but it has a long flavour. When you chew it, it becomes more vibrant as the natural oils come out."

His first offering, wild blueberry flax bread, made with the blueberry-flavoured milled seed, doesn't quite work. Roasting flax reduces moisture in the seed and concentrates the flavour. Add too much roasted flax in cooking, and a dish can take on a slightly fishy taste, the case here. But his wild mushroom soup, the milled flaxseed stirred into the stock, is shockingly good—nutty and earthy. Coating bison carpaccio in flaxseed sweetens the meat ever so slightly. And flaxseed sprinkled on grilled salmon lends the fish a delicate crust and, as Fuller promised, a longer, deeper flavour. For dessert, the roasted flax perks up a Saskatoon berry crisp. His list of flax recipes goes on—pasta infused with flax oil, sorbet sprinkled with milled flax, flax crème brûlée. But, unfortunately, there's only so much I can eat at one sitting.

When I return home to Toronto, Nancy and I experiment with recipes from The Flax Council of Canada's website and discover a few things. Generally, substituting Cecil's flax for raw works well in cookies, muffins and desserts, but roasted flax tends to be sweeter, so a straight substitution does not always work for bread and can make main-course dishes too sweet. The roasting process also lowers the protein in flax, so if you're looking to add a protein boost, say, to vegetarian meals, consider using unroasted milled flax. Flax should be stored in a sealed container and refrigerated to keep it from turning rancid. And after a week of heady cooking, we also discover that two tablespoons of flax a day (ninety calories) is quite adequate for normal bowel function. Any more and flax can be just too much of a good thing.

But I'm racing ahead of myself again.

On my last evening in Regina, I have dinner with Cecil and his wife, Barb, at The Willow on Wascana restaurant, situated in Regina's massive downtown walking park, overlooking Wascana Lake. Here, chef Moe Mathieu is also a fan of Cecil's roasted flax, experimenting with the apple cinnamon and blueberry flavours in various desserts. And he sprinkles them over salads, adding flavour and texture. Milled roasted flax, he says, makes a "killer" breading for fish. He also mixes the whole roasted seed with wild rice and locally grown chickpeas as a stuffing for roast bison, which seems to me the ultimate Saskatchewan meal. On this warm evening, we start with a chilled blueberry flax soup, so rich and thick it could be a course on its own, and finish with a delicious flaxseed apple crisp.

During dinner, Barb, a warm, soft-spoken woman, tells me that she wasn't really surprised when Cecil—with three grown children, grandchildren and an easy retirement to look forward to—decided to jump into flax processing. "He felt he had more to contribute," she says, shrugging. She's clearly used to his driven nature.

It's a glorious summer evening, with the Prairie sun lingering until well past 8 P.M. Our table on the patio has a glorious view of the province's legislative buildings across the lake. As we eat, rowboats glide past us.

In the fading evening light, I prepare for the inevitable goodbyes—I will fly to Calgary in the morning. Cecil and I trade more stories of growing up on a farm. I can't help but wonder what will become of everything—my brother's farm, Cecil's farm, his company. But Cecil quickly cuts through my nostalgia. He tells me that he will likely sell his farm—when Regina presses toward it. "Why not?" he asks. "There are worse ways of making money." And once CanMar Grains starts hitting healthy sales of $10 million or more a year, he will likely sell that, too, to a larger company. "Farming's a business," he reminds me again. "In business, you can never stay still."

# Saskatchewan

## Cecil's Morning Smoothies

Barb Werner makes this refreshing breakfast-on-the-run treat for Cecil on weekday mornings, varying the flavour by substituting different fruits for the blueberries and strawberries. For a creamier drink, add 1 cup (250 mL) plain yogurt.

| 2 | scoops protein powder (any flavour) | 2 |
|---|---|---|
| 1 cup | frozen blueberries | 250 mL |
| 1 cup | frozen strawberries | 250 mL |
| 1/2 cup | milled roasted flaxseed | 125 mL |
| 2 cups | water | 500 mL |
| 1 cup | unsweetened orange juice | 250 mL |

Place all the ingredients in a blender and blend.

*Makes 2 to 4 servings.*

Credit: Barb Werner, Regina, Saskatchewan.

## Zest's Wild Mushroom Soup

This easy-to-make soup will leave your guests moaning for more. I have made it in a pinch using whatever mushrooms were available, including button mushrooms, rather than the assortment the recipe calls for and it's still full of rich, mushroom flavour.

| | | |
|---|---|---:|
| 6 tbsp | unsalted butter | 90 mL |
| 1 cup | chopped red onion | 250 mL |
| 1 1/2 tsp | minced garlic | 7 mL |
| 1 cup | porcine mushrooms, sliced | 250 mL |
| 1 cup | morel mushrooms, sliced | 250 mL |
| 1 cup | button mushrooms, sliced | 250 mL |
| 2 | sprigs fresh thyme, the leaves plucked and chopped | 2 |
| | salt and freshly ground black pepper | |
| 1/3 cup | port wine | 75 mL |
| 6 cups | chicken stock | 1.5 L |
| 1 cup | milled roasted flaxseed | 250 mL |
| 1 1/2 cups | 35% cream | 375 mL |

Melt the butter in a large pan over medium heat. Add the onion; cook, stirring constantly, until soft, about 4 minutes. Add the garlic; sauté for 30 seconds. Add the mushrooms and thyme. Season with salt and pepper. Cook, stirring, until the mushrooms give off their liquid and start to brown, about 7 minutes. Pour in the port; bring to a boil and reduce to a syrupy consistency, about 2 minutes.

Meanwhile, pour the stock into a medium-sized bowl. Vigorously whisk in the flaxseed. Once the port has reduced, pour the flaxseed-stock mixture into the onion-mushroom mixture. Reduce the heat to medium-low and simmer, uncovered, for 10 minutes, stirring often. Remove from the heat. Add the cream, return the pan to the heat and bring to a simmer. Cook for 5 minutes. Remove from the heat and adjust seasoning to taste.

*Makes 6 servings.*

Credit: Chef Rob Fuller, Zest, Regina, Saskatchewan.

# *Alberta*

# GREEN COWS

*Sacred cows make the best hamburgers.*
—Mark Twain

I arrive in Calgary on the eve of the Stampede, dreaming of beef. Not just any beef mind you, but *Alberta beef.* The very name conjures up the beef bonanza that kicked off here in the 1880s, the golden age of ranching with hundred-thousand-acre leases and ten-thousand-head cattle drives, when the outlaw Sundance Kid hid out at Bar U Ranch and four wealthy cattle barons founded the Stampede in 1912, that ten-day whoop-up celebration of all things cowboy, held in July of every year. Then, markets in London, England, salivated after Canada's prime export—three- to five-year-old steers raised on southern Alberta grass.

Albertans are still deeply proud of their meat. Their province may be the only place in the western hemisphere where consumption of beef shot up during the mad cow crisis. At every Calgary steakhouse I visit during these Stampede days, the menu loudly proclaims that it serves Alberta beef, as if the mere act of growing up in this province might transform a pot-roast peasant into porterhouse prince.

Sadly, it is no longer so.

Most of the steaks I sample in Calgary taste pretty much the same as in Toronto and no wonder. Sixty-seven percent of Canada's beef is produced in Alberta, and, as I would discover, the majority of those cows are now fattened in about twenty massive feedlots in the same manner as at every other large-scale industrial feeding operation in North America: crowded into paddocks, often standing knee-deep in manure, and consuming a diet of grain and growth hormones, and a steady dose of antibiotics to survive this unhealthy stew.

Then I stumble across one very new and very upscale restaurant that boasts about serving Alberta AAAA beef, something I've never heard of before. I make a reservation, thinking that extra A must surely prove there is more to this Alberta beef hoopla than mere volume. But when I arrive, the chef admits that Quadruple A is properly called Canada Prime. But still, this is Canada's highest grade of beef, hallowed stuff you would think. Less than 1 percent makes this grade, yet all it really means is that the meat has slightly more fat—or marbling—than Triple- or Double-A, the two categories nearly 95 percent of our beef falls into. Clearly, the industry, by creating a fetish around beef grades, has distracted us from looking at how that beef is raised. For, predictably, this top-of-the-class strip loin arrives on my plate perfectly grilled rare, as ordered, but like most beef these days, wet and flavourless. Tender, yes, but tasteless.

Here, the chef is good enough to speak to me about my disappointment, but this is a variation of conversations I had with chefs at other Calgary steakhouses. I ask where he gets his meat and he tells me Cargill, which is the largest processing facility in Alberta. This is a little like telling me he gets his wine from a distributor, but never mind. What about the rancher, I ask? He knows nothing about the rancher. Well, how was the cow raised? He does not know. A sommelier could easily supply the answers to the same questions about a $45 bottle of wine—$45 being about the going rate for a Canada Prime steak in Calgary—yet the chef cannot, and this in a city that once proudly called itself Cow Town.

"So what makes Alberta beef so special?" I ask.

"Well," he says, "it's Alberta beef."

"But what makes it special?"

"Because everyone says it is," he laughs uncomfortably. "It's Alberta beef."

Our conversation continues on like this for quite a while. Finally, the chef admits that he does not really understand all the fuss about Alberta beef. He actually prefers what he ate as a child growing up in Egypt. That beef was so full of flavour, he tells me, it was almost sweet.

"And what did these wonderful cows in Egypt eat?" I ask.

"Grass, I guess," he says. "That's all there was."

*Grass.*

Now I am beginning to see a connection between those four-year-old, grass-fed steers and Alberta's much-lauded reputation for beef.

Then, at River Café, I taste it. This rustic pavilion, nestled in the pretty gardens of Prince's Island Park, a stone's toss across the Bow River from downtown Calgary, seems an unlikely place to go for steak. But Scott Pohorelic, the thirty-six-year-old executive chef, is obsessed with all things local and, in good part, that means grass or, at least, anything that feeds on it.

On the night I visit, the star chef has just returned from representing the province's cuisine at The Smithsonian in Washington, where he didn't even cook Alberta beef. Rather, Scott showcased grass-fed bison—or buffalo, as ranchers called the original prairie cow that once grazed the ancient native grasses covering the foothills of southern Alberta. "I'm all about the bison," Scott tells me, grinning like a boy who's discovered something new and astonishing that it is actually very old and precious. "It's got this deep beefy flavour, it's leaner than beef and, nutritionally, it's better for you."

Grass-fed beef also has a flavour and nutrition superior to cattle raised in industrial feedlots, Scott tells me. A grass-fed, six-ounce loin may have ninety-two fewer calories, one-third to three times less fat, more omega-3s (a good fatty acid), a natural balance of omega-3s and omega-6s, and two to five times more conjugated linoleic acid, all the positive stuff that can reduce dietary ills, including cancer, diabetes and cardiovascular disease. As author Jo Robinson put it in her book *Pasture Perfect,* a person eating sixty-seven pounds of beef a year can trim off 16,660 calories simply by switching from industrial to grass-fed. And nature's banquet of grass, she writes, enabled hunter-gatherer tribes to survive "without taking a course in fatty acid chemistry."

So back to that rarified beef. And I'm lucky, because Scott has two choices on the menu tonight and they're not always available. One is organic tenderloin from Producers of the Diamond Willow Range, a group of ranchers in the southern foothills who start their cows on grass and finish them at a leisurely pace on grain and hay in small feedlots. Scott says it took him three years to secure a supply and he hopes it stays steady throughout the year. The second, a strip loin from Pine Terra Farm, an organic family-run ranch fifty kilometres northwest of Edmonton, is even harder to get because it's from cattle that have been grass-fed *and*-finished, making it more of a summer and fall product. Plus the family finishes just one hundred animals a year.

Scott features these ranchers' names prominently on the menu to acknowledge that the preparation of a great steak starts in the field, long before it ever hits the kitchen. "Not all beef is created equally," Scott insists. "If beef is raised conventionally, that beef is rushed through the feedlot, with an emphasis on tenderness rather than taste. It's stressful and crowded for the animals, so they get sick and need antibiotics. On the other hand, the foothills offer a perfect life for a cow. And if we care about a cow's feelings, it will taste better. I really believe that."

Indeed, Scott's steak rubs consist of a barely there dusting of herbs—thyme and rosemary to let the feel-good flavour of the meat shine through. And whether it's the grass or that loving care, the meat from these pampered bovines definitely has structure: There's a satisfying chew without being chewy. It's firm and dense rather than wet and listless like so much industrial beef is. And a bite releases a robust, mature flavour with a surprising zing at the end, a hint of—dare I say it?—ancient, succulent fescue grasses.

HONESTLY, I can amaze even myself at the lengths I'll go to for a great steak. Tonight, my rental car skitters over a pitch-black, twisting gravel road somewhere outside, well, I don't exactly where I am other than in the foothills of southern Alberta. Did I say it was very dark? And, because of the dust roiling up behind the car ahead, I have to back way off the tail lights I'm supposed to be following. And now those tail lights are gone.

In the passenger seat beside me is Keith Everts, husband of Bev, who's driving the car ahead. This organic cowboy presumably knows the way to their ranch, except he got tangled up in a drink or two of whisky earlier and now he's hollering things like "Where's the Alberta Ranch? It's right by the bridge. Did we go over the bridge already? What's that sign say? All the roads used to be named after ranches. Now the roads have names like RT001. That's so if we die, the ambulance knows where to come and pick us up."

We do not die on the road, but the night's still young.

We've just come from a potluck dinner where I met the Producers of the Diamond Willow Range, responsible for that tasty tenderloin I enjoyed at River Café. The group is intriguing, not only because it's on a mission to bring its organic version of Alberta beef to the rest of Canada but also because I know from growing up on a farm that it's easier to round up a hundred steers than corral just a few farmers into working together. I wanted to see how the seven families of Diamond Willow managed this close co-operation for going on ten years now. So I called up Keith, the group's president, and he invited me down for a visit.

Eager to fit in with the crowd, I headed to the Alberta Boot Company and bought a pair of black cowboy boots and matching hat, then showed up with a bottle of organic wine at our designated meeting place, the ranch of one of the Diamond Willow group members, Janet Main, just south of Pincher Creek. Keith arrived a few minutes later wearing bashed-in hiking boots and a brown-felt Stetson with two inches cut from the brim so it looks more like a fishing hat. Keith and Bev, both fifty, were vegetarian hippies before they started ranching, and Keith still sports a blond, braided ponytail. His nickname is Holly, short for Hollywood, perfect given his perpetually sunny grin and entertaining wit.

There are what Keith calls "real" cowboys in Diamond Willow, too, third- and fourth-generation ranching families. They call Keith the "ideas man," the "energy" and the "passion." He's also "funny as hell" and "can talk to anyone." He pulled together this group some thirteen years ago, after the scare at Alberta's Feedlot Alley—a concentration of massive feedlots northeast of Lethbridge, about a two-hour drive from Keith and Bev's ranch. As Calgary-based journalist Andrew Nikiforuk reported in a June 12, 2000, *Maclean's* article titled "Water Kills," the area's 1.3 million head of cattle, 25,000 in some feedlots alone, were producing raw sewage equivalent to a population of 8 million people that was flowing untreated into the surface water. Between 1989 and 1991, E. coli killed twelve children in the area, and residents registered the highest rates of intestinal disease in the province.

That situation no doubt sparked a group of University of Calgary graduate students to see if ranching could be carried out in an environmentally sustainable way. They contacted University of Calgary professor Norm Simmons, who owned an operation that Keith managed along with running his own. Norm and Keith knew it was possible to ranch this way—they were already doing it. But they were less sure it would be *economically sustainable* in this age of cheap industrial beef, so they asked the students to expand their study to survey consumers on whether they would be willing to pay more for beef raised on green ranches. And maybe because Keith and Bev came to the profession as outsiders—his father ran a trucking operation in Pincher Creek, while Bev grew up in Toronto—they didn't adhere to the lone-cowboy mentality of so many farmers. They invited a group of families who ranched in a like-minded way to hear the results. Words like *natural* and *organic* were fuzzy terms then, but consumers said they would support what Keith dubbed "green cows."

For the next three years, the families met for potlucks, as Bev told me, "to share information and celebrate what everyone could bring to the table besides appetizers." Their children grew up together, calling themselves the Diamond Willow kids; some are now starting to ranch. The families shared ideas on combating weeds and growing crops without chemicals. They talked about labelling their beef "natural" but didn't think that was a rigorous enough term. Most were close to operating organically, so getting certified was no big deal, and they did so, with the International Organic Crop Improvement Association. Keith jokingly refers to the association as "the organic police" but says its yearly inspections are crucial in assuring consumers that the beef meets its stringent standards.

What stumped the group, however, was the logistics of producing a steady supply of fresh meat year-round and in sufficient quantities to fill customer contracts. That meant extending its current operations from raising calves for feedlots to running its own feedlot, growing crops for feed, and contracting with a slaughterhouse, butcher and distributor—all of which would have to be certified organic. "We moved really slowly on this," says Keith, "and the only thing happening at the potlucks was I was getting fat. Then I asked, how much does it cost to produce a green cow? The price of beef goes up and down according to the world market, but that has nothing to do with the way we're doing things here. I said, we have to turn this whole thing around. We have to take control of this. We have to be price makers, not price takers. That was the turning point."

Keith is continuing this story of Diamond Willow as I drive us home, straining to navigate the dark, loose gravel roads. And I must confess that I don't really follow his leap in logic from the cost of green cows to solving the logistics. But Keith, who jokes about dropping out of school in grade six, has a visionary's mind that works in the bizarre leaps of a calf being let out onto spring grass. His excitement ratchets up as he explains variations on the theme, such as how much does it cost to sustain the farmer who protects the water, the air and the fragile native grasses on the land that the green cow grazes and which also happens to be the key watershed flowing into southern Alberta?

"What's that clean land and water really worth?" he asks me. "Consumers think they're getting cheap meat, but it's at the expense of the environment—and then they're really paying through the nose in taxes to clean things up."

I tell him I'm not sure what a green cow costs, but a Diamond Willow tenderloin steak set me back $48 at River Café.

"Really?" he says. "Jesus, we're not getting *that much.*"

Finally, we turn off the gravel road onto a long laneway leading into Keith and Bev's Stillridge Ranch, a raw quarter section they bought in 1980, with no house, power or water. In fact, the only thing the homestead came with was a hefty mortgage and interest rates spiking in the double digits. They raised their three children here. "People saw us and said, this is a young family that's not afraid of work," says Keith. "As soon as the farm community finds that out, you're okay."

He directs me past the old house that he and Bev had moved here and placed on a foundation, which they dug out themselves with shovels. We turn by the shed and barn they also built, then Keith tells me to stop at a black wall of bush. "I hope you don't mind staying in the bunkhouse," he says. "It's cooler than upstairs in the house."

"No, that's fine," I say. "I really appreciate it."

"Good," he says, "'cause if not, I would have told you to suck it up, princess."

*Princess,* I think. Keith had warned me earlier that everyone in Pincher Creek gets a nickname, but, I swear, mine will not be this.

I get out of the car and grab my backpack. There's no moon, and the sky's blacker than my fancy new cowboy boots. I take a step and a pine branch whacks my face. Two more and I smack into the giant rear tire of a tractor.

Keith cracks up laughing. "I forgot I left the tractor there," he says. Between haying, fencing and looking after his cattle, he's been trying to build a new barn in time to host his daughter's wedding in a month. No wonder two drinks hit him so hard.

After we squeeze between the pines and the tractor, Keith trips over a pile of gravel he also forgot was in the path. Then I trip over him. Luckily, we're both pretty short, so our legs don't get tangled up.

Finally, we reach a barbed wire fence that Keith holds low enough for me to step over, except he's not exactly holding it steady. I heft my knapsack onto my back and safely step over, only to run face-first into a hot, wet nose. It's a horse, I hope, because then two more slobbering noses are suddenly butting into my chest.

Keith has already started down the path ahead of me, through waist-deep grass, followed by his black dog (at least, I hope it's a dog). I consider asking him to call off his overly friendly horses but, biting against that word *princess,* I push their heads away and hurry to follow. The horses rush after me, hooves scraping the back of my new boots, noses snorting greetings of warm saliva down my neck.

Eventually, we reach the bunkhouse, a two-room affair with a tiny kitchen in front, a bunk bed in the back. Keith points out the outhouse, tucked back into the bush.

"You need anything?" he asks.

"So, are there any grizzlies, black bears, cougars around here?" I ask. It's a silly question, I know. I heard a few stories about ranch wildlife at the potluck earlier.

"I'll leave you the dog," he says, calling good night as he bangs out the door.

I pace the width of the bunkhouse—about two steps—and listen to the horses snorting and stomping around outside. Finally, Rusty and I make the fifteen-yard dash to the outhouse, then I crawl into bed and shut off the light. It's so black that I can't see my hand when I hold it in front of my face.

THE PRODUCERS OF DIAMOND WILLOW own or lease about forty thousand acres between Longview and Twin Butte, along the historic Cowboy Trail, Highway 22. This is stunning landscape, known as Big Sky Country, where a sea of grass-covered prairie laps against low-rolling foothills before crashing into the Rocky Mountains. You've probably seen the expansive vista—scenes from the Oscar-winning *Brokeback Mountain* were shot here. Locals packed into the Pincher Creek theatre to see that one, but were a little unsettled when the two cowboy protagonists fall in love, with the scenery and each other.

I'm on the road again, this time armed with a municipal map Bev and Keith gave me. Keith had promised I could join him on a cattle roundup, but he has fences to repair first—with 130 kilometres to maintain on his four thousand acres, that's an ongoing chore. Plus he thinks I'll understand the cost of green cows more if I meet up with Mac Main and pick blueweed along Pincher Creek.

In addition to ranching, the Diamond Willow producers have started several environmental organizations. Mac, Janet's son, volunteers with Cows and Fish, and also the Pincher Creek Watershed Group, both of which bring together ranchers and conservationists to manage and protect the watercourse. "These ranchers are the true environmentalists," one conservation officer tells me. "They've been managing the land for a long time, moving their cows off the river in the winter, then back in the summer, to keep the vegetation healthy. It's in their best interest to make their operations sustainable."

A few years back, Mac bought a ranch along Pincher Creek and built a house, where he lives with his wife, Wendy, and their two children. He's a postcard cowboy—tall, square jawed and as taciturn as Keith is outgoing, but he has his own perverse sense of humour, at least when it comes to blueweed, or viper's bugloss. The invasive plant was brought in by oil and gas companies, on vehicle tires or in landfill. If workers had picked the blueweed when it first appeared, that would be the end of this dreadful story. But according to locals, exploration outfits have a habit of trampling over land and leaving messes behind with little regard to the consequences. When the blueweed hit the waterways—which can't be sprayed even if Mac's organic principles allowed it—the lupine-like spike spread like crazy and now threatens to choke out the native vegetation protecting the banks of the river. Mac's suggestion? Organize a community weed-picking day, get Shell Oil to pay for the barbecue and beer, invite the company's executives, and pull the weeds by hand. They have little hope of eliminating the weed, but, at least, Mac reasoned, the day would be educational.

That it is. Some eighty people show up, including a few from Shell, at the Alberta Ranch, host site for the annual pick. Following Keith's befuddled driving directions given the night before, I miss the pancake breakfast. To catch up to Mac's picking crew, I have to scramble a mile up the creek (scraping up my new boots on the rocky shoreline), pass Mac's ranch and cross the creek a few times (whereupon I learn that cowboy boots aren't waterproof). Arriving breathless, I tell Mac I've never had to work this hard for an interview. He hands me a shovel and tells me to make sure that the roots come out with the plant.

I jam the shovel into the ground around a clump of blueweed, only to hit rock, then jam it in again, this time hitting willow roots. This goes on for six long hours under a hot July sun. I didn't bring any drinking water along, but Mac assures me that Pincher Creek, even with all the ranches in the area, is clean enough to drink from, so I press my face into the cold, clear glacial runoff and suck in the most delicious water I've ever tasted.

At the end of the day, the ten or so crews have filled a few hundred garbage bags with weeds, with the top picker winning the Brokeback Mountain Award, a cow spine broken in three places and wired together on a stick. I don't win, but no one's calling me princess either.

Over cold beers, as the cooks prepare dinner and with fiddlers playing by the campfire, I get a chance to talk to Mac about how Diamond Willow raises beef that tastes so good. Behind us, kids shriek and holler as they chase each other through the creek. Mac chews on his moustache for a time with my first question—how many cows does he have? Apparently, that's like asking a rancher how much money he makes. Not polite. Finally, in a barely audible voice, without a hint of conceit, Mac tells me he has fourteen thousand acres and five hundred breeding cows—easily the largest of Diamond Willow's operations.

What makes the company work, he says, is that each rancher runs a cow-calf operation independently, selling the heifers and steers to the joint company, Diamond Willow Organics, which fattens the yearlings to market weight in an organic feedlot before selling them to the distributor. Although ranchers make their own management decisions, they follow a similar approach to raising cattle. They focus on keeping the cow healthy to avoid using antibiotics. (If they have to treat a cow, they will remove it from the organic program and sell it on the regular market.) Whereas the regular system pushes cattle through growth cycles, Diamond Willow's system moves more at the animal's pace. For instance, most cattle go into industrial feedlots at less than a year old, whereas Mac's cattle don't go into the organic feedlot until they're nearly fifteen months old. "We don't push them," says Mac. "We let them build their frame, put on weight. You tend to get better meat, with more body. It's a lot better. When an animal's too young, it's got no body."

Ever the forthright cowboy, Mac tells me that the beef he butchers for his own freezer is even older, usually three or four years, and never sees a feedlot. He also dry-ages the meat by hanging the carcass in a cool area (at temperatures just above freezing) for fourteen to twenty days, though some ranchers age beef for as long as twenty-eight days. That dry-aging tenderizes and brings out the deep beefy flavour. But aging is also expensive. Hanging carcasses takes up space, and meat dehydrates by more than 15 percent during the process, key reasons why, decades ago, the beef industry switched to wet-aging in vacuum-packed bags: water equals weight equals money.

Oh, but to hear a cowboy talk about steak in the fading evening light, a range of snow-peaked mountains in the background. Mac speaks quietly, with dramatic pauses, as if remembering each savoury morsel. "The beef comes off the hard grass in the fall," he says, "when the native grasses are cured. That gives a great flavour. Fat carries the flavour of what the animal has been eating for the last month. With grass, you get that yellow fat running through the meat. It cooks like bacon rind. You don't cut that off. That's the real beef cowboys like to eat." He pauses even longer. "It's too bad the average consumer doesn't get to taste that."

That, I think, is the four-year-old, grass-fed steer of Alberta's hallowed past, and it's sitting at home in Mac's freezer.

I gulp down my beer and squeeze the can in my hand, wondering how to wrangle an invitation to dinner. But Mac, a true gentleman, notices the empty can and leaves to fetch me another.

HAVING GROWN UP on the back of a horse, I'm pretty sure I can prove my mettle rounding up cows, but Keith puts off our adventure yet again. Instead, I'm relegated to playing chuckwagon chef at breakfast, making Keith and Bev French toast while Keith tells me about an abandoned house they moved into when they were starting out, working on ranches and taking agricultural courses. The owner made them pay rent so that they would appreciate the place more. "And we really did," says Keith. "We had goats living in the basement, but, if we saved enough milk, we could have Kahlúa with goat's milk on Friday nights. We didn't have any money, but we were living in this beautiful place, and we felt like kings and queens."

The truth is, I am actually starting to feel a little like a spoiled princess in my little bunkhouse castle. Around 2 A.M., Rusty and I saunter to the outhouse, me buck-naked except for my new cowboy boots. On the way back, we stand on the front deck of the cabin, drinking in the warm summer night and the movie-set view—a green pasture, the forest beyond and the blue wall of the mountains. Hanging over it all is a massive full moon that crawled over the ridge at about midnight and now sits so low in the sky I feel as if I can reach out and hug it.

Since I arrived on Friday, Keith hasn't stopped working, even though it's the weekend. With cattle feeding on grass, a rancher doesn't have set chores but is always doing something—moving bulls to breed with cows, calving, branding, moving cows between pastures, fixing fences and water pumps, cutting and baling hay for winter feed and, in Keith's case, growing organic crops for the feedlot—rye and barley. As president of Diamond Willow, Keith also speaks at organic and slow food conferences around the world, represents the group on agricultural committees, works on marketing and coordinates the activities of the producers, feedlot, slaughterhouse and distributor to ensure the cattle are moving through the system in an orderly fashion.

But after ten years of pouring all their profits into building their system, the producers have a problem: The company is growing at a rate of 25 percent a month and it needs to bump up production to keep up with demand, twelve hundred cattle a year now, a projected ten thousand in five years. Since the ranchers can't simply put more cattle on their grazing land and remain environmentally sustainable, Keith is off today to talk to other ranchers about producing organic cattle for Diamond Willow. And that means another problem. Keith has a dream of marketing beef from the entire southern Alberta Foothills region, as a way of making ranching economically sustainable and therefore protecting the area from development. But the challenge is persuading other ranchers to go organic, even though their beef would fetch as much as thirty-five cents a pound more, twice as much after it comes out of the organic feedlot. Until now, Diamond Willow has kept a deliberately low profile. As Keith says, "It's hard enough being a cowboy with a ponytail without saying you're organic. You say that, and everyone thinks you're saying their beef's no good. And suddenly, you're the Diamond Willow weirdo."

"Ah, suck it up, princess," I tell him.

He nearly spits out his coffee laughing.

Still, I know from talking to ranchers at the blueweed pick that it is difficult going against the grain of a rural community. One said he thought organics was "lazy farming," as if using chemicals to grow crops and blast weeds is harder than building soil by rotating crops and growing nitrogen-rich legumes for green manure—and picking weeds by hand and shovel. But when the going gets tough, the Diamond Willow group draws courage from its toughest member, Janet Main.

"She's our mentor," Bev says. "She's our inspiration. You really have to talk to Janet."

And so I am back in the car, with another bottle of organic wine, timing my visit for lunch in the hopes that Janet will serve leftover prime rib roast from the potluck a few days ago. She does. Even cold, the pink, thick-cut slices are superb, with leftover pasta and bean salads and a cold glass of white wine—or two, for it takes the better part of the afternoon for Janet to explain why she's "Big Momma to the group."

At seventy-three, she's a slim five foot six, with wispy silver hair framing penetrating eyes, but her hands are weathered bibles, square and strong. Just when her four children were entering their teenage years, Janet's husband, Bill, developed Huntington's disease, a debilitating nervous disorder that eventually killed him. Janet quit her teaching job and took over running the ranch. She had grown up on one and had a passion for cattle and the land. While he was able, Bill taught her the scientific side of ranching that he had learned at university. After he "really went downhill," she would hear his encouraging voice in her head—particularly on those nights during March snowstorms when every tenth or so cow needed to be lassoed and tied so that Janet could deliver the calf, when calves needed rescuing from snowbanks or warming up in the bathtub in the house. When Janet found one mother cow without her calf, she gave the momma a push and was led across a pasture through a howling squall to the edge of the bush. Janet followed the cow's stare into the trees and saw the calf—and a grizzly eating it. "I was a bit startled," Janet admits. "I guess I hollered so loud I scared the grizzly off." Too late for the calf, though. "But she was a brave cow," Janet says, "leading me there."

Maybe Janet channelled some of that cow's grit, for she didn't just maintain the ranch after her husband's death but expanded aggressively. She implemented an extensive breeding program to improve and expand her herd. A good breeding cow, Janet says, is one that can have her calf on her own, wards off predators and will be lean with a big rib-eye. Unfortunately, some are good mothers but turn out to have small rib-eyes, and then it's into the freezer for them, often Janet's. That's hard, she admits. "You've had some of these cows for twelve years. You form relationships. Some of them I just loved. We used to have names for them all, but now, with the organic tagging, we go by numbers. But you still know them."

Being a woman, Janet ran into the usual prejudice: banks that wanted to increase the interest on the ranch's line of credit when Bill could no longer sign for loans, a real estate agent who overestimated the acreage on a ranch she was buying with Mac.

When a friend from Montreal phoned to ask her to take on a family friend as an apprentice, Janet was forthright. "Does he have any ranching skills?" she asked. "Because I'm doing just about all the caretaking I can do right now." Charlie Straessle showed up, as he told me at the blueweed pick, "knowing nothing. I was in my twenties, and Janet was near fifty then, and she had way more energy than I did. She worked longer and harder on the ranch, and then she went into the house and did all the work there and looked after her husband." After Bill died, Janet helped start two of her children in ranching—Mac (along with his wife, Wendy) and her daughter, Cas (along with her husband, Jamie)—and also Charlie, all now Diamond Willow producers. When Janet wound down her operation, she had one of the largest cattle and land holdings in the area.

And that's just half her story. Through it all, she waged a thirty-year battle with Shell Oil, which moved in next door. Says Janet: "The oil companies were starting to explore in this area, and it was totally new to people, to let them on your land to do seismic testing. And then you find out there's a big price to pay."

The Mains lived just a half mile from the emissions stacks. Their children developed rashes, the youngest asthma. Somehow, the family got used to the drills, often at night, of collecting the kids and rushing from the house when a particularly obnoxious blast of hydrogen sulphide blew down their valley. "We should have acted then," Janet says, "but I was just trying to hold things together with my family, and then I started to manage the ranch."

One winter night, the grass on their pasture caught fire, likely from a spark from the emissions stacks. Another night, liquid mistakenly released from a holding pond flowed down their creek—the company sent in bulldozers to damn the creek, then set it on fire to contain the mess. Berry bushes died within two seasons. In spring, the new alfalfa crop turned black. One morning, Janet found a bull and seven cows dead in the field. Shell Oil and the family finally agreed that the family would move to another section of the ranch. But they still ran cattle on the original section. A few years later, Janet discovered the cows wouldn't drink from the creek. When a University of Calgary professor brought students out to see the effects of the oil industry on ranching, four cows had dropped dead during the night. "The students helped me move the rest of the herd," Janet says, "and on the way, another cow dropped." Janet herself suffered through two bouts of cancer.

When a group of ranchers invited her to speak at a meeting, she donned the mantle of environmentalist well before it was fashionable. The ranchers were trying to decide whether to let a pipeline run through their properties. Says Janet: "I found myself presenting my case to sixty people, and they could hardly believe what I was telling them. These days, with what we know, I would get all sorts of support, but back then everyone just thought I was off my rocker."

Janet could never prove a direct link between the incidents and the presence of the oil company, but she moved again, to a new ranch, after reaching a settlement with Shell that included a non-disclosure agreement, something she regrets signing. But now her first ranch has a conservation easement on it, meaning no one can ever develop or live on the property or even camp on it. "I didn't want anyone else going through what we went through," Janet says. Her new ranch is eleven kilometres north of the plant.

Diamond Willow, at least, heard Janet's message. About the same time the producers were meeting to form that company, Keith, Norm Simmons and a third producer, Francis Gardner, along with Janet Main, founded the Southern Alberta Land Trust Society, a rancher-run organization with a goal of protecting the fragile foothills grasslands. They've already persuaded about forty ranchers to put conservation easements on their land, protecting it from future development. Their latest initiative calls for a temporary halt to all gas and oil exploration in the area.

Some five hours after I arrived at Janet's, the wine bottle sits empty between us and the batteries have ground down on my voice recorder.

"Grass, of course, is the lifeblood here," she says. "It's crucial to keep it in good shape."

LARRY FRITH is Diamond Willow's grass specialist, a former grass-seed salesman and self-described "peripheral visionary" who quotes George Carlin—"I can see way ahead, but it's off to the side."

Larry and his wife, Jan, a nurse, have the smallest operation in Diamond Willow, with just forty breeding cows that they move between pastures by foot. Conveniently, I again time my visit for lunch. Jan has made the human version of grass—a salad of lettuce, beet tops, spinach, Swiss chard, green onions and a couple of edible flowers that we picked from her garden—which she serves with broccoli soup.

Over lunch, Larry tells me that ranching is critical to maintaining the health of these foothills grasslands, one of the last unbroken tracts of native grasses in Canada. By moving cattle through various fenced pastures, sometimes seven or eight times a year, ranchers mimic what millions of bison did here for the past ten thousand years: harvesting this natural crop by grazing it, churning up the soil with the cattle's cloven hooves, then replanting and fertilizing native grass seed with the cattle dung. "Without grazing, this grassland would deteriorate in a hurry," says Larry.

Over the past thirty years, ranchers have gotten better at practising this holistic range management on delicate native grasses, but Larry says there were plenty of mistakes before that. Ranchers arriving in the late 1880s and early 1890s—after the last bison were driven off—encountered huge grasses. "They thought that was the norm," says Larry. "They hit it hard." At the turn of the nineteenth century, new arrivals started to farm, but when the drought hit in the 1930s, causing massive erosion to the tilled soil, they realized the land should have been left in grass. The provincial government seeded the farms down in new grasses. But the introduced timothy and brome crowded out native ones. Says Larry: "These [introduced] grasses give lots of top growth but not much root growth, which gives organic matter to the soil. The native grasses are slower to grow, but they have deep roots that grow in low-moisture areas and prevent soil erosion. When new grasses mature in the fall, there's nothing left but straw. The nutrients in native grasses are more concentrated."

Indeed, these hard grasses, as ranchers call them, have more protein and carbohydrates—a good pasture can feed cattle through the winter, especially with chinooks blowing in from the Pacific Ocean to melt the snow. As Larry sees it, this grass is a crop that nature provides, evolved through thousands of years. And now imagine a bulldozer taking a spin through that lush crop. "That's why we're so concerned about oil and gas encroaching. They carve up grass for pipelines and roads, then non-native grasses and weeds come in and suddenly the whole ecosystem changes."

At this, Larry works up a good head of indignation. "This grassland isn't rocket science," he says. "It's far more complicated than rocket science will ever be, because you're dealing with a whole living system. Look at the ground and see how many pounds of stuff are living on top of it. There's as much if not more underground, and we don't know what it does. We don't even have names for most of it. Yet, here we are, fucking around with it, making changes without knowing what effect it will have."

Although many ranchers raising cattle on these grasslands are not far off Diamond Willow's organic model, Larry still sees it as a steep challenge to bring more into the fold. Going organic is not just a case of eliminating chemicals and antibiotics but also requires relearning the art of farming, to work with nature rather than trying to dominate it. "Over the last year, Diamond Willow has had tremendous growth, and we need conventional ranchers to switch over," he says, "but it's hard for kids who have grown up with a certain mindset to see outside it. Agricultural businesses want to maximize sales, so they tell farmers to maximize yield. Farmers are saying, we can't make money producing wheat for $2 a bushel, so the chemical companies tell them to produce more. They really tell them that. You almost need a counter-revolution to offset that. Farmers need to look at their net sales. Gross sales don't matter. What's the cost of your inputs? What's the long-term health of your resource—your land? With organics, you replace inputs with management. You work with the natural systems, rather than force them."

For Larry, that means going back to growing crops that are indigenous to the area. And here, that means native grasses. So it wasn't easy, he admits, for Diamond Willow to introduce a feedlot to its system.

BILL ELTON ran a conventional feedlot for twenty years before joining Diamond Willow. Over tea in their kitchen, Bill, a thoughtful, quiet man, and his wife, Carol, a former nurse who now studies alternative healing, tell me about the struggles they faced setting up an organic feedlot. As Bill says, "Some organic people don't believe in feedlots and think that, ideally, we should be grass-finishing."

But that ideal would be tough to achieve without consumers making huge adjustments in the way we buy and cook meat. Earlier, I spoke to Louise Phillips at Pine Terra Farm, which produced the amazing grass-finished strip loin served at River Café. She says it takes nearly two and a half years to finish a cow on grass, which makes it a far more expensive product for the fresh-meat market. But the farm can still sell a side of beef at comparable prices or even cheaper than a supermarket—if the customer buys a whole side of beef directly from the farm. But that means freezing and using all the cuts, not just the prime roasts. Freezing for less than six months doesn't really alter the quality of the meat and may even enhance the taste through aging. And off-cuts such as flank steak, stewing beef and chuck roast are actually more flavourful than the so-called top cuts. But, as a nation of weekend grill chefs, we have to relearn the art of braising, sautéing and roasting to make those mouth-watering cuts tender.

As well, Bill believes, people are "sold on the romance of grass-fed," but not on the reality. "That's a small niche market. The taste of the animals varies—whether they're coming off soft or hard grass. Grass-fed is more difficult to cook, as it's leaner. It's more like cooking wild game. Most people like that taste of grain-fed beef."

To serve that fresh-meat market year-round with organic, grain-fed beef, Diamond Willow set about to establish a feedlot that would be humane and environmentally sustainable or, as Bill says, "cattle friendly and people friendly."

Bill offers me a tour of his feedlot, just a short walk from the house, and here's where I really begin to understand Keith's rants about the cost of green cows. Compared with industrial feedlots that have ten thousand cows or more, this one, with just five hundred, is tiny. Bill's land base of 880 acres is large enough to handle the manure he hauls out and spreads as a rich natural fertilizer. The cows have ample room to move around in four large paddocks, a configuration that enables Bill to keep cows from the same range in the same pen, "to keep the social herd together."

As we approach, the cows watch us, curious, calm. They are incredibly clean, standing on a bedding mixture of woodchips with a bit of straw. The smell is actually pleasant, tame and woodsy. "Wood chips keep them cleaner," says Bill, "and that's healthier for the cow and more hygienic for the slaughterhouse."

When the cows first arrive here, Bill slowly eases them from grass onto a grain-based diet of wheat, barley, rye or oats. He continues to feed a healthy ratio of hay to keep the cow's digestive system—designed to work on grass and hay—from becoming stressed. And he doesn't even try to fatten the cows to a Triple-A rating—Diamond Willow's beef grades to a leaner A or Double-A. "We've never had an abscessed liver," Bill says, referring to the consequence of stressing the cow's digestive system by feeding the cow too little forage.

In addition to this go-slow approach bumping up expenses, the feed costs 50 to 60 percent more: It must all be certified organic, meaning no genetically modified grains, no pesticides on the grain. Organics also ban drugs, whether growth hormones or antibiotics, both regularly used by industrial feedlots. If a cow does become sick, they will treat it with antibiotics but then remove it from the organic program and sell it on the conventional market. However, Bill says that only about 1 to 2 percent of cows in their feedlot system ever become sick enough to warrant antibiotics. "We take about 10 to 15 percent longer to fatten a cow from 900 to about 1200 or 1300 pounds," says Bill. "We avoid sickness by keeping the animals in a low-stress, healthy environment." Diamond Willow's challenge will be maintaining its high-health record with its rapid expansion to meet the growing demand for organic meat. Since my visit to Diamond Willow, it had set up a new feedlot, for between fifteen hundred and two thousand cows, near High River, Alberta.

From Bill's feedlot, about fifty to one hundred "fats" are trucked every other week to a meat processor north of Calgary. That facility must also be organically certified, which requires following organic regulations and passing an intense audit annually. To make their relationship "no hassle," Diamond Willow guarantees that the cows will be at the processor in the morning, to be the first kill of the day, as the processor must clean the facility and equipment with organic solutions before processing, and use a separate butchering bay and keep organic beef from coming into contact with other beef. It must also keep meticulous records of each carcass, so that a consumer can trace meat from the store right back through all the stages of production, to the calf and the ranch where it grew up.

Otherwise, the kill is the same—as calm as possible, since a stressed cow will produce either pale soft meat or dark red, dry meat. The cows funnel one by one through a chute and separately enter a knocking box. A door closes behind the cow so that the ones following see nothing. Inside the box, a stun gun shoots a bolt against the cow's forehead, killing the animal instantly. A conveyor carries the carcass out of the box, to be hung up, bled out, skinned, washed and then butchered into the primal parts, which are vacuum-packed and shipped by refrigerated truck to the distributor, Hills Foods, in British Columbia. Hills Foods wet-ages and custom-cuts the meat according to a customer's order, shipping it to retailers across Canada and now a few upscale restaurants in Calgary—Rouge, Belgo Brasserie and River Café—though that city has been its toughest sell.

FINALLY, Keith gives me a chance to do some real ranching. The roundup is on. A buddy of Keith's, wearing real cowboy gear, shows up to help out. Even Keith pulls on riding boots and leather chaps. I saddle up Sully, a temperamental gelding according to Keith, which secretly pleases me. Would he give a princess a temperamental gelding to ride? I think not.

We load the horses in a trailer for the ten-minute drive to the pasture. From there, it's five minutes at a slow walk to the cattle, Sully's temperamental antics involving little more than stopping to eat grass. The scene that greets us delights me: About thirty cattle have escaped from Keith's field into a neighbour's. Our goal is to push the cattle from the bush across a muddy stretch of pasture, through a narrow gate and back into Keith's without them hightailing it for higher ground. This will be a roundup.

"I don't know if the cattle will go," Keith says as he steers his horse through the muddy stretch to test the foothold. He rides back, mud flying. "I don't know," he says again.

Scenes from western movies flash through my head—the bellowing cattle bulking at the mud, charging in all directions, and Sully and I at a dead run, chasing down stray calves.

Keith motions me to ride to the left, his buddy to stay behind. He reins his horse to the right. "C'mon, ladies," he calls to the herd. "Let's go, ladies."

Something is wrong with my notion of how things will go. Keith sounds like a tour guide herding a group of churchwomen onto a bus. He is unfailingly gentle, patient, even polite. "Time to go, ladies," he says. "C'mon. Picnic's over."

And the cows respond like a group of churchwomen, mildly complaining and a bit flatulent but leaving the bush as told and setting off across the muddy pasture.

The three of us ride in a V formation behind the cattle, in a magic zone of pressure—exerting just enough to keep them moving, not so much that they break from their leisurely pace. They funnel through the open gate. Keith slides off his horse, shuts the gate. And our roundup is over, inside ten minutes.

"Bet you thought that was going to be more exciting," Keith smirks.

Back in the truck, he tells me that the cowboy arts, like the holistic management of grass, have improved tremendously over the past few decades, adapting horse-whisperer methods to managing cows. "We could spend eight hours on the same job," he says, "but we've learned to take the low-stress route to moving cows. Cows get to know what you want, and you just need to ease them there. If you put too much pressure on them and they get stressed, it doesn't work. It's cow psychology 302."

And so I am left to prove myself in the only way remaining to me: dinner. That evening, Keith and Bev barbecue up a platter of rib steaks, with baked potatoes and a garden-fresh salad. I'm sorry that Nancy, who is back home working, is missing this dinner. Keith and Bev are, too. They insist I bring my partner next time I visit. As we sip wine on the side deck overlooking the bunkhouse and valley, we chat as farm families do after a hard day's work—teasing each other about the day's triumphs and mishaps, until our stomachs cramp from laughing. Keith jokes that the meat is from an old cow culled from the breeding herd. But, clearly, the cow wasn't butchered for her scant rib-eye. The steaks are massive, an inch and a half thick and the size of a dinner plate. I cut one in half, and still the portion is huge.

Whether from an old cow (as Keith teases) or not (as Bev indicates), organic beef again proves to be a revelation. There may be all sorts of sensible reasons to eat clean meat—proper feed, humane handling, sustainable ranching—but the seductive reason is taste. I eat the first half, then the other half, and then another half. And fine, it may only be for my queenly appetite, but Keith, I can tell, is impressed.

I MAKE ONE FINAL STOP on my way back to Calgary, at what Bev calls "Diamond Willow's showcase ranch," Francis and Bonnie Gardner's Mt. Sentinel. Their 8500 acres sit north of the Chain Lakes, on the edge of the southern foothills of the Rocky Mountains, one of the most ecologically threatened grasslands in Alberta and an aquifer that provides water for southern Alberta. It's a half-day ride from the historic Bar U Ranch and the EP Ranch, once owned by Prince Edward VII, who later abdicated the throne for Wallis Simpson. "Edward used to ride twelve miles straight across to have Sunday breakfast with the crew here and just be one of the men," Francis tells me over breakfast. And, yes, like Edward, I have timed my arrival for flapjacks and sausages.

Francis, sixty-three, looks every bit the grandson of a British naval commander that he is. His grandfather bought the ranch in 1898, when this area was still unfenced, open range. When the First World War broke out, he returned to England to serve in the navy, leaving his wife to run the operation until he returned. Now a war has come to Francis's doorstep: oil and gas exploration, and development pressure from Calgary that has sent land prices skyrocketing.

"Most people see this as a piece of real estate that you can alter," he says. "Most people don't understand that you're disrupting something far more ancient and valuable."

A flapjack or two later, he tells me about oil and gas dynamiting a property nearby. "My well went dry. The oil companies don't seem to see that the veins where the gas might be and the underground aquifers are all connected."

He became an environmental activist the day an oil company showed up at his door asking to run a pipeline across his property. He invited Janet Main to speak to a group of neighbouring ranchers, and eventually he became the founding president of the Southern Alberta Land Trust Society (SALTS). A few years ago, local municipalities, the oil industry and a few concerned citizens paid $60,000 for a study that looks at the potential effects of development in the southern foothills. SALTS has asked oil and gas companies to stop exploring until everyone can consider the study and decide if the short-term profits are worth the long-term devastation to the land. Since the late 1980s, Bonnie says she and Francis have devoted more time to protecting the ranch than actually running it, though the work gets done with hired help. They're hoping their oldest daughter will return home from training horses in Australia to manage their ranch.

After breakfast, we take a walk up a steep hill behind the house, the calving field, though there are too many wolves to actually calf in this pasture anymore; increased recreational activities in the mountains have pushed down grizzlies, cougars, moose and elk. But this knoll, covered with thirty-five or so species of native plants and the rough fescue grass, is stunning. It overlooks a spring-fed lake and a thick stand of diamond willows. It is apropos the ranchers named their company after these tiny twisted trees, which grow by waterways: Their roots filter water and prevent erosion by stabilizing shore banks.

When I first arrived in the southern foothills scant days ago, the range land seemed to stretch forever. Since I've been here, my perception has changed. It takes four hours to drive from Calgary southward to the U.S. border. And the land in between is precious. "You're looking at ten thousand years of evolution since the last ice age," Francis tells me. "That to me means something. This range produced millions of bison without fossil fuels. And we can do this for thousands more with cattle, if we look after the grass."

But every incursion into the area—whether it is a road, driveway or pipeline—will degrade the grasslands, Francis suggests, for three kilometres on either side. And degradation to the land also erodes what Francis calls "the caring capacity" of ranchers to look after it. In other words, few people would put up the fierce fight to protect their land as Janet Main did. Or as Francis and Bonnie are now doing.

"Organic production is an approach to how we view resources in an area," says Francis. "It's not about disrupting the land but working with it in a complementary way. It's what this country needs to do. But now it seems as if we have no tears. We'll go down a road as if there were no implications."

LEAVING THE RANCH, I begin to understand, maybe for the first time, my own conflicted feelings about my family's farm, now run by my brother. After developers bought our first farm—a piece of land I loved desperately— I found it hard to mount much caring capacity, as Francis puts it, for the second. We always knew the nearby city of Barrie would land on our doorstep, and now it has, swelling from a population of 30,000 to more than 120,000 in the past twenty-five years and creating some of the ugliest urban sprawl in Ontario. Just a half kilometre away from our farm, vehicles thunder along Highway 400. There's already a mishmash of development just two kilometres north and east of the farm—a casino, an industrial park, a subdivision. It doesn't much feel like farm land or a community anymore. Neighbours on our road have all sold their farms to speculators, their land likely to become industrial "parks" within the decade. For our farm, it's just a matter of time.

Shockingly, just five minutes up the road from the Gardiners', on the Cowboy Trail back to Calgary, I arrive at the edge of their frontier. At Longview, oil and gas pumps and wellheads line the hills, more than I can count, the pumps driving into the land, boom, boom, boom. From here, tiny rural villages now stretch well beyond town limits with their new shopping malls and huge paved parking lots. Between villages, massive modern country estates have sprung up on quarter sections bought for the view, the precious native grasses untended. And then the Cowboy Trail crests a hill and, suddenly, the prairie is gone and Calgary is here, a solid wall of houses and strip malls, though the road sign indicates downtown is still twenty-three kilometres away.

I turn off the highway and the first city intersection is anchored by four fast-food chains. Their signs wage a heated battle to offer the cheapest hamburger. Today, McDonald's is winning.

# Alberta

## Bev and Keith's Witches' Brew

Bev says this is her family's favourite take on chili con carne, satisfying after a day of skiing. Since this chili reheats well, she makes it in batches, which she freezes to have on hand for easy weekend meals.

Although the recipe calls for just one can of tomato paste, you can add up to two extra cans, to give the chili a real tomato zest.

| | | |
|---|---|---|
| 1 1/2 lb | organic ground beef | 750 g |
| 1 tbsp | each salt and pepper, or to taste | 15 mL |
| 1 tbsp | cayenne pepper, or to taste | 15 mL |
| 1/4 lb | organic bacon, cut into 1/4-inch/5 mm dice | 125 g |
| 2 | large Spanish onions, cut into 1/4-inch/5 mm dice | 2 |
| 2 | large red or green bell peppers, cut into 1/4-inch/5 mm dice | 2 |
| 1/2 lb | button mushrooms, sliced | 250 g |
| 3 | large ripe tomatoes, peeled and chopped (or 1 28 oz/796 mL can diced tomatoes) | 3 |
| 2 | cans (each 19 oz/540 mL) red kidney beans | 2 |
| 2 cups | cooked brown rice | 500 mL |
| 1 | can (5 1/2 oz/156 mL) tomato paste, or more to taste | 1 |

Preheat oven to 350°F (180°C).

Fry the ground beef in a large, heavy oven-proof pan over medium heat. Season with the salt, pepper and cayenne pepper. When the beef is cooked through, remove from heat and drain off the fat.

Fry the bacon over medium-high heat. Transfer to a plate lined with a paper towel; drain off any fat remaining in the pan. Add the onions, bell peppers and mushrooms to the pan; sauté until soft, about 3 to 5 minutes. Add the tomatoes, beans with their liquid, rice and tomato paste. Stir in the ground beef and bacon. Adjust seasoning.

Bake, covered, for about 30 minutes or until heated through and bubbling.

*Makes 6 to 8 servings.*

Credit: Bev Everts, Pincher Creek, Alberta.

## Braised Beef Short Ribs
## with Blueberry Sauce and Gremolata

Organic meat can be nearly as economical as regular if you buy off-cuts, or
a quarter or side of the animal. Of course, the latter demands a little more
ingenuity in the kitchen to cook all the cuts, nose to tail. This is one of
chef Scott Pohorelic's favourite ways of serving short ribs; they're exquisite
enough to make the menu at Calgary's River Café. The recipe calls for
juniper berries, Canada's only indigenous spice. Look for it at fine food
stores selling dried spices but, if not available, you can leave it out; the ribs
will still taste great.

You can prepare ribs a day or two in advance of making the sauce and
gremolata; keep tightly wrapped in the refrigerator until ready to use.
Braised meat dries out quickly, so don't leave it uncovered.

| | | |
|---|---|---|
| 3 lb | good-quality beef short ribs, cut between the ribs to 3-inch/8 cm pieces | 1.5 kg |
| | salt and freshly ground black pepper | |
| 12 cups | beef stock | 3 L |
| 1/2 cup | dry red wine | 125 mL |
| 2 tbsp | balsamic vinegar | 25 mL |
| 1 | stalk celery, chopped | 1 |
| 1 | carrot, chopped | 1 |
| 1/2 | yellow onion, chopped | 1/2 |
| 1 | clove garlic, minced | 1 |
| 1 | bay leaf | 1 |
| 1 | star anise | 1 |
| 10 | juniper berries | 10 |
| 1 | sprig fresh rosemary (or a pinch of dried) | 1 |
| 1 | sprig fresh thyme (or a pinch of dried) | 1 |
| 1 tsp | black peppercorns | 5 mL |
| | coarse sea salt, for assembly | |

**For blueberry sauce:**

| | | |
|---|---|---|
| 8 cups | braising stock (leftover from the braised short ribs) | 2 L |
| 1 cup | fresh blueberries | 250 mL |
| 2 tbsp | cassis, optional | 25 mL |

**For blueberry gremolata:**

| | | |
|---|---|---|
| 2 tbsp | chopped dried blueberries | 25 mL |
| 2 tbsp | chopped flat leaf parsley | 25 mL |
| 2 tsp | lemon zest, minced | 10 mL |
| 1 tsp | chopped fresh mint | 5 mL |
| 1/2 tsp | grated fresh horseradish | 2 mL |

Preheat oven to 300°F (150°C).

Season the beef with salt and pepper. Sear on all sides in a hot pan or on the barbecue over high heat. Transfer the ribs to a roasting pan; choose one large enough to allow the ribs to be submerged in the stock. Pour in the stock, wine and vinegar. Add the celery, carrot, onion, garlic, bay leaf, star anise, juniper berries, rosemary, thyme and peppercorns. Bring to a gentle simmer over medium heat on the stove.

Cover the pan and place in the oven. Cook for 4 hours or until the ribs are fork tender. Let the ribs sit in the braising stock until they are cool, or drain, reserving the stock. Tightly wrap ribs in plastic wrap and set aside until ready to use.

To make the sauce, let the braising stock cool, then remove the fat that has congealed on the top. Reserve 1/2 cup (125 mL) of the stock. Bring the remainder of the stock to a gentle boil, skimming any film that forms on top. Continue to boil until the stock is reduced to about one-quarter of its original volume; it should have the consistency of a sauce. Strain through a fine sieve. Add the blueberries and cassis, if using; keep warm.

To make the gremolata, combine the blueberries, parsley, lemon zest, mint and horseradish in a small bowl.

**To assemble:**

Warm the short ribs by placing in a hot pan with the 1/2 cup (125 mL) of reserved braising stock. Reduce the stock in the hot pan until it is thick and the ribs are sticky. Season the beef with coarse sea salt.

Transfer to a serving dish. Spoon the sauce over top and sprinkle with the gremolata. For a richer sauce, stir in 1 to 2 tablespoons (15 to 25 mL) of butter just before serving, or add two spoonfuls of blueberry jelly.

*Makes 4 to 6 servings.*

Credit: Chef Scott Pohorelic, River Café, Calgary, Alberta.

*Yukon*

# THE FARM
# AT THE TOP OF THE WORLD

*During the Alaskan Klondike gold rush (1897–1898) …*
*potatoes were so valued for their vitamin C content*
*that miners traded gold for potatoes.*
—Potato Facts, Potato Growers of Alberta

Feidhlim trots from the greenhouse, a fat red tomato stuffed into his mouth. He is a sturdy fellow, three years old, with a rakish halo of curly blond hair. Although his Irish name—pronounced FEE-lim—means "ever good," that high moral ground doesn't much interest him. He has the smug smile of a boy who has just discovered gold, as if he knows exactly how dearly Yukoners would pay for that juicy homegrown fruit in his fist. He spots us in the field picking Yukon Gold and Russet Norkotah potatoes and barges into the vegetable patch. At first sight of these golden-fleshed nuggets, these ruby-skinned gems, he drops the half-eaten tomato, picks up a dirt-crusted spud and splits it cleanly in half with one chomp. His sun-freckled cheeks bulge. I expect the snack to fly from his mouth, along with a spew of mud and spit. But no. Another spud has caught his eye. He grabs that one, eats it.

His parents, Heidi Marion and Garret Gillespie, aren't the least bit worried about their son hoovering up the harvest, dirt and all. They have the largest organic vegetable farm in the Yukon, whimsically called Wild Blue Yonder. They use no synthetic pesticides or chemical fertilizers; rather, they weed by cultivator and a propane torch flame weeder and enrich the territory's glacial silt soils with animal and vegetable compost. Heidi, forty-one, an energetic woman, quick to laugh, is a stubborn idealist prone to saying things like, "The whole notion of farmers putting poison on food is ridiculous. Would you stir dish detergent into your coffee?" Garret, thirty-three, has more the air of a brooding poet. He calls himself a soil specialist, an agronomist, but talks more about the "yoga of farming"—how every molecule in our body comes from the ground via the food we eat; hence, farming is a "spiritual exercise" that connects us, through food, to the land. "In a healthy society that connection is honoured," he says, "farming is honoured." And, no, he does not think the direction we're heading is all that healthy. "The modern generation is eating mundane crap," he says. "And they're turning into mundane flavourless people."

Although Heidi and Garret are absolutely convinced of the nutritional and even spiritual superiority of their organic food, there is still considerable debate about that in scientific circles. But in gathering research prior to my trip, I stumbled headlong into author Thomas Pawlick's *The End of Food.* And he puts forward a convincing argument. Scientists have identified at least seventeen nutrients that plants feed on, but synthetic fertilizers supply crops with just three: nitrogen, phosphorus and potassium—NPK. Without compost that returns diverse nutrients to the soil, vegetables will "mine" elements such as calcium, carbon, zinc and iron. When those are depleted and the soil is exhausted, veggies will still grow with doses of NPK, usually into the big robust beauties that appear voluminously on our supermarket shelves. *The miracle of modern agriculture!* But that beguiling beauty is only skin deep. According to Pawlick's reading of the United States Department of Agriculture's food tables, the nutritional content of our industrially produced vegetables has decreased steadily since the 1960s, a decade after North American farmers turned en masse to chemical fertilizers for a steroid-like boost to productivity. The Canadian potato, once a rich source of vitamin C, has lost 57 percent of that vitamin over the past fifty years. As the soil starves, so do plants. And the people and animals who feed on them. Heidi sees the difference: "Our plants feed on soil, not chemicals, so they're smaller and denser but more nutritious."

Whatever science might say, Feidhlim knows what he knows. When he plunges into his parents' vegetable patch, I'm guessing he's not thinking about minerals or vitamins. He sizes up the rows as if aisles in a Wal-Mart-sized candy store. And holy cow, he is allowed to eat anything he wants! As much as he wants!

The next day when he arrives at the field to feed, his parents are trying to decide whether to harvest carrots. The small juicy shoots are the size of an index finger. Heidi takes the pitchfork and stumps up and down several rows, digging up clumps here and there, trying to find a sizeable batch. Garret takes over the pitchfork and has a go, finds nothing larger than Heidi has unearthed. Their debate see-saws back and forth. Left to grow another week, they will look more impressive at market. Maybe, but people may be eager to buy the summer's first carrots now.

There is some urgency to their talk: Although their veggies may be packed with nutrition, their bank account is as empty as an industrial potato. They have been staring down that chilling reality for more than a year. Now, whether by bankruptcy, fire sale or foreclosure, they will lose their farm in two months.

None of us think to consult the raw-food expert. As Heidi and Garret take their tense discussion into the workshop, Feidhlim marches past me, picks up samples lying askew on the ground. He barely gets one chewed before he shoves another orange treat into his mouth. At market on Thursday, the carrots will sell out.

WHEN I TOLD FRIENDS I was heading to the Yukon to visit a farm that grows Yukon Gold potatoes, they all responded with a variation of this question: *Wow, is that where our Yukon Golds come from?* I suppose that proves half of Garret's point—that our connection to the foods we eat has stretched so thin, it is nearly at the breaking point.

It's a different story here in a territory that starts north of British Columbia and stretches to the Arctic Ocean. Since 1898, when this wild mountainous land ignited the world's largest gold rush, the Yukon has been a magnet for wonder-seekers from around the world—some on the run from social bonds, some fleeing city pollution, others lured by the vast wilderness. And then there are those, like my good friend from Toronto, Miche Genest, who came for a visit and found that the place would not let her go. She told me how newcomers quickly bond with the land, can't help not to when winter temperatures rip below minus 40°C for a string of never-ending weeks, then summer kisses you on the forehead—well, it's more of a gob smack really—with nineteen hours of 25°C-plus sunshine. Transplanted urbanites take up pastimes such as moose hunting, berry collecting and gardening. Miche writes a column in *North of Ordinary* magazine about her obsession with what folks here call country foods; she tells of her first attempts at smoking salmon, gives recipes for rhubarb—hers raided from a neighbour's garden. The afternoon I arrived in Whitehorse, the capital of the territory, she took me for a bicycle tour as we picked up supplies for dinner. The city of just twenty-four thousand is a tasty slice of foodie heaven, with a seasonal roadside vegetable stand, several organic shops, a cheese boutique and deli, a handful of great independent cafés, a daycare that serves organic food to the children, a weekly farmers' market. Of course, with the heavy cost of transporting food here, everything costs a small fortune.

When Heidi and Garret started farming in the Yukon six years ago, they also helped build the market for local foods. They started a community supported agriculture (CSA) marketing system on their farm, which forges a direct link between farmer and customers. For about $480 for the summer growing season, consumers can buy a share of the harvest upfront, which provides them with fresh local organic produce every week and their farmers with a predictable income. Heidi and Garret also helped start the Whitehorse Fireweed Community Market: Every Thursday, eight or so farmers gather in a park by the Yukon River to sell produce, meat and eggs. Heidi and Garret even persuaded some supermarkets to carry local organic produce and, in 2003, their peers named them Yukon Farmers of the Year.

But the Yukon is one tough place to farm. The growing season is too short for crops such as corn and soybeans. Frost can strike at any month in the summer and often does, so delicate vegetables, including cucumbers and tomatoes, require a greenhouse. With a shortage of flat arable land, existing farms are in short supply and expensive. Only a few farms grow grain for livestock, so there are no large beef herds or dairy barns. Of the 150 farms in the Yukon, perhaps only twelve support full-time farmers. Their output is not nearly enough to feed the territory's thirty-two thousand people, let alone export Yukon Golds to the "outside," as locals call southern Canada. Most of the food consumed here is shipped in, and Yukoners feel their dependence keenly. They care about good food almost as much as they care about having food.

When Food Secure Canada launched in 2004, organic farmer Joan Norberg volunteered as Yukon's representative. The non-profit organization has three primary goals: reduce hunger, advocate for healthy and safe food and promote local sustainable food systems. But Norberg has had one overwhelming priority. "The North is a fragile environment," she told me when I phoned her. "If we have our road cut off [say, by a storm] for more than a week, we have no food. I have gone shopping and there was absolutely no butter, no eggs, no milk. Food supply is a very real issue here. If we don't have a local food supply, we're vulnerable. If 9/11 had happened in Canada, I think the North would have starved."

I was to visit Heidi and Garret the next day. I passed a restless night thinking about the irony of their situation—farmers who can't make a go of it in a land that so desperately needs farmers. Most of us don't lose sleep worrying about our food supply in southern Canada, where grocery stores overflow with thousands of products. But we should. I struggle to find local produce in supermarkets at the height of the season—an apple from Nova Scotia's Annapolis Valley, a B.C. peach, Ontario greens. Instead, retailers stock shelves with cheaper produce from California, Mexico, South America and China. But what does it mean when local foods start to disappear? Canadian farmers are suffering through the worst economic crisis since the Great Depression. Shockingly, few of us know that crisis even exists. Fewer still understand how that crisis is affecting us, not just farmers, but us.

I DRIVE OUT to Heidi and Garret's on Monday morning. Their 220-acre farm is about a hundred kilometres south of Whitehorse, just outside Tagish, a village of 360, and down a dead-end gravel road that threads through the White Mountain Valley. Beyond this gently rolling plain, the mountains rise up in every direction, friendly weathered giants. It's a beautiful place, though remote and, it strikes me, rather lonesome.

When I arrive, however, the house is a flurry of lunchtime activity. The kitchen dominates the main floor of the small two-storey; the adjacent living room surrendered long ago to children's toys and books. Heidi is just in from the field, along with Megan, a fiercely bright university student here to learn about growing food and, as she puts it, "social justice issues in our food system." Feidhlim of the insatiable appetite is already at the table, fork in hand. His older sister, Fionnuala (pronounced fin-NOO-lah), is a six year old with dark, thoughtful eyes. She must, as always, be coaxed from her book. Garret manages that with a flavourful curry packed with lentils, onions and turnips—in August the root veggies are ripening and plentiful, he says, so you figure out things to do with them. He serves the curry with brown rice and dark Chinese greens. I have not done a lick of work, but the meal is so tasty, I polish off seconds.

As my hosts invited me to stay the week, I had asked Heidi what I could bring. She suggested milk and cheese. I picked up four cartons of milk, three blocks of cheese, added four bottles of wine, maple syrup, huge bars of good-quality chocolate for the children (a mistake—Garret says they avoid processed sugars) and a bag of groceries leftover from a canoe trip I took with Nancy on the Yukon River, before she returned home to her own work, gently reminding me that her research help applies to tasting and cooking, not potato picking. Heidi and Garret had told me about their situation when I first contacted them months earlier, hence my stash of groceries. There was some discussion about whether I should chance the visit, whether they would still be farming in the spring.

Then a couple of things happened. Word got out that Heidi and Garret were in financial trouble, and their customers were shocked. They could lose *their farmers*. They reacted in a way some communities might at the loss of a local doctor. And maybe that shouldn't be so surprising—good food keeps us healthy, after all. When Peter Coates heard, he recalled having bought Wild Blue Yonder potatoes. They must have been some spuds because he picked up the phone and called the couple and "basically offered to bail them out for a while." He bought some of Heidi and Garret's farm equipment for $37,000 to give them an infusion of cash, though he left the machinery on the land for the couple to use. Coates is not a man of endlessly deep pockets, he assured me when I phoned him to talk about his gesture. The computer programmer said he had moved to the Yukon to escape the "toxic pollution" of southern California and immediately recognized the "extreme need of local farming." And that investing in a local enterprise might be a good idea. "I must have been in a strange mood," he said of that day. "And Heidi must have been shocked when she picked up the phone. But if they didn't have a sudden chunk of cash, they would have disappeared just like that." Over the next year, he said he extended another $20,000 or more to help with mortgage payments.

Christina Sim, a nurse and mother of a five year old, belonged to Heidi and Garret's CSA. Her family relied on them for affordable organic food, produce that, as she told me, "has a face," rather than being transported in from who knows where. When she heard about Heidi and Garret's plight, she, too, took the potential loss personally. "A lot of us said, wow, we really depend on them." She also wanted to help.

Garret and Heidi floated the idea of starting a co-op, a CSA of sorts, but on a grand scale. Members would buy shares for $5000, which the co-op would then use to buy the farm. Heidi and Garret, relieved of the burden of a mortgage, would continue farming the land. In return, shareholders would get first access to the food the farm produced. When I first heard the idea, I have to admit it sounded wacky—co-op members would invest $5000, not for any return, not for free food, but simply for first access to buy food? Yet, within a couple of months, the Great Green Growers Co-Operative had a name, elected a board (Sim and Coates became directors) and sold fifty shares to raise $250,000. It wasn't enough to buy this farm, which Heidi and Garrett purchased for $720,000 three years ago and listed for a quick sale at $550,000, but it was perhaps enough to buy another, smaller farm. It was also the start of something strange and wonderful and, as Garret might say, *connected.*

Still, the co-op cannot relieve Heidi and Garret of their immediate loss. To buy the farm, Garret says they staked all that they had—an early inheritance of $250,000 offered by Garret's parents, Heidi's inheritance from her grandmother. "If I think about the money, I'll be sick," Heidi says. She prefers to look forward. "We have our health and two beautiful children and customers who care about us. Everything is going to work out. It's already working out." But Garret is clearly having a harder time dealing with the failure of their operation. He thanks me for the food I have brought; later, he will make a crack that it's a sad state of affairs when farmers can't feed themselves.

THE 220-ACRE FARM has a woodlot, 90 acres of hay, 100 acres for grazing thirty head of cattle and 6 acres for the forty types of vegetables they grow, down from the 11 acres Heidi and Garret planted last year, which produced more crop than they had hands to plant, weed, thin and pick. Some three dozen volunteers have worked on the farm over the years—WWOOFers (volunteers with the organization Willing Workers on Organic Farms) or students passing through Whitehorse who help out in exchange for room and board and an opportunity to learn about farming. Heidi keeps a book with photographs of their smiling faces and gushing thank-you notes.

Megan, taking a break from her studies, answered the call for help this year. Her living quarters is a barebones apartment above the workshop, with a toilet and running water, though no hot water. Mine is a white-canvas prospector's tent shaped like a tiny house. It sits on a raised wooden platform tucked into the bush. I use the toilet and cold-water-only wash basin in the workshop and fall asleep to the yips of coyotes prowling about the compost pile in an adjacent field, the barking of the farm dogs, Cash and Banjo, chasing them off.

Vegetable picking can be back-breaking and monotonous, yet, as the week passes, I find my body strengthening to the effort, even appreciating it. This steady toil with my hands frees my mind to leap and drift and dream, to talk politics with Heidi and philosophy with Megan. But there are also hundreds of lessons to learn—like the exact slice that frees the bok choy from the ground without damaging it. And, of course, there is a constant search for more efficient ways to perform a task—a more efficient way, for instance, to pick and move bins of lettuce from field, through hydrating stations of water, to the shade of the truck. And at the end of the day, there is the deep satisfaction of seeing what I often can't in my office work at home: progress, physical evidence of effort, the mounting piles of vegetables.

That first afternoon, Megan and I gather several hundred pounds of Yukon Golds, the buttery yellow nuggets developed in Ontario by the University of Guelph's potato breeding program and licensed in 1980. Sweeter and less starchy than white potatoes, these golden orbs grow even sweeter in this land of the midnight sun, with the plant feeding on long hours of sunshine. Garret had told me proudly that when his parents visited from Ireland, land of the spud, they were "blown away" by the taste of the territory's potatoes.

Next day, we move on to picking mange-tout—also known as sugar peas—which you eat pod and all, and those contested carrots, then broccoli and bok choy on Wednesday. Thursday, the morning of market—how did it come around so fast?—is a frenzy of last-minute harvesting: the more perishable lettuces (four kinds) and, from the tiny greenhouse, basil (three kinds) and nasturtiums. Along the way, we wash and weigh everything, bundle and package—processing chores that take as long as the picking did. It makes me wonder, when did we come to expect produce to look as if it sprang from a sparkling laboratory rather than from the ground?

Heidi orchestrates the harvest, working along with us when she is not caring for the children. Her shadow in the noon sun is no wider than a sapling, yet, with one arm, she can heft a five-gallon pail full of water onto the back of a truck—a task that takes me two hands and considerable struggle. She says she loves growing good food for people though admits to being tired of her and Garret's complete focus on farming, misses having the time to do her sculpting and painting. "But art, it's kind of insignificant compared with growing food, isn't it?" she shrugs. As we sort potatoes, I discover she grew up in Barrie, Ontario, where I went to high school, and attended my alma mater, University of Toronto, where she took art history and women's studies. She visited the Yukon with a friend, took a job in social work and "just never left"—save for a brief stint working in Britain, where she met Garret.

Garret grew up in Ireland, helped out on his uncle's dairy farm, then spent a decade travelling and working on farms in Romania and Kenya before returning home to do a master's in soil conservation. After the couple met and Fionnuala was born, they moved back to the Yukon, onto a small rented farm, and set up a market garden. They enjoyed enough success for Garret to think about expanding. Heidi says she was reticent to borrow money, wanted to expand gradually on their own steam, but Garret had an abundance of confidence and big ideas—to sell local organic produce to restaurants, cafés, supermarkets. Three years ago, they bought this farm. Ever since, the couple has run headlong into problems that Megan describes as "biblical."

Garret makes the odd foray into the garden but spends most of the week I am visiting inside the house looking after the children, cooking meals or worrying at the computer over the bleak business of the future. There is a lot to do—the harvest to finish, the workshop tools to pack up, machinery to move, the thirty cows to slaughter, a new home to find. But, save our harvest work, the farm seems in stasis. I suspect Garret is sinking into a deep funk.

Heidi tells me one day that she's having disaster dreams. Garret admits to being "really burnt out."

Late one afternoon, he invites me to take a tour of the farm. The last few days have been tense. Fionnuala, whom I tease is six going on thirteen, has been weepy and withdrawn. Her parents blame the heat—although it's the middle of August, it grows hotter and hotter through the day, until the sun finally burns out about 10 P.M., slipping behind the mountains at eleven. Maybe it is the heat, but Fionnuala absorbs every mood, every conversation we have around the kitchen table, and I suspect she is the one expressing the uncertainty looming before the family, the one calling attention to her father's increasing irritableness and lethargy. The family's horse, Honey, ran away days ago, and no one has gone to look for her. The story spilled out at lunch one day. Seeing my reaction, Garret went searching the next day, said he found her safe, but he did not bring her home. Now, as we amble across the front pasture, he tells me that he is sick of tractors, wants to try farming with horses. That's why they bought Honey, to get the family used to horses.

This all feels too much like home to me, reminds me too much of my own family. At fourteen, I was like Fionnuala, powerless as our first family farm was sold to developers. Worse, a year later, when we moved onto our next farm, I could only watch as my father drifted off, his behaviour increasingly irrational, his mood ever darkening. Why was this happening? I did not know. What could I do? *Nothing.* My accident with my horse, Rebel, and his death came almost as a penance for some sin committed, though I was at a loss to name the wrong then—as I am now.

I am taking in too much.

I walk alongside Garret as he pushes a jogger's stroller across the field, the sleeping Feidhlim inside. Garret is a tall, good-looking man, with gleaming white teeth and sandy brown hair. He can easily charm with his high-minded ideals of farming, but he is also hurt and angry about his and Heidi's predicament. Before I visited, he practically demanded that I read the National Farmers Union (NFU) report on "The Farm Crisis and Corporate Profits." It would help me understand the pitiful state of modern farming, he said. When I arrived, he asked me if I had read it. If I hadn't, if I didn't agree, I wasn't welcome at his table. He laughed. He was joking, sort of.

The gist of the report: Between 2001 and 2006, some 17,500 farms went out of business in Canada, most of them small family farms like Wild Blue

Yonder. The farmers who managed to hang on are getting older, and their farms are getting larger and more specialized, a trend the federal government encourages to maximize efficiency. Shockingly, market net income for Canadian farmers—what a farmer gets from selling, without government subsidies, programs and support payments—fell to near zero in the mid-1980s, stayed there through most of the 1990s, then plunged to negative $10,000 per farm in 2003. The only year worse was 2004, when income was negative $16,000. Meanwhile, the NFU claims that while farmers were suffering their worst years since the Great Depression, other players in the agri-food chain—fertilizer, chemical and seed companies, processors and retailers, farm-machinery manufacturers—were lapping up record profits. Consumers are paying more for food, and more money is being raked in by players in the food chain—except for farmers. Statistics Canada confirms as much. The farm input price index—what farmers spend for supplies such as seed, fertilizer, pesticides and fuel—jumped by 19 percent between 2000 and 2005, well above the consumer price index. And so the farm crisis becomes easier to understand: Big agribusinesses have hooked farmers on expensive inputs such as fertilizers and pesticides, while massive processors and retailers—the Krafts and the Loblaws—have flexed their worldwide, low-tariff buying power to squeeze Canadian farmers on price. Caught in the middle, our farmers are working harder to produce more, yet are earning less.

*Poor farmers.*

But Garret says we should also be thinking, poor us. Without local farmers growing diverse crops in all of the country's regions, we must rely on fewer massive specialized farm operations, which in turn rely on chemical and pesticide companies, to produce our food. We must rely on profit-driven multinational retailers accessing food in foreign markets where we have no control over farming practices or chemical use. And we must swallow this system's notion of safe food.

*Poor farmers, poor food, poor us.*

The tour of Heidi and Garret's farm leads us to a huge limestone pile. Garret stares at it, a man haunted by decisions made, paths taken. Now he holds off on his lecture, waits for me to ask questions.

Of course, every farm failure has its own unique story. Being organic farmers, Garret and Heidi do not have the expense of chemical inputs, but Garret admits that they paid too much for the farm. With the high cost of farm land, many people cannot even contemplate starting farming without inheriting a land base. Looking at it this way, a farmer has to sell a lot of vegetables to make $4000 monthly mortgage and debt payments, and Heidi and Garret have a low-volume, labour-intensive operation. That squeeze left them little room to deal with what followed.

The first year, they suffered an extensive crop failure, which revealed a calcium deficiency in the soil. Garret, the soil specialist, says the land had been beaten down by years of growing hay, but chemical fertilizers had masked the deficiency, made the land seem more fertile than it was. Through the summer and fall, he tilled, composted and reseeded the hayfields. Limestone—rich in calcium carbonate—was too expensive to truck in from Edmonton, so Garret went "ag prospecting" in local highway quarries over the winter, found a supply and, in spring, spread about four and a half tons to the acre with his manure spreader.

In year two, Garret mustered up his old confidence. Believing that the hayfields and vegetable patch would perk up with composting and the calcium correction, the couple increased their market garden and borrowed $40,000 from the bank, which they used to hire employees to help with their increased crop. Really, how can anyone blame them for this? It's what the government advocates to farmers—get bigger, bigger, bigger. Then caterpillars invaded. An organic spray from British Columbia took two weeks to arrive. Not that the delay mattered: The fuzzy beasts destroyed the root vegetables practically overnight. Thankfully, the hayfields responded to Garret's work and produced, for the first time, a luscious second cut in August, exactly when thousands of migrating Canada geese passed over the valley on their route south. Enticed by the sweet clover, they made the field a pit stop and ate their way through about $15,000 worth of hay before continuing their journey. The winter that followed was not a good eating year for their cows.

We continue our walk to the hayfields. The geese are back this year. Garret has erected two scarecrows, pathetic waving figures at either end of the field, in an attempt to stave off the raid. My guess is that they will work, for a few days. Garret laughs sardonically. "When we bought the farm, we didn't exactly work back-to-back crop failures into our business plan."

But the brutal reality is that he probably should have. Taking a farm from chemical dependency to organic is a tough transition, one that requires the soil to be chemical-free for three years before the farm can be certificated organic. It often takes longer to properly amend the soil with compost fertilizer so that it can produce bountiful crops. And nature is a wicked pitcher, with an endless supply of curveballs.

What the NFU report leaves out is the individual challenge of farming, that the food giants have money to attract deep talent and diverse skills to their teams, whereas farmers are largely left to go to bat on their own. Even big farms can draw on the marketing acumen and science of the agri-giants—biased against the farmer as they may be. But small farmers like Heidi and Garret must possess a near superhuman arsenal of skills: They must know how to grow crops and raise animals, often several kinds, and fix machinery; they must also devise business plans that account for the unaccountability of nature and master financial spreadsheets that keep them on budget; and then they must be able to process food, package and market it. Science, mechanical, business, management and people skills. Garret says he and Heidi are craftspeople, farmers with abilities that are becoming rarer "than a hen's teeth." Perhaps he's right, and perhaps it's not enough.

On my last evening at the farm, after the children have gone to bed, Garret, Heidi and I talk about their struggles over a bottle of wine. The wine helps. Garret, who normally exudes considerable confidence in his abilities, now admits they need help. He hopes the Growers Co-Operative can pitch in with business planning, relieve them of some of the hard decision making. They talk about the skills the co-op team brings—one director, a wind energy consultant, is working on a system for selling carbon credits to local businesses for the carbon the new organic farm will sequester, another revenue stream. Garret has come around to the notion that a smaller farm might suit him and Heidi better: They can concentrate on growing vegetables and improving their productivity. And Heidi has convinced Garret that they need a year off farming to re-energize before they plunge into the next venture. They hope to rent a house near Whitehorse, working at whatever might pay the rent for the year. Garret says he's looking forward to spending time dawdling and "redreaming" and finding the balance between family and farm and Heidi's artistic work. He wants time to think out how the next farm might operate, "from the ground up." He looks happier than I have seen him all week. "We want this to work out," he says. "We are very much living our truth. We are the change we want to see. Without a doubt, this is what we want to do."

If the co-op manages to buy a farm in the next year, and Heidi and Garret become its farmers, this will be their third farm in seven years.

MY LAST DAY in the Yukon is market day. People start arriving in the afternoon before the farmers' market opens at three. Unlike a grocery store where everyone is on a frenzied mission to get in, buy, get out, folks come here to hang out. Customers visit with their neighbours, chat with farmers. Some stroll by, coffees in hand, simply gazing at the profusion that overflows the stalls this time of year.

A young man, a skateboarder type covered in tattoos, stops at our booth, asks for a bag of Yukon Golds, potatoes I helped picked. Heidi has listed them for $2 a pound, nearly three times higher than the supermarket sells potatoes shipped in from the outside. Megan weighs a bag and tells him the price: $6. He looks from Heidi to Megan to me. Then he thanks us. He nods his head solemnly and thanks us again for growing his food.

CSA customers drop by in steady streams. The summer abundance makes up for the thin allotments in spring, but for some people there is too much—a few hand back a second bok choy, offer it as a donation to the farm, to sell at market.

Heidi tells me that she and Garret receive thank-you notes at the market and in the mail, sometimes envelopes with five and ten dollar bills tucked inside.

Their customers are like this. Take Mary-El Kerr, who runs a catering business in Whitehorse. She buys local when it's available, trying to support as many local farmers as possible, and she gushes about their work. "Our organic growers are really interesting people who love to try growing new things. Heidi brought one vegetable to market in the spring—she called it joy choy. It was the most delicious thing I've ever eaten, because, of course, those were the first greens of the season. It was *joy* choy." But now it is nearing fall and the new potatoes have her attention. "Oh," she says, "you can almost taste the dirt, they are so fresh."

This makes me think of Feidhlim. And Fionnuala. And the struggles and joys that lie ahead for their family. But it is time for me to go. All I can think to do is to buy a bag of potatoes I have picked. Heidi doesn't want me to pay for it, but I insist. They're a bargain, I tease. I am taking home Yukon Gold, after all.

# Yukon

## Yukon Gold Fries

These are so easy to make, and so delicious, you'll give up packaged french fries. These fries make a classy bistro side for meat and fish, and kids love them. You can cut potatoes into fry-sized strips or into wedges, for home fries. Count on about one and a half potatoes per person, as guests always want seconds.

| | | |
|---|---|---|
| 6 | large Yukon Gold potatoes | 6 |
| 1 | medium or large onion, chopped | 1 |
| 3 | cloves garlic, minced | 3 |
| 3 tbsp | olive oil, or enough to coat potatoes | 45 mL |
| | salt and freshly ground black pepper | |
| | basil and oregano, or spices of your choice | |

Preheat oven to 375°F (190°C).

Cut rounded sides off the potatoes, creating a square. Cut the potatoes into strips 1/4 inch (5 mm) thick. Place the potatoes, onion and garlic in a plastic food-safe bag. Drizzle the olive oil over the top of the potato mixture, twist the bag closed and shake to coat the potatoes with the oil. (Alternatively, place the potatoes, onion and garlic in a large bowl, drizzle the oil over top, and stir to coat well.)

Spread the potatoes on a lightly greased baking sheet. Season with the salt, pepper, basil and oregano. Bake for 15 minutes, turn fries over and bake for another 15 to 20 minutes or until cooked through and slightly brown.

*Makes 4 servings.*

Credit: Margaret Webb, Toronto, Ontario.

## Yukon Gold Brandade

Brandade is a Basque dish made with salt cod. It can be used to flavour and season soups or as a dip or spread, as Mary-El Kerr does. She uses Yukon-grown Yukon Gold potatoes for the flavour of their yellow buttery flesh. The salt cod comes from the East Coast. On a cold Yukon winter night, the hot, steamy brandade is perfect with sourdough bread as a hearty appetizer or served with bouillabaisse.

This recipe requires some planning, as the cod needs to be soaked for up to 2 days, to leach the salt from the fish.

| 1 lb | packaged salt cod | 500 g |
|---|---|---|
| 2 1/2 lb | potatoes (about 6 medium), peeled | 1.25 kg |
| 1 cup | 18% cream | 250 mL |
| 1/4 cup | olive oil, and extra for drizzling | 50 mL |
| 2 | cloves garlic, minced | 2 |
| 2 tsp | chopped fresh rosemary | 10 mL |
| 1/4 tsp | cayenne pepper | 1 mL |
| | freshly ground black pepper | |

Soak the salt cod for up to 2 days in cold water in the refrigerator, changing the water at least 4 times. The cod should be slightly salty but not overly; to test it, taste a little piece of the cod taken from the centre of a large section. Once it has soaked, drain it and set aside.

Boil the potatoes in a pot with lightly salted water for 15 to 20 minutes or until they are cooked through. Add a dash or two of the cream and mash the potatoes to a smooth consistency.

Heat the olive oil in a pot over medium-low heat. Add the garlic, rosemary and cayenne pepper and sauté until fragrant, about 1 minute. Stir in the remainder of the cream and bring to a simmer. Add the drained cod, stirring until the fish begins to break apart. Stir in the mashed potatoes. Season with black pepper. Transfer the mixture to a shallow baking dish.

Turn oven broiler to high.

Flatten the surface of the cod and potato mixture with a fork. Drizzle olive oil over the top. Broil to brown the surface slightly.

Serve with crackers, bread and an assortment of sliced raw vegetables.

Leftover brandade can be cooled and stored in a tightly sealed container in the refrigerator for up to 3 days.

*Makes 6 to 8 servings.*

Credit: Mary-El Kerr of Mary-El Fine Food & Catering, Whitehorse, Yukon.

# To Finish

# British Columbia

# AN APPLE IS NOT AN APPLE

*No mortal has ever enjoyed the perfect flavor of any fruit,*
*and only the godlike among men begin*
*to taste its ambrosial qualities.*
—Henry David Thoreau, *Wild Apples*

To have eaten of the tree of life, to have had our eyes opened, to be as gods with knowledge of good and evil. Yet, for all that, we really don't know much about the apple anymore.

Take apple picking. On my trip to sample Canada's most exciting new apple variety, I would discover that you don't actually pick apples. Perhaps the scriptural prohibition booms in our subconscious for good reason—tugging will rip off the stem, leaving an open wound on the apple, and can also damage the fruit bud on the tree, destroying next spring's bloom. If an apple is properly ripe, you simply *lift* the fruit or, at most, give it a slight twist to free it.

But then, who among us urban mortals has recently plucked an apple from a tree, tasted the fruit in a state of perfect ripeness so that we might properly judge the grocery store offerings that are too often delivered upon us, relegated to uncooled bins to quickly grow old and soft and mealy?

Which leads me to my second revelation: An apple is not an apple. I would hear this curious aphorism from a fruit-tree breeder in British Columbia. When we want bananas or strawberries or cherries, we simply ask for bananas or strawberries or cherries (though there are hundreds of cherry varieties). Not so with apples. We request a Granny Smith or Gala or, if we're feeling particularly patriotic, the McIntosh, a Canadian variety discovered by John McIntosh in Dundas County, Ontario, in 1796.

We crave choice, yet modern commerce has all but taken the temptation out of the apple, reducing it to a high-volume, low-quality, cheaply traded commodity. Produce departments stock maybe two or three reds, a green, perhaps a yellow—even though computers and modern IPU stickers make it possible to price code many more.

What a fall from paradise! What a loss of delicious knowledge! For, by some estimates, there are more than ten thousand varieties of apples in the world. When European settlers first arrived in North America and migrated toward the setting sun, they brought along the staples, "the dog and horse and cow," and "the seeds of the apple," wrote Henry David Thoreau, in *Wild Apples*. The apples were nearly a prescription for good health through the harsh winter months, and the pioneers planted millions of their favourite trees. With each passing wave of immigration, the seeds and saplings of these early orchards continued westward, making our Pacific province of British Columbia a pomologist's paradise, with some two hundred heritage varieties of apples.

One such apple flourished in the orchard on my family's farm. My brother Joe remembers it as a green-and-red-striped orb with snow-white flesh, a sweet thing, almost spicy, like a bite of fall pie. Maybe it was a Fameuse, the Snow Apple brought to Quebec in the 1600s. But who knows? The tree was lost when my father sold the farm to developers. My brother has been pining for that apple ever since, searching it out, to no avail.

In 1991, the Friends of the UBC Botanical Garden, on the grounds of the University of British Columbia, held a one-day apple festival to offer tastings from their forty or so varieties. The volunteer group expected modest interest, but more than five hundred people showed up to treat the much neglected fruit with the reverence of an Okanagan Pinot Noir. By 2006, organizers were scouring orchards and valleys for heritage apples and new varieties, as the festival had expanded to two days (now held the weekend after Thanksgiving) to accommodate the twelve thousand people seduced by the rarified opportunity to sample sixty or more varieties and see another hundred on display. As organizer Tish Davis suggests, "There's such pleasure in rediscovering the apple."

At the 1997 apple festival, Sally and Wilfrid Mennell brought along the fruit of a chance seedling that grew up on their orchard in the Similkameen Valley. Wilfrid dubbed the new variety the Ambrosia, food of the gods.

Clearly, he thought it was pretty good. But the Mennells wondered what others might think. The festival was a veritable garden of plenty. To put it as Robert Frost did in his poem "Apple Picking," "there were ten thousand thousand fruit" to taste. Still, Davis says a mad rush descended on the new apple. "The Ambrosia was met with absolute amazement."

But a festival in Vancouver is still miles and miles away from getting that apple into the commercial market, where sellers move volume (the state of Washington, in the United States, produces one hundred million boxes a year, British Columbia four million), concentrating their efforts on just eighteen to twenty varieties.

The probable fate of the Ambrosia is that it would be relegated to obscurity, like a heritage apple, perhaps available at a local farmers' market. But that's not the story at all. Not only has the Ambrosia cracked the commercial big league, it has become a price leader for growers in British Columbia, which strikes me as another kind of miracle.

As THE AMBROSIA is not yet widely available in central Canada, I wanted to be like Eve and eat my first one right off the tree, at its magic hour of ripeness, so I set out to visit the Mennells on the last day of summer, leaving Nancy behind in Toronto to work and rake leaves. In Vancouver, apple season is in full swing. It is a glorious fall day, with maple and ash leaves flaunting their gold flambé against an azure sky. At the Trout Lake farmers' market in East Vancouver, shoppers pick through bushels of heritage gems, creamy Gravensteins, tart Bramleys and early Grimes Goldens, the richly aromatic dessert apple. At the Granville Island Public Market, vendors spill onto the sidewalk, selling sweet Fujis and Elstars, juicy Honeycrisps and tangy Galas.

I buy one of each, along with my old favourites (a Granny Smith, a McIntosh). The woman serving me is long-haired and pretty and shyly bundled up in a red-plaid jacket. On hearing of my mission to eat the Ambrosia right off the tree, she leans in and whispers that she can save me the trouble of the drive. That morning she had picked two that had ripened early. She then produces the forbidden fruit from behind her cash box.

And oh what spectacular beauties they are. Neither red nor green nor yellow, these bicoloured globes show a blush of red that is almost pink and a creamy green background that is almost yellow. And the sheen! In the autumn sun, they glow, almost fluorescent.

She had been saving them for her lunch.

But I remembered my promise to myself. I had travelled all this way to eat one right from the tree, and so I resist, thinking smugly that Adam was a pushover.

That night, I stay with friends in the south end of Vancouver, and my market finds make a splendid appetizer (or would that be appletizer?)—slices of eight varieties served with wedges of havarti and a Wild Goose Vineyards Pinot Blanc, which pairs splendidly.

More epiphanies ensue. That the apples make us forget supper should not shock: Just one with its scant eighty calories contains half the energy-boosting carbohydrates of a PowerBar but without sodium or fat. Its whack of potassium, pectin, boron and fibre (more than a bowl of most cereals) helps reduce blood pressure and cholesterol, build bones, aid digestion. The three of us quickly polish off eight apples and feel pretty smug, considering our moms' admonishment to eat "an apple a day to keep the doctor away."

But the true surprise is that the tasting makes me reconsider almost everything I had previously thought about that humdrum lunchbox staple of my school days. My favourites were now my least favourite, clearly just the best of a sad lot possessing the virtue of being regularly available. I had always thrown myself in with northern folks who prefer a tart apple, one that bites back. But enough Protestant denial. How I swoon with Mediterranean dramatics over the sweetest of the sweets—the Fuji and the Elstar.

AT DAWN, I embark on the five-hour drive into the southern interior of British Columbia, more curious than ever to sink my teeth into an Ambrosia.

The Coquihalla Highway is a zippy route through the Cascade range of the Rockies. Frequent signs along the way warn me to slow down, focus on the road and not the silver-backed rock faces that slide from the sky, sheer and breathtaking. Ah yes, the road.

From the Coquihalla, the 97C gives way to the Okanagan Valley, a lush green vein of arable land that threads along the Okanagan water system, some two hundred kilometres long, from Vernon in the north to Osoyoos on the U.S. border. To eastern eyes, the scenery is surreal. Cactus, sage and rabbit bush cling to steep hills rising up from the verdant valley. The Sonora Desert thrusts up from Arizona, through California and into the southern tip of the Okanagan, making this Canada's only warm-weather desert.

In the past three decades, more than sixty wineries have opened in this valley, but settlers arriving in the late 1800s confronted the Northern Pacific rattlesnake and beheld a paradise for fruit trees—apple, apricot, cherry, peach, pear and plum all thrive in the long warm summers and temperate winters. The problem of a scant 36.64 centimetres of precipitation a year was solved by irrigating with water piped up from Lake Okanagan—and, indeed, fruit trees prefer that to rain and humidity, which can cause scab and brown rot. Towns with names like Peachland, Fruitvale and Summerland sprang up.

To settle returning veterans after the Second World War, the federal government developed irrigated benchland in a second, smaller valley, the Similkameen, about forty-five kilometres west of Osoyoos. But this is not the fruit-growing paradise of the Okanagan. It is something even closer to heaven.

I arrive at the Mennells' at sunset, which comes early in this deep mountain valley. Their home orchard, nestled on the bench overlooking Cawston, looks more like a vineyard from the road, with the Ambrosia planted on modern high-density dwarf rootstock, branches primped and trained to climb horizontally along wire trellises. But a few rows in, traditional trees loom up, casting quiet, lush shadows. The lane ends at a spectacular view: the bench ridge plunging a hundred feet below to the valley and river, the mountains beyond flaring in the day's last light. The Mennells' house perches on the very edge of this ridge.

I am still taking in the glorious view when Wilfrid bounds from the house to welcome me. Since the harvest started more than two months ago, he has been working seven-day weeks, sun-up until sundown. Yet, even at fifty-nine years of age, even after the long hours, he's a tight coil of energy with a trim elfin beard and kindly hazel eyes that dart after his thoughts, here then there, then over there.

He interrupts his greeting to explain that his wife, Sally, is running errands in town with their son, which leads into a story about Roger, nineteen, who's heading off to university soon to study political science. "He's become the recycling dictator. He wants us to convert the tractors to cooking oil." Then his thoughts jump to his middle daughter, Olivia, twenty-four, who should be home by now, but maybe she's at rehearsal. She's studying business at Okanagan College and also sings in a band. "She has this beautiful operatic voice," says Wilfrid. "She's the artistic one." Then he corrects himself. Philippa, twenty-six, their oldest daughter, is artistic, too. "She has an incredible visual," he says, breaking off the sentence to leap into the next, "… really talented." She lives in Vancouver and studies industrial design. Sally just returned from visiting, Wilfrid tells me as he reaches for my luggage and heads inside the house.

"You should also talk to my brothers, Brian and Robert," continues Wilfrid, leaping ahead to business, "and Brian's partner, Linda. She was the driving force behind organics [taking off in the valley], and that was crucial to the success of the Ambrosia. You see, there was a confluence of events…."

My week's stay with the Mennells will be like this, rushing through the orchard trying to keep up to Wilfrid's hurried strides, to follow the gush of his thoughts.

Let me try to untangle some things.

Confluence number one. Wilfred's brothers, Brian, fifty-six, and Robert, fifty-two, always wanted to farm, but Wilfrid dreamed of a life in the theatre, as a director and playwright. He studied English at university, then moved to London, where his grandfather, a tea merchant, Quaker and pacifist, served time in jail for protesting against the First World War with the likes of Bertrand Russell. Then Wilfrid's father, Tuke, fell ill with cancer and Wilfrid returned home. His father recovered, but in that year, Wilfrid discovered that he rather liked looking after the orchards. His brothers were buying land in the valley and so Wilfrid did too.

Confluence number two. Sally is a tall, striking woman with silver hair and a sure will, as precise in conversation as Wilfrid is kinetic. Born in South Africa, she joined a political writers' group in university, some of whom agitated against apartheid. When the police started visiting her family's home—"it was intimidation"—her father suggested she travel for a while. She ended up in Vancouver and was working as the executive director of the Association of Book Publishers of British Columbia when she met Wilfrid and became his partner in this adventure.

Confluence number three. Wilfrid worried that Sally wouldn't take to country life, but she quickly fell in love with gardening and work in the orchard. "We used to get up at 5 A.M., put together a picnic basket and bundle the kids into the car," says Sally. "They'd nap while we picked, then they'd wake up, have breakfast and play under the trees. It was wonderful being able to stay home and watch them grow up. And when they were older, they worked along with us. We had great times, singing songs, telling stories and laughing." And in the winter, there was time to pursue creative passions—Sally began editing books and Wilfrid occasionally directs plays with a community theatre group. After moving to the valley, Sally bought her own apple orchard—where they later discovered the Ambrosia.

Confluence number four. Wilfrid and Sally were in the process of replanting Sally's orchard with high-density dwarf rootstocks that produce more fruit per acre and serve as a base for grafting on new higher-earning varieties. But times were lean and the investment was huge, $20,000 an acre on the ten-acre patch.

And yet, when a seedling grew up amid the delicate and expensive new cultivars, Wilfrid did not pull it. "If we had been more assiduous in our management of weeds, we would have pulled it out," admits Wilfrid.

The seedling became a tree, and still Wilfrid did not pull it out. He's unable to say why not. Perhaps he was thinking about his grandfather exchanging letters with Bertrand Russell while in prison or helping organize lectures for Gandhi, or about directing one of his own plays. He made a note to check on the tree when it began to produce fruit, but by the time he did, the pickers had stripped it clean. "The apples just disappeared and, you have to understand, pickers get really sick of apples," says Wilfrid. "Pickers hate eating apples. So then I really began paying attention."

The following year, Wilfrid and Sally beat the pickers to the tree and discovered that not only did its apple taste, as Wilfrid argues, like "food for the gods," but, cut open, the flesh would remain white for heavenly hours, making it a perfect apple for salads. It was all very, very strange.

Robert and his wife, Jane, own the orchard next to Sally's. Robert describes himself as "a doer" compared with Wilfrid, "who thinks too much." Robert watched the drama unfold, more than a bit bemused. "But what was Wilfrid thinking?" he laughs now. "The damn seedling was growing right up in the middle of a new planting. Anyone would have pulled it out. I would have pulled it.

"But that's the family joke," says Robert, who became captivated by the tree and took the first graftings. "Because of Wilfrid's ..."—what is he going to say—deep thinking, curiosity, distraction? But he can't find the word. "... Well, we have the Ambrosia."

IT'S 6:30 A.M. and Wilfrid is giving me a tour during morning rush hour in the orchard. The pickers have arrived and Wilfrid is assigning rows, jumping on his tractor to haul empty bins to them, finding me a basket for picking. The Spartans are on. And the Ambrosia?

Wilfrid pulls out a pocket-sized colour chart with enough chips to make Benjamin Moore jealous, with several reds and creamy greens to gauge ripeness. According to the chart, the Ambrosia has coloured up nicely, but that's not the final test. He slices one in half, douses the white flesh with iodine. "It's a trick you can do at home," he says. If the apple is ripe, the iodine should blacken just the outside edges. But almost the entire flesh darkens, indicating the starch has not yet started converting to sugar. Another day until harvest, he predicts.

I get the sense there's a giant minute clock roaring in the orchard, for there is an exact tick of ripeness for each variety Wilfrid grows: at the beginning of August, Sunrise; then pears, then Galas at the end of August; Spartans and Ambrosia in September; Fuji and Granny Smith in October.

We reach the nursery, a swath of ten rows where Wilfrid grows rootstock. He drops to his knees to demonstrate the marvel of creating new trees by cutting a tiny chip-shaped wound in the bark of a rootstock, then inserting the bud of another tree, say an Ambrosia. The healing of the wound will engage the bud and the Ambrosia will grow up on the rootstock, a clone, identical to its parent.

Without this grafting process there would be no true apple varieties, Wilfrid tells me, for apple trees are not self-fertile and must cross-pollinate with other varieties. That means the seed from an Ambrosia would never produce another Ambrosia; rather, every single seed in the tree would reproduce a variation of its parents. And there is a good chance one parent would be a crab tree, for it is a prolific pollinator, likely why most wild apples are small and green and mean tasting.

It takes me a minute to realize that Wilfrid is talking about one of my favourite subjects—sex. I had never thought of apple trees as having sex, but they do, much like humans do, only with a little help from the bees, of course. They carry pollen from the male stamen in the blossom of one tree to the female pistil in the blossom of another. The process is crucial, for a large lovely apple develops around fertilized seeds—all the better to protect the seeds and for eating.

In the spring, to give his orchard a Viagra boost, Wilfrid occasionally buys pollen and will bring in hives of bees when, tick, the temperature reaches 14°C. He places the pollen at the entrance to the rent-a-hives so that the busy bees have to walk across it before flying out to do their matchmaking among the blooms.

A few days later, when, tick, the blossoms are at 25 percent fullness, Wilfrid sprays them with lime sulphur and fish oil, an organic means of thinning about two-thirds of the blossoms, so that the tree's energy goes into producing fewer but larger Canada Extra Fancy apples.

Which brings me to the work of picking. Wilfrid helps me into a picking bag, a sort of backpack that I wear on my chest and is all the more ungainly for being clad in metal to protect the apples. Wilfrid warns me that they bruise easily. When the Golden Delicious was their highest priced variety, shipped to markets in New York in the 1950s and 1960s, Wilfrid's father made his sons wear white gloves during picking to prevent fingerprint bruising on the skin. Now Wilfrid assigns me a row of Spartans—not the lovely dwarf trees that are eight to ten feet tall and easy to pick—but full-size behemoths. He shows me how to work the ten-foot ladder, find an angle in the tree so that I can reach several branches without leaning too far and falling off the ladder.

"Don't do anything heroic," he says.

I assure him I will not.

He instructs me to pick from the top of the tree to the bottom so I am not lugging twenty pounds of apples up the ladder. He assigns me a bin that holds eight hundred pounds.

Some pickers love Spartans, like Guy, originally from Quebec, who is a gazelle on the ladder. Indeed, many Quebecers come out to pick for a season, then return year after year, often spending winters in Mexico. And there are locals who have worked for the Mennells for years, as well as seasonal pickers, such as snowboarders earning money to see them through winters in the Rockies. The Mennells provide living accommodations for out-of-towners and the money's not bad—orchards in the valley pay $20 or more a bin, and experienced pickers can fill five to eight in an eight-hour day.

But I am a novice. Finding the correct angle to place the ladder among the tree limbs is an art. Or geometry. Or just bloody impossible. So up I go for ten apples, down to move my ladder, up for ten more. Unless I keep emptying my paltry pickings in the cavernous bin, I am constantly lugging apples up, up, up. And as I do, the big clock in the orchard slows down, down, down. An hour passes. Two. And already I feel the weight of the tree's bounty on my back, feel the strain of yawning branches in my arms, feel sleep coming on.

I AM STROLLING through an experimental orchard perched on a hill high above sun-drenched Lake Okanagan. It feels like heaven, though it is just a reprieve from picking Spartans. I am with Dr. Cheryl Hampson, an apple research scientist, and Richard MacDonald, a research technician, on an abbreviated version of the four-hour walk they take each day through summer and fall, twenty-five kilometres of orchard rows, tasting apples from some thirty thousand trees they've bred from 250 different parents.

They keep up a lively banter.

Cheryl: "My dentist's always asking me, what the hell are you doing? The enamel's wearing off your teeth."

Richard: "There's a lot of farting and burping that goes on."

The two work for Agriculture and Agri-Food Canada at the Pacific Agri-Food Research Centre here in Summerland, developing new varieties for Canadian apple growers. B.C. apple growers—the conventional ones at least—are struggling. When New Zealand's Gala arrived here, it saved the B.C. industry in the 1980s, fetching growers nearly a dollar a pound. Now everyone's planting them—Washington State, Europe—and prices have plummeted over two decades, to twenty-five cents for conventional Galas, barely more than the cost to produce them. The summer before my visit, twenty-odd growers sold their orchards in the Okanagan. Many more are pulling out their trees to convert to vineyards. Now B.C. growers are grasping for innovative niches such as price-leading new varieties. But with all things in the apple industry, this is easier said than done.

Richard hands me an apple from a row of Braeburn-Gala crosses, this tree coded 9N192. It looks beautiful but tastes like, well, nothing. Then he hands me a 9N188, which is flagged with a pink ribbon, indicating potential. This apple looks exactly like the apple I just sampled, but it at least tastes like something, though nothing great.

"It's okay," I say.

We move on.

Richard: "It's bite and spit, bite and spit."

Cheryl: "We only bring in about 1 percent of the apples [to the laboratory for further testing]. Most of them taste yucky."

Richard: "Over twenty years in an experimental orchard, you might breed 750,000 trees and only about a hundred are any quality."

Those select few are subjected to a series of tasting panels that rate the apple on hedonistic scales similar to those developed by the wine industry. Tasters judge for texture, flavour, skin toughness, crispness, hardness, juiciness, aroma, sweetness and sourness. And—a big one—aesthetics. Does the apple look good? To pass all these tests, an apple has to be at least as fine if not better than varieties currently available. If it shows promise, it's then subjected to another battery of tests—how well does it store, pack and ship? If it passes all these tests, they then send it out to a few growers to see if they like growing it. Some apple trees may turn out to be prone to disease or will not grow well in certain regions or only bear fruit every other year—and orchardists simply won't want to plant more.

Cheryl estimates that developing and bringing a new variety to market takes about twenty years. Agriculture Canada's recent introductions include the Silken and Aurora Golden Gala, neither of which has cracked British Columbia's commercial market. When Ag Canada held a contest to name the yellow Aurora, one person submitted this suggestion: "I wish I was red."

Richard: "You develop a fruit and you get really excited about it and you think, this is going to go, and you take it to market and the seller says no. It doesn't pack, there's no volume, the retailers don't want it, the consumers don't want it, we don't want it. It's no, no, no, no. I don't know how the Mennells did it. I would have slit my wrists."

DAY FOUR and the Ambrosia is still not ready. Before anyone can say Spartan, I duck out to visit Wilfrid's brother Brian and his partner, Linda Edwards, who have a fifty-six-acre orchard down the road. Brian was the first to plant the Ambrosia commercially.

Which brings me to confluence number five. Brian and Linda became partners about the time Wilfrid was puzzling over the wild seedling rudely sprouting among his new cultivars.

Linda grew up on a farm in Saskatchewan. Back then, girls could marry farmers, but they did not become farmers, so she became an expert, taking a master's in entomology. She worked as a consultant to fruit growers in the Similkameen and Okanagan, for both organic and conventional orchards. One of the main pests affecting orchards then was the codling moth. Organic farmers, unable to use the synthetic, petroleum-based pesticides used by conventional growers, were losing up to 80 to 90 percent of their crop each year to these insects. At that time, Linda began to see pesticides as the problem, rather than the codling moth. "Some of the conventional pesticides were toxic," she says. "I'd get headaches going into the orchards. I learned to ask when sprays were applied and not to be in the orchards until the required number of days had passed. The sprays will kill off many insects—the bad pests along with the good predators like ladybugs, which eat the pests. But sprays won't get that 1 percent of the pests, and then that [resistant] population grows out of control and you can't kill them."

To combat the problem on their own orchard, Linda and Brian stopped spraying conventional pesticides, to re-establish a balance of predators and parasites. They also brought in a non-toxic control recently developed and tested at pioneering organic orchards, called mating disruption. That entails confusing the hell out of male codling moths by tying twist ties to trees that have been drenched in a synthesized version of the scent female moths send out to attract males. When it worked in their orchard, neighbouring orchardists took note and some followed their lead. Some farmers, watching the codling moths wreak havoc, paced in one spot all day, dying to spray, but they waited it out and eventually mating disruption cut the population of codling moths.

The more Linda learned about working with nature rather than against it, the more sense organics made to her. "I was really fortunate because, over a number of years, I got to see what the organic guys were doing, and the conventional, and to compare the results."

For one, she saw that organic orchards using compost were producing apples that were as good as conventional ones. And the Similkameen also proved to have a perfect microclimate for growing organically, with a dry climate and a constant breeze swirling through the long narrow valley.

Linda encouraged Brian to go organic, then Robert and Jane followed, and, finally, Sally and Wilfrid. Linda says that, as a way of winding up her consulting business, she "downloaded my brain" into a book, *Organic Tree Fruit Management*. It has become the bible of the B.C. fruit industry.

And what happens when one of the leading fruit-growing families in the valley goes organic? Today, Linda estimates that nearly half of the Similkameen's 2000 acres of fruit trees are now organic. The Mennells also invested in a local fruit packer, Nature's First Fruit, helping to make it the largest organic fruit-packing company in Canada.

And the organic market proved to be a boon for the Ambrosia. The conventional, big-volume sellers, according to Wilfrid, looked at the new apple "with a kind of blank expression and said, come back when you have a thousand bins." The organic market, on the other hand, greeted the Ambrosia with "absolute excitement. Brian sent a bag of apples to a seller in the United States, and he said, next year, I want everything you can produce."

But, once again, Wilfrid stalled. "I was under considerable pressure from Brian and Robert to do something with this apple," Wilfrid says, "to establish some sort of ownership and brand" so that they could grow and sell the variety. Sally and Wilfrid spoke to a few nurseries but ultimately decided to develop the identity of the apple themselves. Says Sally: "We had the incredible fortune of this apple coming to us, and one does feel a strong sense of responsibility. We asked ourselves, how do we do what's best for this apple in the long run? Wilfrid felt very strongly that growers should benefit."

Without a model to follow, they turned to the newly founded Okanagan Plant Improvement Company (PICO) for guidance and eventually agreed to develop the new variety together. Wilfrid and Sally obtained a patent on the Ambrosia, under Canada's then-new Plant Breeders' Rights legislation, giving them exclusive ownership for up to twenty years and royalties for the sale of each tree, which they share with PICO. But what do you do now that you own a tree?

Confluence number six. The Ambrosia could have grown up in a wild orchard or on another commercial operation, but it landed in the hands of nurturing parents—Sally with her publishing experience and eye for marketing opportunities, Wilfrid with his anxious overthinking and stubborn insistence on getting the details right. The Mennells embraced the challenge of bringing the apple to market. "The toughest thing is being out changing the hydraulic drive on the tractor and then getting called to the phone to deal with a lawyer," says Wilfrid. "But it exercises parts of my brain that I don't usually use on the farm, so I enjoy it."

To help market the new apple, Wilfrid and Sally turned to those they wanted it to benefit: B.C. growers. After gaining approval from British Columbia's minister of agriculture, B.C. growers established the New Varieties Development Council, a democratic, grower-driven organization. "The industry was quite skeptical," says Jim Campbell, a key organizer. "Growers became champions of the variety and it had never really been done before." And the risks for a single grower planting a new variety are huge, with as much as $25,000-per-acre investment and a three- or four-year wait for the new trees to produce a crop. "You want to make sure the market is there," says Wilfrid, anxious about friends, neighbours and brothers taking the gamble to grow the Ambrosia. "I was excited, but you have to qualify it. There's huge risk."

To build a market for the new apple, the council voted a $1 levy on each box of Ambrosia sold, to pay for development and promotion costs, which attracted matching industry and government funds. It hired a public relations firm to create media buzz, held an Ambrosia recipe contest, which attracted top Vancouver chefs—Karen Barnaby won for her Tunnel of Ambrosia Cake, laced with bourbon. Meanwhile, to ensure consumers were getting not just a new variety but a top-quality one, the council coordinated workshops for growers, brought out the starch and colour chart to ensure the apple is picked at its peak, and researched optimal storage lengths and conditions. Says Tish Davis, of the Friends of the UBC Botanical Garden: "When you get the growers marketing the apple, they become super conscious of quality."

When it was time to take the apple to consumers, the Mennell brothers and their partners travelled to trade shows, fairs, apple festivals and stores to conduct tastings—a crucial move. Once consumers tasted the Ambrosia, they wanted it. Growers sold early shipments of organic Ambrosia for $1.10 a pound, and it continues to be a price leader among B.C. apples. And what did this mean for the growers?

Linda laughs when I ask her that. "My God," she says. "We paid off our mortgages."

THE NIGHT BEFORE THE AMBROSIA HARVEST, Sally and Wilfrid invite the Mennell clan over for a potluck dinner. Wilfrid's mother, Margaret, a sharp ninety (her husband, Tuke, passed away the year before), is also there. There's a sense of celebration in the air during harvest time, especially with times this good. We feast on organic chicken; fresh sweet corn, new potatoes and juicy tomatoes from the garden; pickled asparagus; Sally's homemade bread; and a stunning Pinot Gris I bought at the Orofino strawbale winery just up the road.

Although conventional farmers are struggling, organics has given new life to the valley. Wilfrid says many young couples have moved to the Similkameen over the past few years specifically to farm. They're confident they can make a living at it. Brian's sons, Tristan and Andrew, with their partners and children, recently moved back and will become the third generation of Mennells to run orchards in the valley.

And "a living" here has much to do with actually living. The Mennells all keep massive gardens, learning to can and jam and dry fruit from Margaret. Linda and Brian raise their own turkeys. Robert and Jane keep chickens for fresh eggs. Sally and Wilfrid trade their organic fruit for organic beef and lamb. Tristan, thirty-one, who trained as a chef in Montreal before returning home, recalls that his mother was "paranoid" raising him and his brother with all the agricultural chemicals being used in the orchard then. Recently, the Environmental Working Group listed conventional apples among its "dirty dozen" of the most pesticide-contaminated foods. Now, Tristan says, he doesn't have the same worry about toxic pesticides in the orchard for his children. He's excited about the quality of life his family will have in the valley. "It's about access to fantastic food, a fantastic garden and fantastic fruit. It's a healthy place to be." His dream is to open up a bed and breakfast one day and bring people to the Similkameen to taste the Ambrosia as he believes it should be eaten, "right off the tree, shined up on your pants a little. Perfect."

Tonight, everything is positive, moving forward, and I confess that I have never seen a happier group of farmers.

"So," Robert teases me, "when are you going back to your farm?"

DINNER FINISHED, Wilfrid and I stay up late talking, after we discover that both our fathers suffered from dementia—Tuke for the last six years of his life, my father for the last twenty or so of his. Is this a coincidence, or confluence number seven?

I have realized on my tour that it's easy to make farmers cry—just ask about their fathers. But this time, Wilfrid turns the tables on me.

"How old were you?" he asks softly.

I was fifteen. And it's hard looking back, let alone going there.

Farmers look over their shoulders now—my brother Graham to the hydrous ammonia he and my father once injected into their fields, to fix nitrogen in the soil. And then one day Graham noticed that there were no seagulls behind his tractor when he ploughed or cultivated. Which means no worms breaking down organic matter. Which means the soil is all but dead. My brother stopped using the chemical. Now researchers are linking other chemicals, such as paraquat, one of the most widely used weed killers in the world, to Parkinson's dementia. After some twenty years of suffering from mental confusion and increasing paralysis, my father died of a stroke. It took an autopsy to finally confirm what had ripped him away from us all those years earlier—he had been suffering from Parkinson's dementia.

Wilfrid looks back to his childhood, to the professional sprayers who came to his father's orchard. "We're talking real chemicals, like lead arsenic they'd spray four or five times a season, and others that were just as nasty. I can remember as a child watching the operators. They used spray guns and wore little more than a jacket, rubber gloves and a hat, and they'd be standing under these huge trees with the sprays just raining down on them. Sprays were cheap. You took them for granted. Virtually all the custom sprayers I knew died of cancer. In one family, four brothers died of cancer, all at relatively young ages. The operators are always at the greatest risk."

Wilfrid says that even before he went organic, about six or seven years earlier, he stopped using what he calls the "heavy duty" organophosphate pesticides. "You really shouldn't be in or around the orchard for a number of days when it is sprayed. But as the operator, you often need to be in the orchard. I'd end up with excruciating headaches just from walking through it."

He pauses, then adds that pesticides "work by disrupting the nervous system of pests."

Our conversation hangs there.

So many health studies now are drawing strong links between pesticides and neurological disease such as Alzheimer's and Parkinson's, as well as other diseases that disrupt the immune and hormonal systems. For our fathers, the past is unfortunately the past. But Wilfrid and I admit we're both worried about people still working on conventional farms, and especially children growing up on them.

But it's late. Morning comes early in the orchard. We say goodnight.

ON THE LAST DAY OF MY VISIT, Wilfrid decides that the Ambrosia are ready to harvest. Compared with the Spartans, it is easy work lifting the bright bulbs off the dwarf trees. Now, I could pick for hours, soaking up the glorious fall day, summer's last fling in the valley. But there is something I still have to do: see the chance seedling in Sally's orchard, what started everything, what they now call the Mother Tree.

This quiet lush parcel lies on the lower part of the bench, below Margaret's house and set far back from the road. The land here pitches and rolls, feels wilder, primordial. At the end of one undulating row is the Mother Tree. And it really looks like a mother that has produced about a million baby trees. The trunk is thick and gnarled and gashed, with slashes from a thousand wounds to extract bud wood. The canopy is a head of writhing snakes—the branches grown out to provide scion wood rather than carefully pruned for fruit. Wilfrid and Sally marvel at the tree. It must be nineteen years old now, they guess, and this is the first summer they haven't raided the branches for wood. Left alone, the tree has produced a bounty of apples.

Strangely enough, I forget to pick one. For even stranger, I am moved by a queer stirring, a feeling of cosmic connection between this tree and this family and this valley. And maybe also with something larger—some knowledge of working with nature that we might all learn yet.

Luckily, Wilfrid remembers to pick an Ambrosia, one from the highest branches, sun-warmed, perfect. Back at the house, Sally orchestrates a tasting but, of course, it's not that simple. Nothing is with the Mennells. They've set up a taste test, the Ambrosia along with four other varieties they've collected at their exact moment of ripeness. I decide to go along with it, blindfolded.

I can eliminate one right away—the soft, bland McIntosh. The other four all lean to sweet and juicy, fresh delicious zings on my tongue. How to distinguish one that rises above all others? The choice before me, four fresh-picked organic varieties in their prime, a sweet and tart, a sweet and mild, a honeyed and spicy, and one honeyed and balanced. I sample them several times and I love them all.

And yet one apple stands out. It is crispy, with a satisfying bite, and sweet but not overly. It's juicy yet has a clear, clean, refreshing finish and, I'll give Wilfrid this, notes of the divine.

# British Columbia

## Sally and Wilfrid's Ambrosia Waffles

Polenta waffles are delicious on their own, but with Ambrosia apples, they're heavenly. If you don't have polenta, cornmeal works almost as well, though it lacks some of the crunch. If using cornmeal, increase the amount of flour and decrease the amount of cornmeal so that the proportion of flour to cornmeal is approximately 3 to 1, or 1 cup plus 2 tablespoons of flour, and 6 tablespoons of cornmeal.

| | | |
|---|---|---|
| 1/3 cup | walnuts or pecans, halved or chopped into large pieces | 75 mL |
| 1 cup | all-purpose flour | 250 mL |
| 1/2 cup | polenta | 125 mL |
| 1 tbsp | baking powder | 15 mL |
| 1 tsp | granulated sugar | 5 mL |
| 1/2 tsp | salt | 2 mL |
| 2 | eggs | 2 |
| 1 cup | buttermilk | 250 mL |
| 3 tbsp | vegetable oil | 45 mL |
| 1 | Ambrosia apple, cored and finely diced | |

Preheat the oven to 350°F (180°C).

Brown the walnuts or pecans on a baking sheet in the oven for about 5 minutes.

In a medium bowl, mix together the flour, polenta, baking power, sugar and salt. Add the eggs, buttermilk and oil. (To make the waffles even fluffier, separate the eggs. Add the egg yolks to the buttermilk, and beat the egg whites until they're full of air, then fold into the mixture.) Fold in the diced apples.

Cook the waffles in a hot waffle iron according to manufacturer's directions, until brown. Serve the waffles with the pecans or walnuts sprinkled on top, along with maple syrup.

*Makes 4 to 6 waffles.*

Credit: Sally and Wilfrid Mennell, Similkameen Valley, British Columbia.

## Tunnel of Ambrosia Cake

The Fish House in Stanley Park's executive chef Karen Barnaby invented this recipe for a contest hosted by the growers of Ambrosia apples. The cake, laced with bourbon, earned first prize. It's rich and moist, so no icing is needed—just serve with a generous spoonful of whipped cream and a cup of Earl Grey tea.

### For apple filling:

| | | |
|---|---|---|
| 1/2 lb | cream cheese, at room temperature | 250 g |
| 1/2 cup | dark brown sugar | 125 mL |
| 1/2 cup | bourbon | 125 mL |
| 1 tsp | pure vanilla extract | 5 mL |
| 1 | large egg | 1 |
| 1 1/2 lb | peeled and cored Ambrosia apples, diced | 750 g |
| 1 cup | sweetened flaked coconut | 250 mL |
| 1 cup | coarsely chopped pecans | 250 mL |

### For apple cake:

| | | |
|---|---|---|
| 3 cups | all-purpose flour | 750 mL |
| 2 tsp | baking soda | 10 mL |
| 1 tbsp | dried ground ginger | 15 mL |
| 2 tsp | cinnamon | 10 mL |
| 1 tsp | freshly grated nutmeg | 5 mL |
| 1/2 tsp | ground cardamom | 2 mL |
| 1/2 tsp | salt | 2 mL |
| 1/2 cup | unsalted butter, at room temperature | 125 mL |
| 1/2 cup | granulated sugar | 125 mL |
| 3/4 cup | dark brown sugar | 175 mL |
| 2 tbsp | molasses | 25 mL |
| 2 tsp | pure vanilla extract | 10 mL |

| 2 | large eggs | 2 |
|---|---|---|
| 1 cup | peeled and grated Ambrosia apple | 250 mL |
| 1 cup | buttermilk | 250 mL |

Preheat the oven to 350°F (180°C). Generously spray a 10-inch/25 cm tube pan with cooking spray.

To make the filling, combine the cream cheese and brown sugar; beat with an electric mixer or by hand until well combined. Beat in the bourbon, vanilla extract and egg until the filling is a smooth consistency. Stir in the apple, coconut and pecans. Set aside.

To make the cake, in a small bowl, sift together the flour, baking soda, ginger, cinnamon, nutmeg, cardamom and salt.

With an electric mixer or by hand, cream the butter in a large mixing bowl. Add the sugars and beat until light and fluffy. Stir in the molasses and vanilla. Add the eggs, one at a time, beating well after adding each. Beat in the grated apple. Add one-third of the flour mixture, then one-third of the buttermilk, beating to combine. Continue in this way until all the flour and buttermilk has been added to the batter.

Spread one-third of the batter into the tube pan. Spoon the Ambrosia apple filling evenly over the batter. Spread the remaining batter on top of the apples.

Bake for 1 hour. Let cool in the pan on a rack for 30 minutes before turning out of the pan. Let cool completely before slicing.

Credit: Executive chef Karen Barnaby, The Fish House in Stanley Park, Vancouver, British Columbia.

# Quebec

# C'EST CHEESE

*To us it is a glorious theme,*
*To sing of milk, and curds, and cream.*
—James McIntyre, Canada's cheese poet

Even among farmers, the dairy farmer is considered a workaholic, less envied than pitied, a saint—or slave—to his cows. Frédéric Poulin, for instance, rises at four o'clock every morning to milk his herd at 4:45, an hour-long chore he follows with two hours of feeding and cleaning. He returns to the barn to spread hay for his heifers at lunch, returning at 4 P.M. to repeat his chores and milk the gals again at 6 P.M. In the past, dairy farming may have been easier, if less mechanized. Families were larger, with many children and perhaps even several generations helping out. But Frédéric, thirty-three, works alone. He repeats his routine every single day, 7 days a week, 365 days a year, without holidays, without sick days. And yet, this is what he says of his lot in life: "I am a lucky guy."

And for the right to work as hard as he does, thanks to Canada's highly regulated dairy system, Frédéric has paid between $27,000 and $31,000 per cow just for permission to milk her. Buying the cows was extra. With that debt load, he can't afford to hire help. Still, he's thankful, even thrilled. "I didn't think it would ever be possible for me to own a farm," he says. "My life gave me this chance, and I took it."

Frédéric grins as he speaks. He is a short man with broad shoulders and a five-o'clock shadow nearly as thick as his crew-cut black hair. But he has a round teddy-bear face and dark, soulful eyes. And he giggles explosively, especially when he thinks I am having trouble understanding him. And maybe I am, but it's not because my French is pathetic and his English a bit rusty. It's more that I have never met a man so thankful for the good fortune that life has slivered out to him. I have come here to learn about an extraordinary cheese that is made from the milk of his cows, but before I can ask a single question, he has one for me. "Why am I the lucky one?"

WE SET OUT for the remote Île-aux-Grues, sixty-five kilometres east of Quebec City, by taking the most meandering path possible, for Nancy, after skipping out on the swing to the Wild West, has rejoined my tasting tour of Canadian farms now that we're in genteel Lower Canada. And with her to indulge and with so many wonderful country inns to stay at, well, one cheese route led to another (there are now nine in the province), which led to a tour of artisanal farms and a week-long binge on local foie gras—"If a goose can gain two pounds a week," Nancy said, "I guess that explains how we packed on six"—which led to a wine route, then a loop through the province's amazing new cideries to sample fabulous apple icewines and dark, moody apple aperitifs.

Artisanal cheese-making has spurred an agricultural renaissance in Quebec, drawing not only money but also talent, creativity and confidence to rural communities, and the tasty results are attracting international attention. *Gourmet,* the influential American food magazine, recently devoted an issue to celebrating the province's culinary coming of age. And agricultural tourism is now a leading draw to the province.

Of course, this delicious story did not write itself overnight. Quebec has been on the leading edge of cheese production in North America since 1893, when the first cheese-making school was established in a barn in Saint-Hyacinthe and Trappist monks arrived in Oka and started making the now-famous washed-rind cheese named for the village. But, while the British held power in New France, producers focused on making English cheddars. Then, in the early 1980s, Quebecer Fritz Kaiser, drawing on his Swiss heritage, started crafting European-style cheeses. He quickly inspired a new wave of artisans who were looking for ways to prevent their small family dairy farms from being swallowed up by larger operations. Determined to keep their families in the countryside, rural cheese-makers set up shop and soon developed an impressive range of European-style cheeses using a variety of raw and heated milks—from rare and heritage breeds of cows, as well as from goats and sheep. Success at international competitions soon followed. Now Quebec produces over three hundred cheeses, many of them truly outstanding: excellent goat cheeses such as the Chèvre Noir, a sharp cheddar; Le Pied-De-Vent, a wonderfully stinky Epoisses-style cheese made from the milk of the Canadienne cow on Îles-de-le-Madeleine; D'Iberville, a semi-soft washed rind accented by the herbs and flowers the farm Au Gré des Champs plants in its organic pastures; Bleu Bénédictin, a blue made by monks at the Abbaye Saint-Benoît-du-Lac; and Le Riopelle, a buttery triple cream from a co-operative of five dairy farmers on Île-aux-Grues.

Nancy and I certainly know the splendid virtues of these cheeses, for we ate our way through a good half dozen on a single visit to La Fromagerie du Marché Atwater in Montreal's Atwater farmers' market, one of the most renowned cheese shops in Canada, with 1000 labels, 150 from Quebec. Alain Besré, a passionate promoter who makes a point of visiting each farm before deciding to carry a cheese, is our kind of guy. "I have a very sensual approach to eating cheese," he told us. "I like to eat just one really good cheese at a time, and I like to eat it with my fingers, without bread or crackers. I eat the rind and everything." He told us about a recent discovery, from the dairy co-operative on Île-aux-Grues—Frédéric Poulin's Tomme de Grosse-Île. It so truly expresses that much-used French term *terroir* that Besré told us we must go to the island. "The story of Canada is in that cheese," he said. "Once you go to that place and see it, for your whole life, there will be a special spot in your heart for that cheese."

A few days later, we find ourselves on a small ferry chugging through a lashing rainstorm into the middle of the St. Lawrence River from Montmagny to Île-aux-Grues. This is the largest in an archipelago of twenty-one islands, though it is only a scant one and a half kilometres wide by seven kilometres long. "You can cycle around it in an hour," the island's tourism official forewarned us, "and that's with lots of stops." Yet, we had to be at the dock at 5 A.M. to win a place on the 7:15 ferry for us and our Jeep, as the boat can cross only at high tide. To get to school on the mainland, children on the island must travel by airplane. And airplanes are the only transportation link in the winter, when ice jams the river.

On this July morning, the ferry is full of rain-suited bird-watchers and cyclists who are coming to explore the island's most outstanding feature: the largest intact wetland in northeastern North America. Locals call it *le foin de batture*. Loosely translated, it means the hay or grass that grows on the part of the river bank that is uncovered at low tide. The term, like the feature, is specific to this area. Île-aux-Grues is located in a transition zone between the incoming salt tides of the Atlantic Ocean and the outgoing fresh flow of the St. Lawrence River. At low tide, you can walk or even drive across the marshland via a causeway, chemin de la Batture, which links two islands, Île-aux-Grues and Île-aux-Oies. But on a full moon, massive salt tides rush in and completely engulf the causeway. The unique grass that survives here tolerates both salt and fresh water and also protects the islands from pummelling waves in summer and ice in winter.

Some two hundred species of birds live in this island habitat, including the little penguin, the marsh owl, and the rare yellow rail that nests in the long marsh grasses—and, of course, the snow goose, that swirling cloud of white that descends from the sky like a flurry of snow during spring and fall migrations. The wetland and its wildlife attracted one of Quebec's most famous painters to Île-aux-Grues, Jean-Paul Riopelle. In 1999, he bought the oldest and grandest house, which the Messeigneurs of the island built in 1769, then set to work painting countless images of the snow goose. Just before he died in March 2002, he lent his name as well as a painting for the label to the farm co-operative's Le Riopelle cheese. His widow still lives in the Monseigneurs' manor, a short walk from the marshland that so inspired Riopelle.

But now it is the exuberant farmer Frédéric Poulin whose destiny is tied to the *foin de batture*.

SHORTLY AFTER LANDING, we meet with Frédéric at the restaurant L'Oie Blanche—the Snow Goose. He tucks his chair up to the table as he offers a quick recount of how he, an *étranger*, as locals call those from away, came to the island. It starts out sounding like so many sad farm stories, except Frédéric refuses to be bitter. "I never keep a bad feeling," he says.

Although he grew up "dreaming of cows" on a dairy farm in Bellechasse, which his father had inherited from his father, the small family operation struggled. To get out of debt, Frédéric's father sold his herd and quota without giving Frédéric a chance to run things. These days, inheriting such an operation is about the only way an independent farmer can take up dairy farming. Canada's highly restrictive supply-management system for milk allows farmers to produce under a quota only, with the total quota roughly equalling the amount of dairy Canadians consume. This secures a dependable local supply, guarantees farmers a relatively stable income and allows federal and provincial governments to enforce made-in-Canada regulations—rejecting, for instance, the import of milk with the rBGH hormone that some American states allow in its supply. But quota for about fifty cows now trades for well over $1 million, making it nearly impossible for a farmer to break in. Frédéric gave up his dream of owning his own farm but not of farming. He took a job at a large modern dairy operation and eventually became a manager, which came with a decent salary, a house and holiday time. When he met his wife, Karina Lemieux, he began visiting her family's summer home on Île-aux-Grues and, as the friendly, hard-working Frédéric is wont to do, he used his vacation time to help out a dairy farmer on the island, Denis Bernier.

Meanwhile, the fromagerie had also endured its share of challenges. Islanders have been making cheese here since it was settled in the early 1800s. The latest cheese factory, owned and run by the collective of five farmers, focused on cheddars—and they still make wonderful two- and three-year-aged blocks—but they could hardly compete with the cheap, mass-produced stuff that comes out of industrial operations like Kraft. When the cheese factory hit a financial wall, the farmers followed the new wave of Quebec artisans making European-style soft cheeses, but they looked to their own island for inspiration. They tested some thirty recipes with islanders to develop the Mi-Carême, a double cream named after a mid-Lent Acadian celebration that sees adults dress up in costumes every night for a week—until masks come off at a Saturday night, Mardi Gras–style whoop-up at the Snow Goose restaurant. This is virtually the last community in Canada where the tradition persists. "It's a long winter," Frédéric laughs. "This passes the time."

The next cheese from the fromagerie, named for Riopelle, was a luscious triple cream with wide appeal, but it also helped that the famous painter died shortly after the cheese's release, bringing it huge attention.

Still, the fromagerie was not yet out of financial trouble. Cheese-maker and manager Gilbert Lavoie was working seven days a week. Saving the fromagerie meant saving five dairy families, which pretty much meant saving the entire community given its scant population, which has shrunk from a high of 900 to just 110 during the winter months. But Lavoie soon got help.

Christian Vinet, whose parents had summered on the island, returned with an economics degree from Laval University, married his summer vacation sweetheart and joined the fromagerie. He secured a federal domestic innovation grant for ten quota to produce milk for a new cheese. And that cheese? An earlier cheese-making factory once used milk from cows that had grazed on the *foin de batture*, and that taste lingered in the island's collective memory. Vinet decided not only that the new cheese would be made from the milk of cows that graze on the *foin de batture* but that the herd would be a different breed from the Holsteins that supply milk for the fromagerie's other cheeses. It would be called Tomme de Grosse-Île, after an island in the archipelago that served as the entry point to Canada and quarantine station for thousands of immigrants, mostly Irish, who arrived there between 1832 and 1837. The cheese would both commemorate those who suffered horrible diseases—thousands were buried on the island—and celebrate those who survived.

The vision for the new cheese was complete—except for the farmer who would tend to this special herd of cows making the milk for this special new cheese. Of course, they didn't have to look far—Frédéric was already devoting his vacation to helping a local farmer. And, they hoped, Frédéric, then thirty, and his wife, Karina, might also have a family, which would address the island's other challenge, a declining and aging population.

Still, says Frédéric, giving up his secure job and taking a chance on his dream "was not an easy decision to make." With the sudden emergence of so many new Quebec cheeses, even excellent fromageries have gone out of business. And although Frédéric could start up with fifteen free quota (ten from the innovation grant, which he must eventually buy, and five that are given to all new farmers starting up), he still had to buy another ten plus his herd of cows, an investment of more than $300,000.

But islanders came forward with a generosity that still surprises Frédéric. "I have so many good people in my life. Why?" A retired farmer rented him an outfitted dairy barn. His friend Denis Bernier would share farm equipment in exchange for Frédéric helping with haying. And his father-in-law, who worked on the ferry before retiring, offered his house as collateral to secure the loan. "Karina and I, we never asked him to do this," Frédéric says. "He's a great man. He put his retirement security on the line for us. He said, if you die, we die together. He did what my own father never did for me. And why? Because I love his daughter."

So Frédéric placed his future with the island, knowing the risks were still huge. "I am doing something no one has ever tried before, with only the taste of that hay in my milk." And making a cheese from a single herd of cows is the trickiest. As Frédéric says, "It's hard to make a good name and easy to lose. One bad batch of milk and I can lose what took ten years to establish."

WHILE NANCY IS OFF TAKING PICTURES of the island's moody sky or trying to secure a fresh loaf of bread for a picnic (the latter is a challenge on this small remote island), I am in Frédéric's barn being bullied by a newborn calf that seems to think I'm her mother. She sucks at my elbows and knees and hands—anything that sticks out. But I suppose I don't mind. Frédéric's herd of Brown Swiss are adorable. The babies are cuddly Bambis, the mothers gentle teddy bears that come in a Ralph Lauren colour palette of luscious velvety browns. Their most distinguishing features are tan, furry ears that extend from the sides of their heads like hands ready to clap and massive black soulful eyes that remind me more than a bit of Frédéric's.

Buying this herd was the first (and likely the last) time Frédéric could choose the breed of his cows. He didn't mind ruling out Holsteins, which comprise close to 95 percent of dairy herds in Canada. They've been bred into milking machines, with each giving an average twenty-five hundred gallons a year. But that has caused problems. The average life of a Holstein in Quebec is just five years, and many are hobbled by poor feet.

Frédéric considered the Canadienne, a small rugged heritage breed that was developed in this country in the sixteenth and seventeenth century. Although they don't produce a lot of it, their milk is rich and full of fat, excellent for cheese. But because of the industry's focus on quantity (which means the Holstein) versus quality, the Canadienne, like so many heritage livestock breeds today, is endangered, with less than three hundred registered in Canada. Frédéric worried about having enough diverse bull semen to keep his herd strong.

He finally settled on the Brown Swiss, thought to be the oldest of dairy breeds, a big cow developed in the Swiss Alps that can withstand extremes in weather. She's also a decent producer, giving on average sixteen hundred gallons a year; this milk, higher in protein and butterfat than a Holstein's, is coveted for cheese. But Frédéric also let his heart guide his decision to buy the big, lovable beasts. "When we saw them, the cows came right up to us. I wanted my wife to have a cow that she loves."

Over the next few days as I help Frédéric with chores at his barn, he mentions Karina often. A civil engineer who designs bridges and roads, she works and lives in Lévis during the week, flying to the island on weekends. Frédéric says she helps deliver new calves and bottle-feeds the babies and has fallen in love with farm life. Karina wants to quit her job when money becomes easier and work alongside Frédéric full time. Certainly, he looks forward to her help. Now, his thirty-six milking cows stand in tie-in stalls, albeit on rubber carpets in a clean, dry, well-ventilated barn that smells sweet and musky, of the *foin de batture*. But between milkings, Frédéric wants to pasture his cows outside with the new mothers and the cows enjoying a dry-out holiday, but he does not have time to round up the milkers twice as day by himself. "The cows know when I'm alone," he says. "The young ones take advantage of me."

But there is another reason Frédéric wants Karina to stop commuting by plane and spend more time with him on the island. They've been trying to have a child for five years. He's encouraging her to apply for a year's sabbatical and slow down, "to see what happens."

And maybe Frédéric is onto something. This dairy barn is a warm, soothing, maternal place. A cow, after all, gives milk after her first calving and, later, when she's pregnant. Everything in this barn revolves around her cycles, her moods. This is something I had not felt in larger barns, where employees work in shifts to keep mechanized milking bays operating throughout the day. But Frédéric knows each of his cows intimately. As we clean stalls, he chats constantly—to the cows, to me, about politics, life, future plans. "Chores are a time to think," he says.

He has names for most cows—Big Sweety, a good milker; Moose, whose moo sounds more like an *oink*. When one young cow not being milked nudges me incessantly, Frédéric identifies the nudges as love taps. She's heading into heat. Frédéric will artificially inseminate her. The process involves poring over a bull catalogue to select sperm. When this liquid daddy arrives frozen in a nitrogen tank, Frédéric will pull on plastic gloves that unfurl past his elbows and load the thawed sperm into a sixteen-inch syringe. He'll then press his left hand into the cow's anus, as far as his elbow, feeling the humps and valleys of her cervix for a give, the opening to her uterus. With the other hand, he'll thread the syringe alongside his left arm and inject the sperm into the entrance to her womb. He completes the session by taking the cow to a bull he keeps in the pasture. If the cow is pregnant, she'll rebuff the bull's amorous advances. If not, the bull will try to impregnate her, explains Frédéric. But even in this tryst, Frédéric plays matchmaker, exciting the bull by singing in a comical operatic baritone as he leads the heifer to him: "*Un gros* bull, a beautiful big bull."

And then there are teats, four to a cow, thirty-six milkers. A good dairy farmer must love teats. In the course of a single milking, Frédéric will handle each of the 144 in his care three times—cleaning each first, attaching the suction cup of the milking machine next, applying teat conditioner after. In the business, this is called "good teat care." Poor care leads to mastitis, an infection that can show up in the milk.

Frédéric is as fussy about the cleanliness of his barn. He's constantly scraping manure into a trough, which is conveyed outside to a compost pile. Before milking he cleans his tanks, sterilizes equipment, pulls on plastic gloves, for that bacteria could also end up in his milk. Even his mood can affect the milk. "If you're tired or stressed," says Frédéric, "that can affect production. If you change the time you come to milk, production can go down by as much as 5 to 7 percent." And so he is fastidious about his routine, milking the cows in the same order, each cow at the same time each day, at the same speed, shunning music so many farmers listen to, preferring to work to the tick-tock rhythm of the milk machine.

The fromagerie tests each batch that arrives. It also thermalizes or heats the milk at 145°F for eighteen seconds, to stabilize the flora or natural bacteria in the milk. But even with the safeguard, handling milk and making cheese is a finicky business. If another farmer's milk has slightly elevated bacteria counts—perhaps from a variation in routine or infection in one cow—that milk will be diluted with output from other farms, making the counts negligible. But Frédéric, being the single source for his cheese, doesn't have that luxury—if bacterial counts in his milk are too high, the milk would get thrown out. Not that that has ever happened. As cheese-maker Gilbert Lavoie told me earlier during a tour of the factory, "It's very important to be consistent. Everything Fred does affects the cheese. He always wants to be better. He's a perfectionist. You can taste his personality in his milk. You can taste that determination in his cheese."

My personality, you may be happy to hear, is not in his cheese. Frédéric shows me how to attach the milk machine's octopus-like hose arms and suction cups. The cow endures my awkward fumbling about her teats, and Frédéric is beyond patient with me. But, finally, the cow is not. She kicks her hind leg forward, roughly in the vicinity of my head, and I conclude that I am, sorry for the pun, an udder failure. This is a job for a master.

That evening, however, I take up another challenge—I ask to drink a glass of raw milk fresh from Frédéric's cows. If this does not impress, consider that raw or unpasteurized milk has only slightly more legal footing in this country than marijuana. If you're a farmer, you can possess raw milk and enjoy your own stash, but it's illegal to sell it to consumers. In 2006, Ontario dairy farmer Michael Schmidt provoked a police raid on his barn for doing just that. In the early 1990s, the federal government even attempted to force cheese-makers to use pasteurized milk rather than raw. (Raw milk cheeses must be ripened for sixty days minimum, which eliminates most pathogens while maintaining the flavour and complexity of the raw-milk base.)

Certainly, dirty and diseased cattle can pass on all sorts of nasty things to humans via their milk—tuberculosis, listeria, salmonellosis and E. coli, among others. Pasteurization kills most of these harmful bacteria. But some argue that the process of heating milk also destroys beneficial bacteria and greatly diminishes milk's nutritious store of vitamins, calcium, protein and enzymes, as well as flavour. And the bacteria killed by pasteurization remains in the milk, which may trigger allergies. Many adults who have become lactose intolerant claim they can drink raw milk. In California, where raw milk is legal, health food stores have been selling it for years, apparently without incident. The neighbours next to our farm drank raw milk from their dairy herd for decades and never suffered ill consequences. And my mother and her siblings grew up drinking raw milk from the cows on her farm. As she told me, some farmers were fastidious about the health of their cows and the cleanliness of their barns and equipment. And some were not.

But the milk industry in Canada is solidly behind pasteurization: It extends the shelf life of milk by 10 to 15 percent and provides safety insurance for slip-ups. Compared with conditions on some dairy farms in 1938, when pasteurization laws were first introduced, Canada has an extremely safe system, thanks to modern equipment and sterilization techniques, refrigeration and a strict National Dairy Code that calls for close testing of cows and milk from every farm. We could well extend that testing to certify safe raw milk from select farms meeting stringent safety codes, in much the same way that we certify organic products. But then safety would have to start with clean barns and healthy cows, rather than at the final stage, pasteurization.

So back to that glass of raw milk, which flowed minutes before from the teats of Frédéric's cows. I am risking my life to try this, at least according to the rather hysterical reaction of government and medical officials to Michael Schmidt's attempts to sell raw milk. They suggest that straight-from-the-cow milk is now some virulent, plague-infested stew.

Frédéric lifts the lid on his huge refrigerated milk tank to reveal 550 gallons of fresh, cold white liquid, not a spec of dust to be seen. I dip the glass in, drink back the contents, and, my God, forget about ice cream! For I swear, this is a milkshake, rich, thick and luscious. If Frédéric's personality is in this milk, I love this man.

THE NEXT DAY, Frédéric, between morning and evening chores, is helping his friend Denis bale and haul hay, so Nancy and I take a walk along the chemin de la Batture, where Frédéric cuts his hay. I have been watching his cows tuck eagerly into the thousand-pound round bales as they milk. I had pressed my face into that hay and discovered that it is like no other. Rather than dry, it is damp (they are sealed in plastic bags for storage, to keep in the flavour, moisture and nutrients). Rather than coarse, it is soft. Rather than smelling of fresh-cut grass, it smells of this marshland and this river.

We pass by two fields that Frédéric cuts, 120 acres of the more than 500 acres of marshland here. Oddly for a farmer, he must work with the tides, waiting for them to recede and the waist-high grass to dry. He also waits until July to cut and bale, after the yellow rail has finished nesting in the long grass. "I don't want to be a bad producer, a wise guy with a big tractor," Frédéric told us. "I try to preserve what nature gives us."

We try to imagine him working alone out here. The marsh, at the northeast tip of the island, strikes us as otherworldly—low-lying, hot, humid and still. The quiet seems to accentuate the surreal sense we have on this island of being quite apart from the world, yet at the very centre. The view is constantly changing: Small neighbouring islands grow vast at low tide and nearly vanish at high tide; the mainland cliffs to the south and Laurentian Mountains to the north loom large on a clear day, yet disappear under clouds blowing in from the ocean. Things around the island seem to evolve, change shape, shift form, while the island itself, in the middle of it all, remains constant.

It is like Frédéric and his cheese. That afternoon, we make a picnic on the ever-changing shoreline with the three soft cheeses from the cheese factory, a bottle of wine and a box of crackers. (Nancy's note to tourists: Buy your bread before arriving on the island.) Frédéric's Tomme de Grosse-Île is by far the most flavourful—earthy and sensual. Yet, this musky mushroom flavour is different from the nutty zest we sampled just weeks earlier in Montreal and different again from the herby tang we will enjoy months later back home in Toronto. For, although Frédéric remains a rock to his cows, their milk changes with the season: fat and nutty in winter; redolent with the musk of overwintered hay in spring; sweet and vegetal during summer and fall. When we savour a slice, letting it melt slowly on the tongue to release the flavour, it is like we are eating the river, the special hay, the summer on the island.

KARINA ARRIVES HOME the evening before we are to leave, so we drop by to say hello and goodbye. She is as shy as Frédéric is outgoing, with dark luxurious hair that swirls about her face. Although they've been married for six years, the two still flirt and tease like young lovers. Tonight, they are particularly excited—and nervous—for Frédéric has just bought three more quota or, as he puts it, "I just borrowed another $90,000 from the bank."

And this comes on the heels of Karina hearing that her sabbatical—a year off work without pay—has come through.

For the time being anyway, their lot is fully with the *foin de batture*. And Karina will see if Frédéric is right—if a baby might come to them when she stops flying to work and spends more time in the soothing company of pregnant cows. As a writer with the luxury of skipping from the present to the future tense, I can tell you that he is. They write me later to say that nearly nine months to that evening, they had a baby girl.

Before we leave that night, Karina and Frédéric show us their wedding picture, taken on New Year's Eve. They are both in their twenties and, although their hair is jet black and their faces vibrant, they seem older, wiser, than their years. He wears a tuxedo and top hat, she a white dress trimmed with fur. They look like they could be the Messeigneurs of this island.

# Quebec

## Frédéric's Fondue

This fondue serves up to twelve people as an appetizer, perfect for an après-ski party. It pairs well with Quebec apple cider. You can usually find Tomme de Grosse-Île at better cheese shops, but ask them to order it in if they don't carry it.

| | | |
|---|---|---|
| 1/2 | wheel of Tomme de Grosse-Île cheese (approx. 1 3/4 lb/850 g) | 1/2 |
| 1/2 cup | apple juice | 125 mL |
| 1/2 tsp | minced garlic | 2 mL |
| 1/4 tsp | nutmeg | 1 mL |
| | salt and freshly ground black pepper | |
| 1/2 tsp | baking soda | 2 mL |

Place the cheese in a medium stockpot or large saucepan. Add half of the apple juice, along with the garlic and nutmeg. Season with salt and pepper. Heat over medium heat until the cheese melts. In a glass, mix the baking soda with the remaining apple juice. Pour the juice mixture into the cheese mixture; stir to combine. The baking soda is a leavening agent and will almost immediately double the volume of the cheese mixture.

As soon as the cheese mixture puffs up, remove from heat and serve immediately, with bread, brioche or apples.

*Makes 6 hearty servings or 12 appetizer-size servings.*

Credit: Frédéric Poulin, Île-aux-Grues, Quebec.

## Tomme de Grosse-Île Cheese Plate

Fine cheese just as it is makes a great finish to any meal. Simply warm the cheese to room temperature and serve with crackers, baguette or an assortment of nuts, such as walnuts, pecans and almonds.

# *Ontario*

# A MIDWINTER NIGHT'S DREAM

*When the wine goes in, strange things come out.*
—philosopher Johann Christoph Friedrich von Schiller

I have a confession to make. When Nancy and I drive to the Niagara wine region, just ninety minutes from our home in Toronto, we almost always take Pelham Road, which follows an old carriage route that twists along the base of the Niagara Escarpment. After the congestion of the city, the whir of expressways, this pretty, shaded country trail works some strange magic on my brain—and this is before tasting stops at the many wineries along the way.

By the time we dip into the valley of Twelve Mile Creek, I can see Butler's Rangers, a ragtag regiment of British, Indian and United Empire Loyalists marching in their tattered green overcoats atop buckskin leggings. Never mind that I am navigating the corkscrew path out of the valley in our new MINI convertible (purchased with these drives in mind, I might further confess), it is the spring of 1813 and the Rangers are in sad shape, retreating from a devastating loss to the Americans at Fort George in Niagara-on-the-Lake. Then, as I round the corner and pass by Henry of Pelham Family Estate Winery, the great heroine Laura Secord appears. Incredibly, she has run thirty-two kilometres from her home in Queenston under the cover of night, braving wildcats and rattlesnakes and bands of roving soldiers. Now she is scrambling up the escarpment behind the Short Hills Bench to warn the British that the Americans are planning a surprise attack to gain control of the entire Niagara Peninsula. And if she does not make it? British North America—Canada—could fall to the Americans. Later, as we lunch at a winery restaurant along the Niagara River, a sudden clap of musket fire breaks the still summer air—yes, Laura made it, I think, and now the British are coming. *The British are coming!* Okay, I realize the muskets are actually bird bangers scaring crows off the surrounding vineyards, but I prefer the historical fantasy. And when friends back in Toronto ask me what goes well with icewine—Niagara's most famous vintage—I tell them blue cheese or foie gras are classics, but what really teases out the complex soul of this delectable wine is a roaring good story.

I first learned of this unusual match while elbowed up to the tasting bar in the cozy stone foundation of one of the first taverns in Upper Canada, established by Henry Smith in 1842, now the Henry of Pelham winery. It was a hot summer day, and we had toured many wineries and enjoyed many icewines, but this one stood out, a 2004 Riesling. But before the tasting, Daniel Speck, the youngest of three brothers who run the winery, did not speak of the many awards their Riesling icewine has won around the world, nor the sophisticated intermingling of flavours that would prompt noted British wine critic Jancis Robinson to declare this one of her top ten favourite Canadian wines, nor that it's the number one selling Riesling icewine in Japan, fetching more than $95 for a half bottle. Forsaking the usual wine talk and the predictable tour of the winery, Daniel took us to see a cemetery behind the winery's barn.

There, laid out under a grove of cherry, pear and apple trees, were the broken pieces of several tombstones. Daniel told us that he and his brothers, Paul and Matthew, while planting the vineyards as teenagers, had found the fragments and assembled them here. On one, in faded lettering, is the name Nicholas Smith, a Loyalist who moved here after the American War of Independence. For serving with the Butler's Rangers and swearing allegiance to the British crown, Nicholas was granted sixteen hundred acres in 1794—one hundred for himself, his wife and each of their fourteen children. (We joked that Canada's immigration policy was rather more generous then.) Beside Nicholas's gravestone was that of his son Henry, who opened the tavern here, signing his name Henry of Pelham, perhaps to honour Sir Henry Pelham, prime minister of England a century earlier, or to lend authority to the toll the Smith clan ran on Pelham Road. (Maybe the place still operates as a toll? I certainly cannot drive by the winery without stopping in to buy something.)

Then Daniel told us that his father, Paul Sr., descended from the Smiths on his mother's side. And that he and his brothers can trace their lineage to Nicholas and Henry. The hot day seemed to cool, even as the breeze grew still. The ghost story took on flesh.

In 1982, the last parcels of land still in the Smith family came up for sale, and Paul Sr. bought them. He had grown up in nearby St. Catharines, became a Catholic priest, then left the priesthood to teach high school in Toronto. Some years later, he and his wife, Bobbi, founded an alternative private school in Toronto, which their three sons attended. Daniel described his father as a man who knew a lot about books and nothing about growing grapes. Yet, he desperately wanted to keep the Smith land in the family. The idea of the vineyard and winery came later. Even the stories of Nicholas and Henry came later.

"We were urban kids," Daniel said, a smiled lodged in his throat. "He wanted us to get a good education, but he also wanted us to get reconnected with this place. It was like he grafted us onto our roots."

Weekends and summer holidays, Paul Sr. and Bobbi sent their sons out to the farm to plant and tend vines. The eldest, Paul Jr., was sixteen. His workmates were his scrawny little brothers—Matthew, then thirteen, and Daniel, just eight. The first summer, they drained and contoured the land and planted fifty acres of vines by shovel (the most they've planted in one season since, with the help of modern equipment, is thirty-five acres). Subsequent summers, through high school and university, the boys lived in the tavern while working twelve-hour days in the vineyards.

And then, as fate usually has its way with stories, a year after the winery opened in 1988, their father fell ill with cancer. Complicating matters was the worst crisis to hit the Canadian wine industry, another threat from the Americans—free trade, which would end tariff protection for Ontario's awful Baby Duck wines and place them in direct competition with California Chardonnays. Sensing defeat, long-time grape growers in the region began yanking out native labrusca vines. But Henry of Pelham and a handful of other start-up wineries continued their radical experiment of planting Vitis vinifera grapes—the "noble" varieties France is lauded for, such as Chardonnay, Cabernet Sauvignon and Riesling. The Speck boys endured their share of stupid farmer jokes. Yet, the brothers, along with the other start-ups, a modern-day bunch of Butler's Rangers, held their ground. And Niagara, now with seventy-five wineries, came out okay in this battle, too.

As Daniel led us from the cemetery, we passed by a black walnut tree the brothers had planted in honour of their father, who died in 1993. His ashes are spread in the nearby vineyard. A plaque, well, the boys have been meaning to get around to that, but they've been pretty busy building not just a winery but an entire industry.

Back in the tasting room in the basement of Henry's old tavern, Daniel poured us a glass of the estate's famed 2004 Riesling icewine. Wine critics have gone to great lengths to describe it: "elegant," "a beautiful balance of tart, bright fruit," "pristine and precise," "a real citrus salad," "fine boned." After the tour of the family cemetery, I also detected notes of nostalgia, heartache, determination, triumph, a haunting depth. And, like any great wine, it left me wanting more.

A LATE FALL DAY and the leaves on the maple trees along Pelham Road are waving in the wind, blazing scarlet, orange and golden banners. There's a snap in the air and also in the step of my Butler's Rangers. The mission today: netting the vines to protect the Riesling grapes from roving bands of deer and wild turkeys, and migrating birds.

With the wine region virtually at Toronto's side door, I have decided to visit Henry of Pelham through the four seasons, a luxury of time I could not afford on my cross-country tour of other farms. And why not indulge other fantasies, like spending a year in wine country running a vineyard?

I meet the three brothers in Paul's office, just off what was once the grand ballroom atop Henry's tavern. If books, papers and rolled maps could constitute a party, then it looks like a heck of a one exploded in this room. "So here's Henry," Paul says, moving artwork for their new label from a chair so that I can sit down. The Henry image on their wine label, Paul concedes, is actually a patron in a bar sketched by Canadian artist Robert E. McGinnis. "The vines behind 'Henry' look more like lightning bolts coming out of his head, so we're trimming that out and moving his head to the back label."

Paul has his father's wit, and colouring—his father's grandmother was an Iroquois who married a Smith. Matthew and Daniel, quick with a joke themselves, have the fair hair of their mother, who grew up in New York. The clutter of the office suggests other traits the brothers share. They're hardworking yet easy going; smart but quick to point out their mistakes, especially if that will win a laugh; confident yet lacking the slightest whiff of arrogance. They might put "family estate" on their wine labels, but they still call their 225-acre property "the farm." They're easy to like.

"Hey, we knew nothing when we started," Paul says. "And we still don't know that much compared with other wine regions. We're still a young industry."

Yet, the brothers are now senior statesmen, having built up one of the most successful labels in Niagara, even though Paul, the president, has just turned forty. And, although taller, his vice-presidents, Matthew, at thirty-seven, and Daniel, at thirty-three, still have the gangly builds of teenagers.

Between slogging out summers on the farm, they followed each other to the same small but demanding alternative university in the United States, Maryland's St. John's College. Each earned a philosophy degree. They say things like *ergo,* not to be pretentious but as a set-up for another brother to land a punchline. They have an obvious respect and affection for each other.

Daniel suggests that their father's example has much to do with why they get along so well. "Dad was always a real grinder. But even though he worked hard, he always put the family first. He wasn't exactly a cuddly guy or anything. I guess we bonded through work." Paul says it also helped that the brothers each have particular talents and that the winery grew along with them, enabling them to carve out separate areas of responsibility. And Matthew points out that they will always have that deep bond: the oldest vines in the vineyard, used to make their premium wines, the Speck Family Reserve, those crooked rows of Chardonnay, Cabernet Sauvignon, Baco Noir and Riesling that they planted so many years ago.

"I hated that," Paul says of those summers. "One minute I was in the city making cash delivering pizza, and the next minute I was in the middle of nowhere planting vines. I thought it was a nightmare." He wanted to become a lawyer but put off law school when his father overextended himself opening the winery. "It was clear we were having trouble, and I said I would work there for a year, and one thing led to another. I got interested in the business." Along with other new wineries, such as Cave Spring and Inniskillin, he helped write Ontario's Vintners Quality Alliance (VQA) rules that established Niagara as an appellation, similar to Bordeaux and Burgundy, though Paul would argue that Niagara's rules are tougher, as they're enforced by a government audit. The VQA became something of a pact of honour among Niagara wineries to follow a quality-first approach, differentiating their wines from the high-volume dreck the previous Ontario wineries produced. "I found it fascinating," says Paul. "There were a bunch of passionate people working together, and we were either going to slay this dragon or not. There were guys who had been in the old industry for a long time, and they said, you can't do this. And these younger guys were saying, we can do it. Free trade had delivered a real shock to the industry. It was going through a major transition. And our winery was starting up in the midst of a new industry starting up. There are not that many times when all those things line up."

Up to that point, Paul did not feel that his father had any grand design for the winery, but when he grew gravely ill, he pulled his eldest son aside. "He made it clear then that he wanted me and my brothers to work in this together, if we could, and that we should have a fair cut, and I just made that happen. Back then we were worried about the business succeeding, rather than how much of it each of us owned." When Paul Sr. died, his wife, Bobbi, closed the school, sold the properties they owned in Toronto and invested her money in the winery, placing her future with her sons.

By the time Daniel graduated two years later, he had an ownership stake waiting for him, but he had already put in fourteen years on the farm and hadn't liked the work any more than Paul. "It was brutal survival," says Daniel. "People look at us like we're the lucky sperm club, but it wasn't like that at all." Still, he honoured his father's rule: Put in one year on the farm. Fortunately, Daniel had read Nietzsche and learned something about the consciousness of method, the causality of the will. "I approached it as a new experience. I would take 100 percent direction and do the best I could in every situation." Gregarious and urbane, he discovered his own niche and is now vice-president of sales and marketing and can't imagine doing anything else.

The middle brother, Matthew, is the only one who actually likes tending vines. He recalls catching the Friday afternoon bus from Toronto and working on the farm by himself through autumn and winter weekends. At fifteen, he had signing rights on his parents' chequebook to pay seasonal workers. He might have become an engineer if the winery hadn't worked out, but he wanted to run the vineyard. "I like anything to do with farming," he says. "I like watching things grow. I like the sense of accomplishment. It's very tactile."

Which is as good a segue as any for getting to the real purpose of my visit on this fall day. Yes, to the vineyards, to net the icewine grapes. As Matthew, the vice-president of viticulture, leads me to the east field, he tells me that his parents raised him and his brothers with what he calls "an odd amount of responsibility and freedom." Even though he's the easy-going brother, the laid-back one, he leans into his lanky walk, his head bent forward, a man with a take-charge attitude. As I stumble to keep up with him along the rutted lane, he fills me in on the work that's already gone into this crop. Although the Niagara region has a longer growing season than the Champagne and Burgundy regions of France, he refers to growing grapes here as "extreme viticulture." He envies the predictable weather of desert climates such as California, but he thinks the wines produced in those conditions are monotone. "Here we get dry and wet weather, heat spikes and brutal cold. But my favourite wines come from continental weather. I think they're more interesting."

The challenge is to make consistently good wines no matter what the weather throws at them. In winter, Pelham staff prune mechanically but leave four or five grape canes on each vine, in case winter knocks off a few. Later, they will hand-prune the vine to two canes. Spring is about managing explosive growth—"the vineyard wakes up quickly here, going from bud break to flowering to clusters in about four or five weeks, that might take twelve weeks in other regions." During that short window, they must prune, bend canes, trellis, cultivate, fertilize, spray. Through the summer, if it's cool or wet, Matthew might have his crew clip leaves to let more sun on the grapes. If it's hot and dry, they might leaf one side, letting in the morning sun, while shading grapes from the burning afternoon rays. The tough question is deciding when to leaf and how, given nature's unpredictable antics through a growing season. "I'm thinking about the weather all year long," Matthew admits. "The romantic view of running a vineyard changes when you realize your destiny is tied to nature. Many don't have the stomach for it. You can do everything right and then a hail storm or frost can take half the crop."

His toughest challenge, though, has been managing the heavy clay soil on the Short Hills Bench. "For the first ten years, I hated this ground," he says.

"Old-timers call it three-day ground. It's too dry the first day. Then it rains and it's too wet. The third day is just right, and so you have one day to work with it." Planting in dry clay is like setting vines into cement: They won't root. Yet, working in soil when it's wet will compact and kill the new plantings.

Over the years, Matthew brought in consultants, watched other grape growers, studied, experimented, learned. He added more drainage—"The Bordeaux wine region was mediocre until the Dutch introduced drainage [in the seventeenth century]." He grows cover crops of rye grass and daikon radish in the rows between vines; it's both a driving surface for machinery and it breaks down into an organic fertilizer. As well, the deep roots of the daikon punch holes in the clay to let in air and moisture. Then, finally, he discovered deep subsoiling, which involves busting up the first twenty inches every fall and letting winter's cycle of freezing and thawing organically cultivate the clay into a finer soil.

Now, Matthew says, the land can produce the kind of vine he wants: well balanced between root, stalk, leaf and grape growth. "A balanced vine on well-drained soil will make the best wine," he claims. "It doesn't have to be the best soil, but the vines have to be healthy on that soil. On clay, the vines tend to grow smaller, produce smaller berries and a smaller crop per acre, but that's perfect for the premium wines we make."

Recently, Matthew brought his expertise to a technical committee developing sustainable agricultural guidelines for the Ontario wine industry, a sort of VQA green code that might one day end up on wine labels. At present, the term *local* means only that, whereas the Sustainable Winemaking Ontario program, developed from the committee's proposals, will offer region-specific sustainable viticultural guidelines for wineries to follow. This will differ from organic certification. Although Matthew uses some organic practices—a few organic sprays such as copper and sulphur, and composting grapes and leaves for green manure—he doesn't want to be boxed into an organic regime. Rather, he picks and chooses practices he believes are most beneficial for the wine. He refers to his method of growing as sustainable. "Organic is an idea that, when really scrutinized, might change," he says. "There's a principle that if something comes from the earth, it's better. But copper (an organic spray used as a fungicide) is deadly poisonous and it doesn't break down. Sulphur is an organic spray, and that's the one that bothers me the most. We use those sparingly. There are lots of horrible man-made sprays, but there are also synthetic sprays that are less harmful than natural ones and break down faster." Matthew works with a consultant to choose chemicals that are gentler on the environment and follows an integrated pest management protocol, spraying only when required and not at all for two months before harvest. "We're in this for the long haul," he says. "We're concerned about our health. We're concerned about quality wine, not volume. Raising premium wine is like raising top-quality beef. Likely, you're not pushing the animals and pumping them full of hormones."

As we reach the icewine vineyard, I ask Matthew about being chosen top grower of the year in 2000 by the Grape Growers of Ontario—the association's youngest-ever grape king. He says he was relieved the award had been updated a little: Rather than donning a regal crown and cape, the winner now wears a more sedate Masters-style sports jacket—albeit a burgundy one—to wine festivals. Still, he's proud of what he's accomplished. "There are few products where the primary function is farming, or where people care so much about how a food is made. Wine is traced to a very specific vineyard." And he points out that how he cares for that vineyard is important to the customer. "Arguably, the highest respect in winemaking is to farming."

Before rushing off to do other chores, Matthew introduces me to Cong Nguyen, one of his senior field staff, who will show me the art of netting vines, a crucial innovation to protect icewine grapes that are left to hang on the vine well into winter, long after they've ripened. As the grape dehydrates, freezes and thaws, its sugars concentrate into a sweet expression of summer, proving irresistible to both wine and wildlife connoisseurs. Inniskillin, one of the first wineries to try producing icewine in Niagara (inspired by German Eiswein), lost its entire first harvest to birds. The next year, a Pelee Island winery developed a netting system that, unfortunately, trapped the birds in with the vines. Matthew has had his own challenges—netting that was so large deer could wedge their noses through it to eat. He switched to nets with smaller loops and then came up with the idea of using a tagging gun, like the kind used to fasten price tags to clothing, to clip the nets shut at bottom and top. Apparently, he also has a knack for finding inexpensive solutions to problems.

His system works well, except that pulling the tightly strung nets closed with one hand while firing the tagging gun with the other requires more hand strength than I possess. Cong is a likeable, chatty man who prefers to work alone—"I can work faster," he says. But he quickly notices my struggle and tells me that we will work together. While Cong pulls the nets closed, I fire the gun, taking care not to shoot the plastic fasteners into his fingers.

Over the next few hours, Cong and I chat about his two sons ("both in university," he says proudly), my book ("lots of work," he comments) and work in the vineyard ("hard work," he says, "hard, hard work"). We pull and tag the top of the net, squat like baseball catchers, pull and tag the bottom, then move on to the next vine to repeat our tag, squat, tag, stand routine.

There are thirteen hundred vines per acre, some thirty thousand icewine vines to net.

JANUARY 17, 2 A.M. Back on Pelham Road. It seems a perfect night for picking icewine. After a rainstorm a few days ago, a cold snap set in, freezing everything into an icy sheen—the branches of trees, the scant covering of snow on the fields. Even the pavement plunging down into the valley of Twelve Mile Creek glistens. But where are my Butler's Rangers? All the wineries I have passed were dark. Then I pull into Henry of Pelham, where the yard lights are ablaze.

At the barn's back entrance, swung open for the night's work, beeping forklifts unload five-hundred-kilogram baskets of grapes from a wagon, manoeuvre them onto four olive presses reinforced with steel strapping to withstand the pressure required to squeeze juice from the frozen grapes. A metric tonne of Riesling produces about 700 litres of table wine, but only 150 of icewine. The golden nectar flows from the frozen, raisined fruit in achingly slow drips. Plastic tubing carries the liquid to a stainless steel tank. After a few hours of pressing, there are just 52 litres in the tank. In total, the winery will produce 35,000 litres of sweet wines this vintage.

I catch up to winemaker Ron Giesbrecht, who, like the four "cellar rats" scurrying about, wears a snowsuit, toque and snowmobile boots. Since my last visit, nature has lobbed a few wicked curve balls—late rains (which can promote fungus; affected clusters must be cut out by hand) and, now, a mild winter. Many wineries will not complete this harvest until well into February, but Ron, amid directing forklift traffic and talking on his cell phone to

Matthew in the field, tells me that Henry of Pelham managed to bring in a third of its crop during two cold nights in December. And it will get the rest in tonight and over the weekend—if the temperature holds at minus 8°C or colder, the temperature required by VQA law for wine to be called icewine. "We like to put everything we can into the harvest and hit it hard. The earlier we pick is the taste profile we like. I prefer December harvests. I like the cleaner characteristics. It's more Riesling-like, with lime and grapefruit notes. The later the harvest goes, you get more of those caramel and apricot flavours."

Suddenly, he throws an arm block at my chest. "Mind the forklift backing up." Then he motions me to follow him to his office for coffee. As we walk, Ron tells me that Henry of Pelham prefers a leaner, cleaner flavour, the reason it has made Riesling its flagship icewine rather than choosing the more commonly used Vidal, a hybrid grape that produces a rounder, more honeyed and, at times, cloying icewine. In the past, Henry of Pelham has made small quantities of Vidal, but this year it is devoting the hybrid to making a range of "almost" icewines—special select, select late harvest and late harvest. Whereas many other wineries make these from second pressings of grapes, Ron uses first pressings at temperatures in the minus 6°C to minus 8°C range—"a tricky window to get," he says. These temperatures produce a lower brix (a calculation of sweetness)—they try to get between twenty-eight and thirty-two, compared with about thirty-eight for icewine, and twenty-one for a Riesling table wine. "You get the connection with icewine, but the selects and late harvests are a little lighter, clearer," says Ron. "And at half the price, it's a deal."

Since joining the winery in 1990, Ron has worked to establish a Henry of Pelham style—"varietal correct," as noted Canadian wine critic Tony Aspler calls it. "When Henry of Pelham makes a wine from a grape, it tastes like it's made from that grape. Ron is a very good winemaker who makes wine that nature gave him, rather than trying to make something that is not there. He's respectful of the fruit he gets from the vineyard."

Hugely respected in the industry, Ron virtually designed his own graduate course in oenology and viticulture at the University of Guelph. By age thirty he was making wine at colossal Brights, finding time on the side to experiment with small batches of premium wines. A then–twenty-four-year-old Paul Jr. discovered that wine at an esoteric tasting event and hired Ron with the promise that he could make premium wine full time. Ron has been with the winery so long now, he says it sometimes feels like he's a Speck brother because of his huge comfort level and creative freedom. "Paul still acts like a twenty-four year old at times," Ron laughs. "He'll say things like, 'If you have an idea, say, to try something stupid like making sparkling wines, go ahead.'" The results—Ron's Cuvée Catharine Brut and Cuvée Catharine Rosé Brut, named after Henry's wife—are splendid sparklers made using the traditional champagne method. With a splash of icewine, they make excellent kirs.

As we return to the pressing area, a wagon pulls up with another load of grapes, and Ron sets down his coffee and jumps on a forklift to help unload. Later—a season later, in fact—away from this frantic buzz of an all-night harvest, he will tell me that his winemaking style is all about expressing Matthew's work in the vineyard. "We're less interested in making a winemaker's statement than a regional viticulture statement. I like certain varieties for expressing that. Rieslings and Riesling icewine come closest to expressing this region. We get concentrated citrus, with petrol coming in earlier, and huge age-ability."

My sense of smell is not refined enough to detect the petrol, thank God, and I can scarcely hang on to a wine for more than a week after buying it, but I do love that citrus zing to Riesling icewine—a concentrated hit of summer—perfect for a cold winter night like this one. Regrettably, I don't have any to take to the field.

I pass by the cemetery, cross the road and enter the vineyard where the Speck brothers planted their first vines more than two decades ago. It's quiet and still. The moon is up. The vines, coated in ice, sparkle. I imagine the tractor returning with the wagon morphing into a horse pulling a sleigh full of happy, singing pickers, jingle bells jingling, even though Matthew had forewarned me not to expect such romance. At Henry of Pelham, the days of handpicking icewine grapes are over. It became one of the first wineries in Niagara to modify its harvester for icewine—another bit of Matthew's handy work—allowing the winery to pounce early and hard on any available windows of weather. Another incongruity: Although the Speck brothers make wines that are more Old World in their elegance and subtlety, they eagerly embrace new technology to help them do so.

In minutes, their $100,000 reconditioned harvester (costing about $300,000 new) roars over a crest of hill. Modern as it may be, this is a prehistoric-looking bird. The front beak takes in one row at a time, splits the plastic fasteners that were keeping the nets closed, shakes out the grapes, then sends the clusters up a conveyor to a bin behind the driver's cab, which looms fifteen-odd feet above the ground. The tall, thin machine teeters on four smallish tractor wheels, looking like it might slide sideways or fall over at any moment. Yet, Matthew strides alongside, making sure the nets are properly feeding through the mechanism. Improbably, he talks on his BlackBerry as he does this. My buddy Cong and two other workers follow, scooping up any grape clusters that have fallen to the ground or remain stuck in the nets. At the end of the row, the driver turns and empties the bin into a basket on the wagon, before the whole procession heads down another row.

Matthew motions for me to walk alongside him, a narrow path between the machine and the next row of vines, a misstep away from the churning wheels. Over the blare, Matthew yells that the picker is only going at half speed tonight, about three kilometres per hour, because of the ice coating the vines. Still, it's far faster than what they used to gather by hand. Now five people working with the harvester can finish a row in five minutes; it used to take twelve people an hour. And Matthew doesn't pine for the old days one bit. "It was brutal," he says. "It was hard to line up crews at the last minute. And people could only work about five hours a night before they got tired and cold."

After scrambling beside the harvester for a few rows, I climb into the warmth of the cab to ride with the driver, Tom. Apparently he doesn't miss the old days either. "It was slow, hard, terrible work," he says. "The first two hours might be fun, and then your gloves got wet and your hands got cold." He usually spent the night hefting boxes of freshly picked grapes onto the wagon. Now, the toughest part of driving the harvester, he says, is staying on the row—and staying awake. To shake things up, he and Matthew will change places throughout the night.

At 5:30 A.M., I head back to the barn. One cellar rat—many are studying to be winemakers—says he's managing to keep his feet warm, though other appendages are getting cold. The first tank is still only a quarter full.

SPRING and, while the vineyard is waking up, Daniel, along with Paul DeCampo, arrive on my turf in Toronto. Henry of Pelham recently hired DeCampo as a key account sales representative; he's also leader of the Toronto chapter of Slow Food International, a non-profit organization that launched in Italy in 1989 to counteract the disappearance of local foods. The two are in the city to stir up sales for the just-released 2006 whites and, as Daniel says, to keep people thinking about icewine through the summer. This is work I can handle—starting with a 10:30 A.M. tasting of Henry of Pelham's Cabernet Franc and Riesling icewines at the Ontario liquor board's upscale Summerhill store, near Rosedale.

Ellen, an in-store product consultant, says icewine is a huge hit with tourists: "It's Canada's little ambassador." Back in 1989, Inniskillin pulled a coup by winning the Grand Prix d'Honneur from Vinexpo in Bordeaux, generally referred to as the Oscars of the wine industry. That foreign acclaim directed the world's attention to the struggling Niagara wine region—and to a wine that Canada could clearly make better than any other country. Since then, wineries have experimented making icewines from a range of grapes. Royal DeMaria Wines, which makes only icewine and late harvest wines, has seventeen, including a Merlot and a Pinot Noir, although, after tasting my way through the flight, I was hard-pressed to pick up the subtle differences among them. The Vidal, a hard-skinned grape that's up to a Canadian winter, and Riesling, which can balance the sugar with its high acidity, remain classics. But Henry of Pelham's focus on Riesling—it makes limited Cabernet Franc—has its challenges. "Those who know wine love the Riesling," smiles Ellen, "but most go for Vidal."

Onto the neighbourhood eatery Allen's, on the Danforth, the first in Toronto to carry an all-VQA wine list. Proprietor John Maxwell has been a huge supporter of Ontario wines ever since, he jokes, "it took an argument on the floor to get people to drink them." He's also a huge fan of Henry of Pelham, though that doesn't prevent him from passing on some pointed criticism. Today, Daniel wants him to taste the estate's dry and sweeter off-dry Riesling reserves. Henry of Pelham first hit my radar years ago with their crisp dry Riesling, and Maxwell calls it "a wonderful wine, a connoisseur's wine." Ah, but the bad news for the Niagara region that grows this grape so well is that, as Maxwell says, "no one drinks it." More folks prefer Chardonnay. And this reserve Riesling, Maxwell says, is still "a bit boxed in, a bit unyielding." His descriptions go on—"ungenerous, edgy, taut." It's not even my wine and I'm feeling a little deflated, but Daniel listens intently. He respects Maxwell's knowledge and wants his feedback. Finally, Daniel asks what a little aging might do for the wine. But Maxwell remains uncommitted. Meanwhile, Paul DeCampo tops up my half glass of the edgy stuff with a sweeter off-dry Riesling—definitely a faux pas in stuffy wine circles, but he winks. The blend is superb. Later in the car, Daniel admits Henry of Pelham has been struggling to define its style for Riesling—how sweet to make it, how dry? There's such a fine line between crisp and tight. He'll take Maxwell's comments back to the winery.

On to the posh Splendido restaurant, where the bar staff have invented a new cocktail for spring: the Winter Summer Solstice. Improbably, it combines Riesling icewine with gin, rhubarb juice and tarragon. "I wanted the coziness of being inside during winter with the freshness of spring," says sommelier Carlo Catallo. This time I'm doubtful, but the drink delivers an exotic hit of ginger and pepper, the refreshing chill of gin, the heat of icewine. I'm happy Daniel is driving as I pour the dregs from the cocktail shaker into my glass.

Finally to a sleek hangout on Toronto's hip Queen West. The bar manager has recently arrived from British Columbia, says he's still getting to know Ontario wines. Daniel immediately invites him to visit the winery. Paul DeCampo, meanwhile, unpacks his case of wines—the taut Riesling, a Reserve Baco Noir, a Merlot, the Cuvée Catharine Rosé Brut. As we taste our way through the flight, Daniel foregoes the Henry and Nicholas story to explain that the Baco Noir comes from the winery's oldest vines, the ones he and his brothers planted by hand. His describes the Catharine Rosé as "a party in a glass" for the summer patio and "a manly pink" that men will enjoy, well, at least those comfortable with their sexuality. Daniel's urbane banter goes over well and, somehow, we're talking about cool bars in Manhattan selling Henry of Pelham wines—The Stir Lounge in the Rockefeller Center, Hearth, and the new Inn LW12. Five wine stores in Los Angeles recently started carrying Henry of Pelham's wines, and now they're available across the United States through its distributor and over the internet. "We like to go into a few upscale places in big cities with our premium brands and let things go from there," Daniel says, adding that "big cities are all about disseminating ideas." A little nostalgia, a little sex appeal, a little philosophy and, by the end of the tasting, the bar manager says he wants to carry all the wines.

It may have taken two hundred years, but the Butler's Rangers are not only defending Niagara, they're taking America.

THROUGH THE WINTER AND SPRING, my wine-loving partner and I find many excuses to head to Niagara, none of them for vineyard work. In January, there's the Icewine Festival. In March, a Cuvée Weekend opens the cellars of some of our favourite wineries for tastings of premier and rare vintages. In May, we watch the vineyards exploding to life while working through a seven-course, three-hour icewine lunch at Peller Estate: suckling pig slow-cooked in icewine, Lac Brome duck glazed with Cabernet Franc icewine.

Although I have long stopped idealizing the work in the vineyard, my year in Niagara has sparked a fierce nostalgia for my own family farm and what might have been—or could be yet? There are more than a few parallels between the Speck brothers and my siblings. When we were still far too young, our father also grew ill, leaving us to fend for ourselves. We also felt the shock to the system of free trade. But, oh, how things turned out so differently.

The Speck's "family farm" of just 225 acres, 175 acres in vines, is now a thriving winery that employs about forty people, brings in more than $8.5 million in sales a year and offers three philosophy majors, all former city boys, fulfilling careers in agriculture that they love. They hope their children might one day get involved—Paul and his wife, Melissa, have two; Matthew and Jillian, three; Daniel and Louise, two. Paul teases his eldest, Sarah, that instead of going to summer camp soon, she'll be heading to Camp Farm. "But, really, they have to want it," Paul told me. "They have to be passionate." Likely, their children will have an unusual amount of responsibility should they choose to join the family business, but they will also have the freedom to choose.

By contrast, my family's farm—and that of the three generations of my family that farmed before us in Canada—is coming to an end. We knew it would come to this, but the end still came as a shock: In the spring, my mother put her half of the farm up for sale, and it's likely only a matter of time until my brother Graham sells his, too. As traditions go, my brother, the oldest son, was the only one who had the opportunity of taking over the farm. For the rest of us siblings, growing up was a matter of growing out of our passion for the family farm; we did not have the opportunity of bringing our talents to it. Not that I wanted to farm then, mind you. I wanted an education, I wanted the big city, I wanted creative fulfillment—none of which I thought could be possible in agriculture.

My brother did well enough farming, but he is bitter about the course agriculture has taken and doesn't want his children involved. Oddly, this spring, while putting in time, he planted about forty grapevines—a crazy experiment given the climate near Barrie, he acknowledges, but he wants to see what happens. For farmers like my brother, the Niagara wine industry offers a different and exciting option, a possibility of what agriculture could be.

The fantasy of what I might do with our family farm, had I the chance to run it, has been percolating on these drives to Niagara, especially following the long philosophical chats I've had with Paul about how to revitalize agriculture in this country. "Why is New Zealand lamb so sexy when we produce great lamb in Ontario?" he would ask. "When we talk about it being better to buy local, well, let's brand the country. Let's create a VQA for agriculture versus shutting down the border and subsidizing inefficiencies. Let's think about what we do well and develop a set of best practices that we trust, to give real meaning to this notion of 'local.'" He has little patience for farmers who refuse to change their practices when the model is no longer working. "Farmers fight things like waterway management and pesticide control and traceability, and that's like so twentieth century. In the twenty-first century, we have to have all those things. Those farmers would do themselves a big favour if they would just get on with environmental sustainability. That's just entry-level. The next step, they have to make a really good product, then explain why it's the best. I don't blame the consumer for not being engaged in farming. I blame the farmer. I think you can make a pretty sexy demonstration of why we need to pay more for a food, and farmers need to show us why we should."

SUMMER and I am back visiting Henry of Pelham.

Laura Secord lopes alongside my car, keeping pace. "So what would you do differently with your family's farm?" she asks.

"Yes, what?" demand my Butler's Rangers marching along Pelham Road. They always look so forlorn, beaten but never quite down.

Well, I'll get to that, in the next chapter. I still have unfinished work at Henry of Pelham. And it's difficult to feel very sad about my family's farm today while eating lunch on the patio of the Coach House Café, with the sun shining down, a tasting trio of chef Erik Peacock's salads in front of me—watermelon and ricotta cheese, octopus with garlic poached in icewine, lightly smoked trout on a bed of fresh herbs—which all go wonderfully with icewine. Later, I can always elbow up to the tasting bar in Henry's old tavern, as though I'm a member of the family, as though I own the vineyard. The Speck brothers don't seem to mind, so long as I pay my toll, buy a bottle or two.

There's Matthew now, in work boots and jeans, striding to the barn, throwing me a wave. Somehow, he has managed to control that explosive spring growth in the vineyard without my help.

And there's Daniel, BlackBerry to his ear, shouting hello as he rushes off on a sales call. I admit, without my contribution to his work, his tasting samples will surely last longer.

And here's Paul returning from a lunch meeting. Much of what he does these days is about building the industry and the region: supporting the Greenbelt Act to protect vineyards from urban development, working on a mayor's committee to revitalize downtown St. Catharines, where the three brothers live.

I have come here today to see my project through to the end, to taste the icewine that I pruned and netted and picked (wild exaggeration, but let me have my fantasies). The Riesling is yet to be filtered and bottled, so Ron holds up a glass to the huge stainless steel tank, turns a spigot. I imagine wine gushing out, holding my mouth to the tap to staunch the flow (I am always ready to be a heroine). Unfortunately, the valve releases just a splash.

Ron grins as he swirls the light golden liquid in his glass, takes a sip. He's thrilled with the sharp notes of lime and grapefruit that edge in with the sweet. He's not sure if it will be as good as the 2004. "Close," he says, unable to stop smiling.

I agree that it's pretty damn fine—tangy, complex, surprising—rather like a couple of stories that Ron and Paul told me earlier about Paul Sr.

Ron used to overhear the tours of the winery Paul Sr. gave to visitors, persisting even through his illness. "He was stubborn and entertaining," Ron said. In various renditions of Paul Sr.'s Nicholas and Henry story, Nicholas was half Iroquois, a translator in Butler's Rangers, a fifer, a bugle boy. "Every time he led a tour," Ron said, "he would say something more outrageous."

Paul conceded that his father, the teacher, the man who never went anywhere without a book under his arm, took a few liberties with history. "But he believed everything he said," Paul laughed. "Telling visitors a story that wasn't a wine story, that was a family story, that really helped us. People loved that story. We're a young country and it connected us to our history. Early on, I realized that story was powerful."

And now, Paul Jr. says, he must continue building on the story, talking about why the Short Hills Bench, where the winery is located, is so important to preserve as farmland. The city of St. Catharines is pressing toward the winery; the border is now just a half mile off.

# Ontario

These kirs, invented by the Speck brothers, make refreshing and classy summertime sippers.

## Kir Catharine

| 3 oz | Henry of Pelham Cuvée Catharine Brut | 90 mL |
|------|--------------------------------------|-------|
| 1 oz | Cabernet Franc Icewine | 30 mL |

In a champagne flute, mix the Cuvée Catharine Brut with the Cabernet Franc.

To create a layered effect, pour the Cuvée Catharine Brut into a champagne glass. Place a teaspoon, bowl side up, just inside the flute and carefully pour the icewine over it and into the glass, so that the red icewine rests on top of the golden brut. Garnish with a frozen grape.

*Makes 1 serving.*

Credit: The Speck brothers, St. Catharines, Ontario.

## Blushing Kir Catharine

| 3 oz | Henry of Pelham Cuvée Catharine Rosé Brut | 90 mL |
|------|-------------------------------------------|-------|
| 1 oz | Henry of Pelham Riesling Icewine | 30 mL |

In a champagne flute, mix the Cuvée Catharine Rosé Brut with the Riesling Icewine.

To create a layered effect, pour the Cuvée Catharine Rosé Brut into a champagne glass. Place a teaspoon, bowl side up, just inside the glass and carefully pour the Riesling Icewine over it, so that the white icewine rests on top of the rosé brut. Garnish with a frozen grape.

*Makes 1 serving.*

Credit: The Speck brothers, St. Catharines, Ontario.

## A Winter Summer Solstice Cocktail

This late spring drink will make you fall in love with rhubarb, or simply fall in love.

| | | |
|---|---|---|
| 1 | 1/4-inch/5 mm piece ginger, peeled and chopped | 1 |
| 1 tbsp | (or sprig) fresh tarragon | 15 mL |
| 1 1/2 oz | gin | 45 mL |
| | ice | |
| 1 oz | icewine | 30 mL |
| 2 oz | lightly sweetened rhubarb juice | 60 mL |
| | lemon zest, optional | |

In a glass, muddle the ginger and tarragon in the gin. Transfer to a cocktail shaker and shake with ice, icewine and rhubarb juice. Pour over a cube of ice in a tall, slender glass. Top with lemon zest.

*Makes 1 serving.*

Credit: Carlo Catallo, sommelier, and Jason Cameron, bartender, Splendido, Toronto, Ontario.

## The Icewine Martini

If you find icewine too sweet or want to give it an extra kick, add vodka to it, for a classy, refreshing martini. The Twist Lounge in New York City serves a variation it calls the Frostbite Martini, which includes a frozen wine grape in the bottom of the glass as garnish.

This is a recipe you can have fun with and personalize as you adjust proportions to taste and use various icewines, such as Riesling and Cabernet Franc or even late harvest dessert wines, which are half the price of icewine. Because I cannot bear to share a fine Riesling icewine with vodka, I often make this martini with a late-harvest Vidal, using equal measures of vodka and Vidal.

| 1/2–1 oz | Henry of Pelham Riesling Icewine | 15 mL–30 mL |
|---|---|---|
| 2 oz | vodka | 60 mL |

If the vodka and icewine are chilled, you can simply mix together and serve in a martini glass. Or shake ingredients with ice in a martini shaker, then pour into martini glasses.

*Makes 1 serving.*

Credit: Margaret Webb, Toronto, Ontario.

# Conclusion

# THE HOME FARM

"It's your move," he says.

We're playing chess, my dad and I. The late afternoon sun pours in through the windows, finds us at the kitchen table starting our third game.

"Double or nothing," Dad says. He's down two games.

I take the challenge because the game is not about winning, which is easy enough. Dad approaches chess like he plays cards, taking wild risks. Our game, however, is about giving us something to do while we talk, which we do constantly through these too-short winter Sunday afternoons, after lunch and before evening chores. My brother Joe is playing hockey on the pond with cousins and neighbourhood kids. My oldest brother, Graham, is snowmobiling with friends. I love having my father to myself on these afternoons because our conversations can go anywhere, from national politics to family history to local municipal issues to feminism.

I am thirteen. Dad will say outrageous things to start a debate, like women aren't strong enough to be farmers or serve in the armed forces or be police officers. Then once I get wound up, he will sit back and listen to my arguments, a grin on his face. He tells me that I would make a good prime minister. And sometimes he even agrees with me, except for the point about women being farmers.

On that issue, I didn't agree with him then, and I don't now. What became clear to me on my tour of Canadian farms was that successful farmers operate as my parents did, as a team. My dad took risks and worked hard farming. My mom worked as hard managing the books and tending the garden that fed us.

As for farming, Dad clearly had other notions of what I should do, but I will never know for sure what he thought.

That was the last winter that I can remember my father being fully with me, before his mood started darkening, his mind and body started crumbling. In many ways, that was also the first winter that I remember him being fully with me. On the farm, he was always around, but he was always working.

My brother Graham and I have these conversations now, sitting in his kitchen on the farm we moved onto the summer after that chess game. Dad sold our first farm to developers, enabling him to buy these fifty acres and my brother the adjoining fifty acres, and give my brother his start. Before Dad grew too ill to work, he also built a new house for us on one half of the fifty acres and helped Graham build a new barn on his fifty acres, and then a house for his wife and two daughters.

Now my brother is about the age Dad was when his mind started to go. Graham doesn't believe the toxic chemicals we used on our farm caused Dad's illness. But then, my brother handled the same chemicals and more. Perhaps he doesn't want to dwell too much on that possibility.

Graham made a comfortable living farming, in good part, he admits, because he bought another farm in his twenties and resold it to developers. Rather than using that windfall to acquire more farmland, he rented land and invested his money outside agriculture, certainly a safer move then. He is winding down his operation now, a move hastened by the loss of his rental land to development from the nearby city of Barrie. Perhaps like my mother, he, too, will sell his farm. With the way farming has gone the past few decades, he doesn't want his children to take over, and they're not much interested. My brother is the fourth generation of our family to farm, and he will be the last.

During our talks in my brother's kitchen, we play the "what if" game. Graham says that if he were starting over today, he would do things differently. He would run a market farm, producing vegetables and meat to sell at farmers' markets or directly to consumers. "It's not about being big," he says. "In fact, maybe you shouldn't be big. It's about the farmer controlling everything, from the field right through to the consumer." Farmers, he believes, should focus on cutting out the middle layers that take their profits and leave the farmer with too little to grow quality food and make a good living. He believes farmers should take back their power over the food they grow.

I agree with him. Forging direct relationships between farmers and consumers is our best option of reducing the power of the industrial farm model. We give close attention to drug testing, yet largely leave the testing of new foods, which we consume daily, in the hardly objective hands of the Big Ag and Big Food industry. Now genetically modified (GM) crops enter our food system without labelling, without consumer notification. The presence of GM canola and other crops in the West has made it impossible for farmers to grow organic crops in those areas, for risk of contamination. Animals on large-scale farms are raised in a way that would horrify most of us, if we cared to look closely. And farms are among the largest contributors to environmental degradation of lakes and streams. The current system is broken and, in many cases, dangerous.

Consumers long for labels that guarantee safety—organic being one. But now we're concerned that industrial farmers are barging into that territory and weakening those regulations. Local is the new rallying cry, but that on its own is not enough. Why support a farmer if he or she is degrading our local environment, simply because that farmer is local? *Environmentally sustainable, naturally raised*—these are still fussy terms without accountability.

Many consumers are frustrated and confused. We are searching for stronger agricultural policies, to protect both consumers and farmers, our food and our land. It would be naive of me to propose what such a policy would look like, without extensive input from farmers and concerned citizens and independent researchers, but I can dream about the kind of farm I would want to run, the kind of farm I would want to buy my food from.

My "what if" scenario is inspired by the stories I heard on my travels across the country, from farmers who are making a difference and presenting us with new models. My "what if" includes our entire family being involved in the family farm, something Dad could not have imagined all those years ago, when a hundred acres could hardly support one family, let alone several. But what if we had the chance to start over, start now, with the demand for local and organic food soaring?

I would call it "The Home Farm," as we've always called this second farm, to differentiate it from the others Graham rented. It would be a field-to-plate venture right on the land, drawing people to us. It's perfectly located, just fifty minutes north of Toronto and beside a major highway that funnels Torontonians to cottage country, and close to Barrie, the fastest growing city in Canada. And surely the land would be worth more growing quality food than sprouting retail stores?

We would have a fresh market (with tasting samples of ten varieties of tomatoes) and a butcher shop (my sister, Carol, the teacher, could manage the retail operation and run cooking demonstrations on how to use every part of the animal). My brother Joe, who always had a special way with animals, could run the livestock side of things, while Graham could take care of the crops. We would offer tours of the farm, both to educate and to foster a closer connection to the foods we eat.

We would be proud to show off the farm because we would use the very best practices available, incorporating organic and sustainable methods to grow quality food in a way that is gentle on the environment. We would raise animals humanely because it's the right thing to do and the meat is better for you.

I suppose, being rather inept at farming itself, I would handle the political side of things, working to get our practices recognized as a brand. Not simply a commercial brand, but a farmer-proposed, government-audited "Made in Ontario" or even "Made in Simcoe County" label, similar to the wine industry's Vintners Quality Alliance (VQA), which guarantees quality as well as locally grown ingredients. It would be a label that consumers could trust. I would encourage other provinces to follow suit, establishing their own guidelines of what local quality agriculture means and then awarding that label only to those farms that qualify.

And let's duke it out for top bragging rights in this country, the best provincial brand, because there's nothing farmers like more than a bit of competition. And there's nothing farmers hate more than ending up on the wrong side of a two-tier food system, quality and local versus cheap and industrial.

The Home Farm would be wildly successful, of course. In time, we would bring the next generation of our family into the business, opening a cheese shop and a restaurant to host spring maple syrup dinners, summer pig roasts and fall harvest suppers. Inspired, neighbouring farmers would adopt our quality-first policies and bring us their harvest to sell. And we would spur others into competition, creating a thriving agricultural scene as exciting as Niagara's wine region, our own little south of France in Toronto's backyard.

All this would demand every ounce of dedication, talent and creativity from every member of my family who wanted to contribute, and wouldn't the results be delicious—a farm that had something to show, had something to say, for its history, the four generations of passion and sweat that went into it.

I believe it is all possible, all exciting, yet the model came too late for us. My sister, Carol, has just retired from teaching. Graham is winding up his operations. My brother Joe is settled in a career as a train engineer. As for me, well, perhaps I had best leave farming to those who do it really well. I am happy to advocate for change and write about their achievements. And I'm even happier enjoying the results on my plate.

So I say goodbye to this book and our family farm, confident that we are at a tipping point, when those who eat food and those who produce it both realize that there must be value in producing good food. As consumers, we have a choice to give food and farming more of our attention, to support quality producers, and to push for a system of agriculture that feeds us well. And farmers, more than ever, have a choice, with enthusiasm swelling for options other than the industrial farm model.

As for my dad, his conversations will forever be frozen in time. Yet, I still hang on to what he said to me so many years ago, over that game of chess. Maybe more than ever, his words take on meaning.

As he said, it's your move.

# *Acknowledgments*

There are so many people to thank:

My farmers and their families, of course, for sharing their stories with me.

The chefs who wooed me with their cooking and contributed recipes.

My family, for beginnings that inspired this journey and support along the way. Graham, you put up with my crazy tractor driving and questions. Mom, you are simply amazing. And Carol and Joe, thank you for sharing stories of our farm.

My wonderful family-in-law has suffered my cooking and still invites me back.

My agent Rick Broadhead and Penguin Group (Canada) editorial director Diane Turbide, for believing in this project and working so hard to help me realize it. And to Judy Phillips, for her careful and artful editing of this book. The fact checking is mine—please forgive any errors or omissions.

I wrote a chapter at The Banff Centre, thanks to its generous Literary Journalism Fellowship. There, director Rosemary Sullivan and editors Moira Farr and Ian Pearson offered insightful editing, inspiration and friendship. I must single out John (Hemingway) Vigna for mountain runs and long talks over scotch. And Susan Bourette, who offered incredible support.

Travelling across Canada for research was a huge and expensive challenge. I would like to acknowledge various publications that published my travel and food articles along the way: *Canadian Geographic, The Globe and Mail, The Toronto Star, Out in Canada, More Magazine* and *enRoute.* And I am truly grateful to the Canada Council for the Arts and the Ontario Arts Council for grants that came at critical moments.

Jesse McLean and my brilliant second-year feature writing class of 2006/2007 at Ryerson University endured my endless farm stories and pitched in with research.

Many friends chipped in with editing advice, title suggestions and a shoulder to lean on when I really needed it: Anne Perdue and Julie Lemieux, Laurie Colbert and Dominique Cardona, Jamie Williamson and Ken Layton, Shena Hinks and Kathleen Urdahl, Laura Tobias and Jennifer Fraser, Jamie Martin and John Szkolka, Richard Almonte, Judy Curnew, Lorraine Gane, Miche Genest, Kathy Guidi, Karen Hanley, Sonnet L'Abbe, John Lorinc, Cynthia Macdonald, Kelly Mansell, Peter Mansour, Dee Shipley, Anne-Marie Shubin and Steve Szigeti.

And, of course, Nancy Lyons, I could not have mustered the appetite for this journey without you.